The geology of the English Channel

BRITISH GEOLOGICAL SURVEY

United Kingdom Offshore Regional Report

The geology of the English Channel

R J O Hamblin, A Crosby, P S Balson, S M Jones,
R A Chadwick, I E Penn and M J Arthur

LONDON   HMSO   1992

Production of this report was funded by the Department of
Energy and the Natural Environment Research Council

The coastline used on many maps and diagrams in this book is
based on Ordnance Survey mapping

Bibliographic reference

HAMBLIN, R J O, CROSBY, A, BALSON, P S, JONES, S M,
CHADWICK, R A, PENN, I E, and ARTHUR, M J.   1992.
*United Kingdom offshore regional report: the geology of the English
Channel.*   (London: HMSO for the British Geological Survey.)

Dd 292033   C20   11/92

ISBN 0 11 884490 3

Contents

FIGURES

Foreword

This report describes the geology of the eastern and central portions of the English Channel from the Dover Strait in the east, to Start Point in the west. It is one of a series of Offshore Regional Reports covering the continental shelf of the United Kingdom (UK), and complements the series of 1:250 000 scale geological and geophysical maps already published by the British Geological Survey (BGS). The report concentrates on UK waters, but mention is made of the geology of both French waters and the coastal areas on either side of the English Channel. The report will provide important background information to the engineer planning offshore structures, the academic geologist, and the exploration geologist seeking offshore minerals or hydrocarbons. It will also be invaluable for students or others with a more general interest in the geology of the area. The report includes a chapter on the Quaternary geology.

The area featured in pioneering offshore geological exploration, with Brunel's survey for a Channel Tunnel in 1866 and Dangeard's sampling surveys of the whole English Channel in the 1920s. However, less work has been carried out by the oil industry in this area than in the adjacent North Sea and South Western Approaches. To date, limited, and so far unsuccessful oil exploration has been carried out only in part of the area. However, surveys related to both aggregate studies and the Channel Tunnel have been important sources of data, and the area has been the subject of much academic research. Geophysical, sampling and drilling operations have been carried out in the area by the BGS since 1973, largely funded by the Department of Energy.

P J Cook, DSc
Director

British Geological Survey
Keyworth
Nottingham
NG12 5GG

24 September 1992

ACKNOWLEDGEMENTS

The report has been compiled by R J O Hamblin, and responsibilities of individual authors during the production of the report have been as follows:

R J O Hamblin—Introduction, Permian, Triassic and Quaternary, as well as contributing to the crustal structure, Pre-Permian, Jurassic and economic chapters.
A Crosby—Cretaceous.
P S Balson—Tertiary.
S M Jones—Pre-Permian basement and economic chapters.
R A Chadwick—Post-Variscan structural evolution.
I E Penn—Jurassic.
M J Arthur—Crustal structure.

In addition to the named authors, the report draws on the pool of expertise in BGS, not only in the Marine Units but also in the Land Survey and particularly in the specialist fields of biostratigraphy, sedimentology and stratigraphy. In particular, the following provided critical comment: B M Cox, C D R Evans, R W Gallois, R Harland, S Holloway, E R Shephard-Thorn and G Warrington. The Offshore Regional Reports Series is co-ordinated by the Marine Geology Group, and is edited by D Evans with the assistance of A G Stevenson. The project is financed mainly by the Department of Energy.

The following companies are thanked for permission to use well data in this report: Conoco (UK) Limited for well 98/23-1, Unocal UK Limited for well 98/18-1, Esso Exploration and Production UK Limited and Total Oil plc for well 99/12-1, and Gas Council (Exploration) Limited for wells 98/11-1 and 2. Transmanche-Link are thanked for allowing publication of information incorporated into Figure 73.

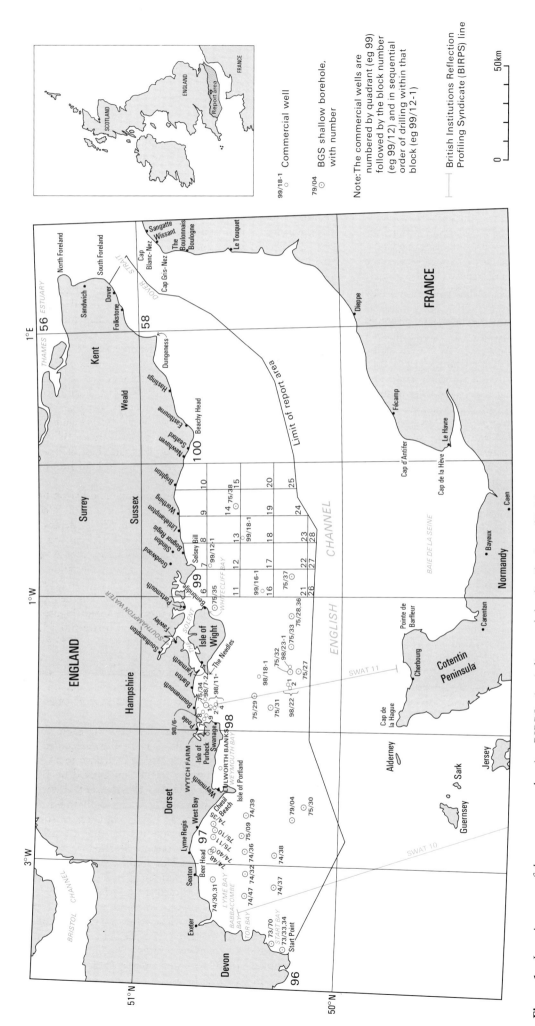

Figure 1   Location map of the report area, showing BIRPS seismic lines and the distribution of BGS boreholes and oil company wells in the English Channel.

99/18-1
⊙ Commercial well

79/04
⊙ BGS shallow borehole, with number

Note: The commercial wells are numbered by quadrant (eg 99) followed by the block number (eg 99/12) and in sequential order of drilling within that block (eg 99/12-1)

|——| British Institutions Reflection Profiling Syndicate (BIRPS) line

0 ————— 50km

1 Introduction

The sea area discussed in this report is delimited to the north by the south coast of England, and to the south by the median line separating French from United Kingdom waters (Figure 1). The western limit is a line running from Start Point towards Cap de la Hague, and the eastern boundary runs from South Foreland in the direction of Sangatte. In order to describe the offshore geology, the text draws upon information derived from the adjacent French waters and from the intensively studied French and English land areas; many geological structures run across the English Channel between the land on either side (Figure 2). The report area lies wholly within the continental shelf, with water depths nowhere greatly exceeding 100 m.

The nature of the English coastline adjacent to the area is very varied. In the west, the outcrop of Devonian strata is typified by rugged cliffs with minimal coastal erosion taking place. Where Permian, Triassic, Jurassic and Upper Cretaceous strata crop out at the coast, there are tall cliffs that are generally steep as a result of continuing erosion, with offshore stacks in places. These cliffs include the renowned red cliffs of East Devon (Permo-Triassic), the varied Jurassic cliffs of Dorset, and the white Chalk cliffs of the Isle of Wight (The Needles and Whitecliff Bay), Beachy Head and Dover. The softer parts of the Jurassic, Lower Cretaceous and Tertiary strata give rise to low-lying coastlines, which are in places subject to rapid erosion, as in Poole and Christchurch bays. Locally, major gravel beaches have been formed against these low-lying coasts, as at Chesil Beach in Dorset, The Crumbles near Eastbourne, and Dungeness in Kent.

The geological history of the area is summarised in Figure 3, which also includes significant events from neighbouring areas. The pre-Quaternary strata flooring the area are largely of Palaeogene and Cretaceous age, underlain by a Jurassic sequence which crops out in the east and west. Permian and Triassic rocks underlie the western part of the area, but with only limited outcrops. Carboniferous rocks are only known to occur at depth in the east, where they include an offshore extension of the concealed Kent Coalfield. The outcrop of Devonian rocks in the extreme west hardly extends offshore, although rocks of this age are believed to underlie the entire area.

PHYSIOGRAPHY

The overall physiography (Figure 4) of the area can be divided into five elements: offshore shoals, submerged cliff lines, incised valleys, tidal sand ridges, and most extensively, a gently dipping marine planation surface.

The marine planation surface (Curry, 1989; Stride, 1990) covers most of the sea bed in the area, and everywhere slopes directly away from the coast. West of 1°W it slopes due south at about 1:1500 to beyond the median line, whereas east of 1°W it slopes to the south-south-east or south-east at a rather steeper angle, but does not extend more than 20 km offshore as it is interrupted by incised valleys and tidal sand ridges. South-east of the Northern Palaeovalley (Figure 4), the surface slopes toward the north-west, away from the French coast, at about 1:1500.

The marine planation surface is considered to be largely of Neogene age, for over most of the area it cuts across Palaeogene and Cretaceous sediments. The overall planation surface is unlikely to be younger, for transgressions and regressions during the Quaternary would have been too rapid to have cut it. However, some nearshore parts of the surface are younger, resulting from coastal erosion during several Quaternary transgressions; in particular, Bournemouth and Christchurch bays are believed to date from the last transgression, the Flandrian of some 10 000 years ago. Furthermore, the solid strata of the sea bed are commonly dissected by fluvially eroded palaeovalleys of Pleistocene age; these have been infilled with sediment such that they cannot be distinguished on the bathymetric map (Figure 4), and their surface must also count as being of Quaternary age.

Offshore shoals are uncommon because of the generally readily eroded nature of the relatively young rocks at the sea bed. However, resistant Devonian strata create a rugged coastline in south Devon where they also form small inshore shoals, but the outcrop does not extend farther than 8 km offshore. East of the Isle of Wight, Owers Bank (Figure 4) is a shoal forming an offshore continuation of Selsey Bill; it is made up of relatively resistant Eocene strata. East of Beachy Head, Royal Sovereign Shoals are formed of hard ironstone of Early Cretaceous age.

Three drowned cliff features off Cornwall and Devon have been interpreted as ancient coastlines (Cooper, 1948; Wood, 1974; Donovan and Stride, 1975). They lie at depths of 38–49 m, 49–58 m and 58–69 m below OD, and are believed to date from the Miocene or early Pliocene, for as with the sea-bed planation surface, Quaternary stillstands are thought to have been too short-lived to allow cliffs to develop (Wood, 1974; Donovan and Stride, 1975). Within the report area, only the 38–49 m feature has been recorded (Figure 4); it has been proved by BGS seismic surveys between 0°55′W and 2°W, and was recorded by Kellaway et al. (1975) from 2°W as far west as Portland Bill, and again off south Devon. It is presumed that the deeper features were older and, where cut into rocks less resistant than those cropping out off the Cornish coast, have not survived the stillstand represented by the 38–49 m cliff.

A shallower cliff line running very near the shore from Portland Bill to Babbacombe Bay (Figure 4) was recorded by Kellaway et al. (1975). It is presumed to be related to a Quaternary transgression. However, a cliff line proved by BGS surveys to run from Beachy Head to Shingle Bank at depths of over 20 m may be of the same age as the 38–49 m feature, the difference in depth being explained by differential subsidence. If this is the case, the feature may be almost continuous from 2°W to Shingle Bank, but not detected where it lies along the northern flank of the Northern Palaeovalley.

Three incised valleys of significant size occur within the area (Figure 4); the cutting of each can be related to Quaternary events. St Catherine's Deep, immediately south of the Isle of Wight, descends some 60 m below the sea-bed planation surface. It is cut wholly into bedrock, and several smaller, parallel deeps may be noted nearby. The Lobourg Channel runs through the Dover Strait, but only descends some 20 m below the sea-bed planation surface. The Northern

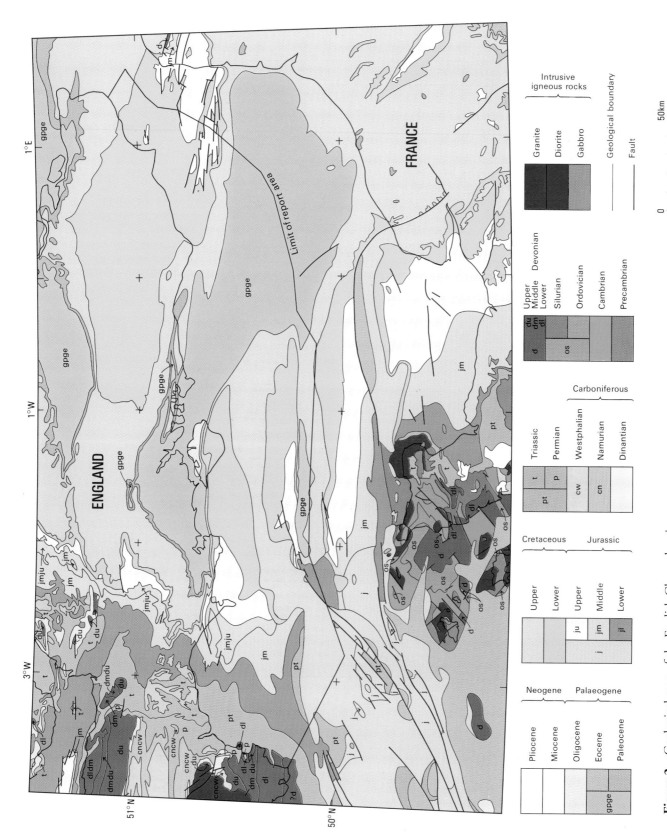

Figure 2 Geological map of the English Channel region

2

Era	Period	Epoch	Age (Ma)	Lithostratigraphic unit	Major events
CENOZOIC	QUATERNARY	HOLOCENE	0.01	(Sea-bed sediments)	Flandrian transgression
		PLEISTOCENE	1.67	(Palaeovalley infill sediments)	Palaeovalleys cut by fluvial action during glacial maxima
	TERTIARY — NEOGENE	PLIOCENE	5.2		Marine transgression (no deposits survive offshore)
		MIOCENE			Formation of cliff line now submerged at -38m to -49m OD
					Marine transgression (no deposits survive)
			25.2		Main Alpine orogeny, major structural inversion
	TERTIARY — PALAEOGENE	OLIGOCENE	30		Sea-level fall associated with initiation of Antarctic ice-cap
		Chattian			
		Rupelian	36	Bouldnor Formation	Lacustrine and brackish-lagoonal sedimentation with brief marine incursions
		EOCENE	39.4	Headon Hill and Bembridge Limestone formations	
		Priabonian	42	Barton Group	Marine and brackish sedimentation
		Bartonian	49	Earnley Sand, Marsh Farm and Selsey Sand formations	
		Lutetian	54	London Clay & Wittering formations	Paris Basin and North Sea linked
		Ypresian		Woolwich & Reading formations	Marine transgression from north
		PALEOCENE Thanetian	60.2		
		Danian	66.5		
MEZOZOIC	CRETACEOUS	LATE Senonian — Maastrichtian	74		Uplift, minor inversion of structure begins
		Campanian	84	Upper Chalk	Most of Europe submerged
		Santonian	88		
		Coniacian			
		Turonian	89	Middle Chalk	
		Cenomanian	92	Plenus Marls	North Atlantic continues to open
			96	Lower Chalk, Chalk Marl	North Sea and Wessex-Channel Basin joined
		EARLY — Albian		Upper Greensand	
			108	Gault	
		Aptian	113	Lower Greensand	Marine transgression and regional downwarping associated with initial opening of North Atlantic
		Barremian			
		Hauterivian Neocomian	116.5	Wealden Beds	Active block faulting, rifting of continental margin. Intrusions in Brittany, Cornubia. Coastal and estuarine sedimentation
		Valanginian	121	Hastings Beds	
		Ryazanian	128	Durlston Formation ⎫ Purbeck Group	London Platform uplifted, North Sea and Wessex-Channel basins separated
	JURASSIC	LATE — Portlandian	131	Lulworth Formation ⎭	
			136	Portland Limestone Formation	Regression, leading to shallow-water sedimentation
		Kimmeridgian		Portland Sand Formation	Renewed extension, maximum Jurassic marine transgression
		Oxfordian	146	Kimmeridge Clay	Uplift, carbonate-shelf sedimentation
			152	Corallian, including Osmington Oolite	Downwarping, renewed transgression
		MIDDLE — Callovian	157	Oxford Clay	
				Cornbrash	
		Bathonian	165	Great Oolite, including Fuller's Earth	Uplift resulting in shallow-water carbonate-shelf sedimentation
		Bajocian	171	Inferior Oolite	
		Aalenian	179		
		EARLY — Toarcian		Upper Lias, including Bridport Sands	Renewed extension, normal faulting coeval with initial opening of central Atlantic; shallow-water sediments of very variable thickness laid down
		Pliensbachian	186	Middle Lias	
		Sinemurian	194	Lower Lias, including Blue Lias	
		Hettangian	201		
	TRIASSIC	Rhaetian	205	Penarth Group	Marine transgression
		Norian	210	Mercia Mudstone Group	Subsidence, normal faulting along basin margins, deposition of supratidal coastal playa sediments
		Carnian	220		
		Ladinian	230		
		Anisian	235	Sherwood Sandstone Group	Renewed extension, alluvial deposition in south-north axial trough
		Scythian	242	Aylesbeare Mudstone Formation	Deposition of floodplain alluvial complex on desert peneplain
PALAEOZOIC	PERMIAN	Tatarian	250	Teignmouth, Exe, Netherton, Oddicombe and Watcombe breccias, & Dawlish Sandstone	Lithospheric extension, block faulting, alluvial and aeolian sedimentation in fault basins
		Kazanian	255		
		Kungurian	260		
		Artinskian	270		
		Sakmarian	280	Exeter Volcanic Series	Emplacement of Cornubian granites
			290		
	CARBONIFEROUS — SILESIAN	Stephanian	300		
		Westphalian	310	Bude Formation — Coal Measures (Kent)	Major Variscan folding
		Namurian	325	Crackington Formation	
	CARBONIFEROUS — DINANTIAN	Viséan		(cherts)	
		Tournaisian		(limestone) (limestones)	
				(volcanics)	
			360	(shales) (shales & limestones)	Formation of nappes
	DEVONIAN	LATE — Famennian		(slates) (schists & limestones)	Emplacement of Lizard Complex
		Frasnian	365	Torquay and Chudleigh lsts (sandstones) (NE France)	Formation of Lizard gabbro
		MIDDLE — Givetian	380	Staddon Grits and	
		Eifelian		Meadfoot Beds	
		EARLY — Emsian	400	Dartmouth Slates (schists)	
		Siegenian			
		Gedinnian			
	SILURIAN	Pridoli			
		Ludlow		(siltstones, sandstones)	
		Wenlock		(black shales) (black shales)	
		Llandovery	425	(mudstones, sandstones) (sandstones)	
	ORDOVICIAN	Ashgill	450	(sandstones) (tillites)	
		Caradoc			
		Llandeilo	460	(sandstones)	
		Llanvirn		(mudstones)	
		Arenig	485	(shales, sandstones) Grès Armoricain (Normandy (Cotentin))	Emplacement of granites on Jersey
		Tremadoc	495	(sandstone)	
	CAMBRIAN	LATE		Alderney Sandstone & (schists, sandstones)	
		MIDDLE		Rozel Conglomerate (grits, sandstones)	
		EARLY	570		
PRECAMBRIAN		Brioverian		(Volcanic Group) (volcanics)	Cadomian orogeny
				Jersey Shale Formation (greywackes, schists)	
			1000	(schists, cherts)	
		Pentevrian		(arkoses, volcanics)	
			2000	(gneiss)	Lihouan orogeny
			2700	Icart & Perelle gneisses (gneiss)	Icartian orogeny

Figure 3 Geological history and lithostratigraphy. Ages follow Haq et al. (1987) and Snelling (1985).

Palaeovalley is somewhat deeper, and falls south-westward into the Hurd Deep. The Lobourg Channel and Northern Palaeovalley form a continuous channel beneath the intervening tidal sand ridges.

Within the eastern English Channel, immediately southwest of the Dover Strait, there is a major suite of tidal sand ridges whose formation is related to the present hydrodynamic regime. They rise to heights up to 40 m above the planation surface and include the Varne Bank, Bullock Bank and part of The Bassurelle; in French waters lie the remainder of The Bassurelle, Le Colbart (The Ridge), Les Ridens, Vergoyer, Bassure de Baas, Battur and Bassurelle de la Somme. Nearshore sandbanks which only rise some 20 m or less above the sea bed include Shingle Bank, an unnamed bank off Brighton, Brambles Bank in The Solent, Dolphin Sand in Poole Bay, and Skerries Bank in Start Bay.

HISTORY OF GEOLOGICAL RESEARCH

A survey of the Dover Strait by Henry Marc Brunel during 1866 in connection with a proposed Channel Tunnel is believed to be the first marine geological survey in the world, and the first record of the use of a gravity corer (Donovan, 1967). Brunel proved a continuous outcrop of Chalk, and Topley (1872) constructed a cross-section and outcrop map of the Dover Strait. Hallez (1899) recorded early dredging surveys in the strait, but the first large-scale sampling surveys of the English Channel were from the ship *Pourquois-pas?* in the 1920s (Dangeard, 1922; 1929). Dangeard did not attempt a geological map, but recorded details of samples ranging in age from Permo-Triassic to Eocene. He also described large angular blocks which he considered to have been transported by ice.

King (1949, 1954) brought together all available information on the geology of the English Channel, including that derived from wartime Admiralty surveys, to produce outcrop and isopachyte maps. A large area of Permo-Triassic strata shown on his 1949 map was later shown by gravity coring (King, 1954) to be Lower Cretaceous, and a Tertiary outlier within Chalk halfway between the Isle of Wight and Cherbourg later yielded samples of Ypresian and Lutetian age (Curry, 1962). Stride (1960) demonstrated the possibility of mapping fold and fault patterns on the sea bed using transit sonar equipment; he initially worked off the Dorset coast and related features to the adjacent land geology. Donovan and Stride (1961) combined this technique with diving and gravity coring to survey the whole of the Jurassic outcrop east of the Isle of Portland.

The formation of the Channel Tunnel Study Group in 1957 resulted in further gravity coring, drilling and diving surveys in the Dover Strait. Additionally, one of the first continuous seismic profiling surveys using sparker equipment was carried out (Beckmann, 1960; Bruckshaw et al., 1961; Bickel, 1966); this yielded penetration of up to 70 m below sea bed in the Chalk, and detected pockets of Quaternary deposits as well as boundaries within the Chalk. More detailed drilling and seismic reflection surveys in 1964/65 (Grange and Muir Wood, 1970) identified zones of major faulting, and also two large channels cut to a depth of over 60 m below sea bed and filled with drift that yielded peat samples with ages spanning the Pleistocene–Holocene boundary (Callow et al., 1966).

During the 1960s, university teams from France and England continued to take samples in the English Channel. Many results were reported at the 1971 'Colloque sur la géologie de la Manche' conference in Paris (Pomerol, 1972),

and Dingwall (1971) produced a geological map of the area from Start Point to east of Selsey Bill. A further conference was organised in London for the Royal Society during 1974 (Philosophical Transactions of the Royal Society, Vol. A279). Both conference volumes contain comprehensive geological bibliographies for the English Channel.

Readings made in submarines first gave the gross outline of the gravity field and structure of the English Channel (Browne and Cooper, 1950; 1952). Combined with later observations, they enabled recognition of three gravity provinces in the English Channel and its Western Approaches (Smith and Curry, 1975).

A 1:1 000 000 scale solid geology map of the whole English Channel was published by the Bureau de Recherches Géologiques et Minières (BRGM) in 1974, and more recent work has included structural syntheses by Smith (1984, 1989). About 2000 sample stations have been occupied by university teams (Curry, 1989), half of which have yielded in-situ solid rock. The deep structure of the continental shelf has been investigated by the British Institutions Reflection Profiling Syndicate (BIRPS), although only lines SWAT 10 and 11 (Figure 1) lie within the report area (BIRPS and ECORS, 1986; McGeary et al., 1987).

Valleys cut into the floor of the English Channel include the Hurd Deep (Hamilton and Smith, 1972), and interest in these features increased as seismic surveys revealed complex networks of infilled palaeovalleys (Dingwall, 1975; Destombes et al., 1975). The latter authors favoured a subglacial origin for these valleys, as did Kellaway et al. (1975). Further detailed studies of the valley systems (Auffret and Alduc, 1977; Auffret et al., 1980) led to a 1:500 000 scale map of these features being produced by BRGM (Larsonneur et al., 1982a). Later, A J Smith (1985) suggested a catastrophic origin for the palaeovalley system by the overflow of an ice-dammed lake in the southern North Sea.

Stride (1963; 1982) elucidated the broad picture of mobile sea-bed sediments around the British Isles; a bed-load parting zone was identified south of the Isle of Wight, with a convergence in the Dover Strait (Kenyon and Stride, 1970). Particularly detailed sediment studies have been carried out in Start Bay (Robinson, 1961; Clarke, 1970; Hails, 1975), and the tidal sand ridges in the east of the area have been studied by several French workers (Berthois et al., 1969; Lapierre, 1975; Le Fournier, 1980). Syntheses of the sea-bed sediments of the English Channel (Auffret and Larsonneur, 1975; Larsonneur, 1977) led to publication of a 1:500 000 scale map by BRGM (Larsonneur et al., 1979).

HYDROCARBON ACTIVITY

In 1942, Dr G M Lees was working for the Petroleum Division of the Ministry of Supply in the planning of the Pipe-Line Under The Ocean (PLUTO) to carry fuel from England to France (King, 1954). His researches led after the war to oil industry interest in the area, examining the hypothesis that the narrow, steep anticlines in the zone between Weymouth and Swanage result from salt tectonics (Lees in King, 1954). The first well was sunk by British Petroleum on the Lulworth Banks in 1963 (Figure 1).

The discovery of the onshore Wytch Farm Oilfield southwest of Poole in 1973 (see Bristow et al., 1991) led to renewed interest in offshore prospects, and a considerable amount of seismic reflection data has since been acquired. Blocks have been awarded in rounds of UK Licence Allocation between 1977 and 1989. The first wells drilled under these licences were 98/22-1 and 98/22-2 (Figure 1) by the

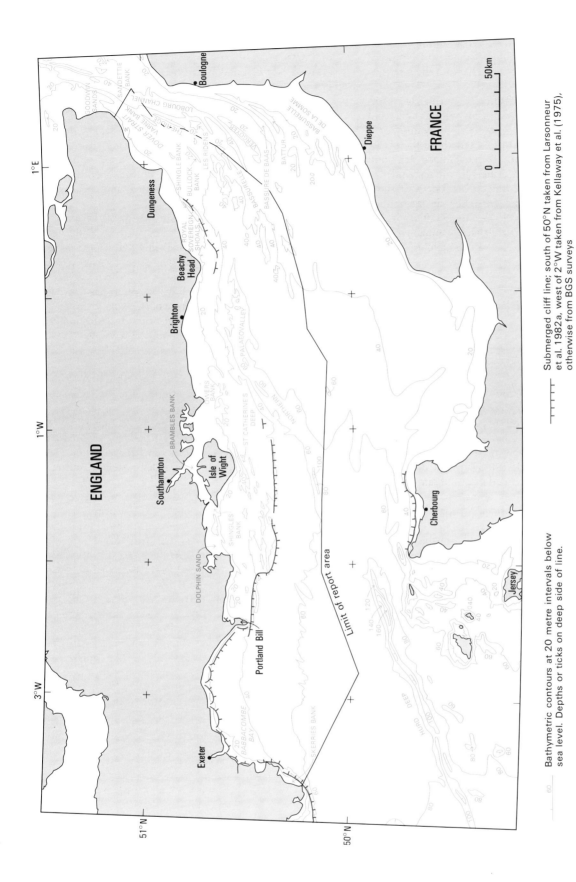

Bathymetric contours at 20 metre intervals below
sea level. Depths or ticks on deep side of line.

Submerged cliff line; south of 50°N taken from Larsonneur
et al. 1982a, west of 2°W taken from Kellaway et al. (1975),
otherwise from BGS surveys

Figure 4 Bathymetry of the English Channel region.

5

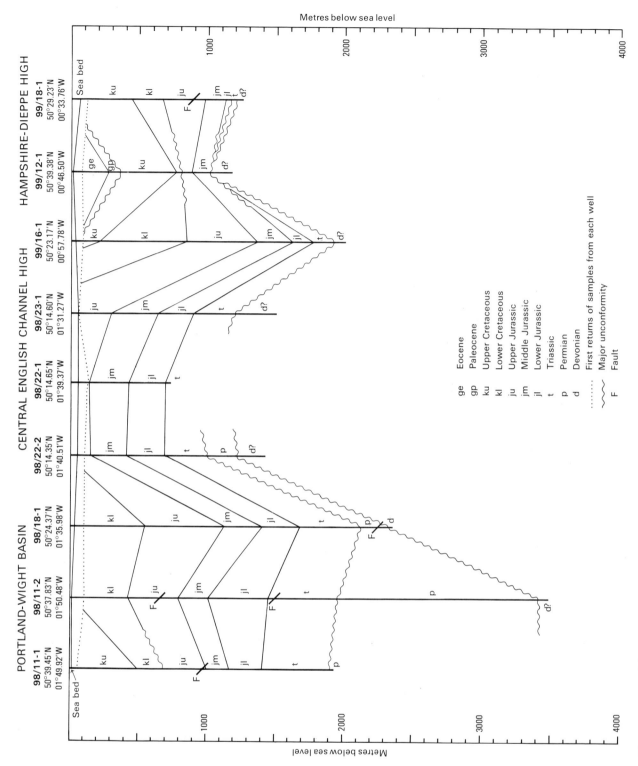

Figure 5 Simplified geological logs of commercial wells in the English Channel.

Gas Council in 1978/9 on the Central English Channel High. These were followed in 1983 by 98/23-1 of Conoco on the same structure, and 98/11-1 of the Gas Council to investigate the Portland–Wight monoclines. Sixteen offshore wells have been drilled to date, and simplified logs of nine of these wells are shown in Figure 5.

ACTIVITY OF THE BRITISH GEOLOGICAL SURVEY

The first offshore activity of the then Geological Survey of Great Britain (GSGB) was the involvement of Dr E R Shephard-Thorn in site investigations by the Channel Tunnel Study Group in 1964/5 (Destombes and Shephard-Thorn, 1971). In 1966, the GSGB became the Institute of Geological Sciences (IGS), prior to being renamed the British Geological Survey (BGS) in 1984.

In 1967, IGS embarked upon a reconnaissance survey of the Designated Continental Shelf of the United Kingdom in order to produce a series of 1:250 000 scale maps and regional reports (Fannin, 1989). This work has been largely funded by the Department of Energy. Geophysical surveys have been run using a combination of gravity meter, magnetometer, air gun, sparker, boomer, pinger, sidescan sonar and echosounder; these have been used to identify sample positions investigated with Shipek grab and vibrocorer or gravity corer. From 1973 to 1975, 27 boreholes were drilled in the area from the converted cargo vessel *mv Whitethorn* (Dingwall and Lott, 1979; Penn et al., 1980). The micropalaeontological stratigraphy of these boreholes, and of many gravity core samples, was detailed by Warrington and Owens (1977). The results of all these surveys, combined with any available commercial and academic data, have been the basis for compilation of the BGS map sheets (see inside back cover).

Additionally, as part of a research programme into geological mapping of coastal areas for engineering purposes, a detailed survey of the sea bed between Lyme Regis and West Bay, Dorset, was carried out (Darton et al., 1981). Furthermore, in view of the importance of marine-dredged aggregates in south-east England, BGS have also been commissioned by the Department of the Enviroment and the Crown Estate Commissioners to investigate the aggregate potential of the English Channel (Hamblin and Harrison, 1989; 1990).

2 Crustal structure

A major seismic boundary within the lithosphere, termed the Mohorovičić Discontinuity (Moho), separates the crust from the upper mantle. Seismic reflection profiles in southern Britain show the Moho (Figure 6), and a threefold division of the crust can be identified above it (Whittaker and Chadwick, 1984; Whittaker et al., 1986). Zone 1, which locally extends down to a depth of over 4 km, shows high-amplitude, laterally continuous, subhorizontal reflectors attributed to gently deformed post-Variscan sedimentary rocks. The underlying Zone 2, extending to a depth of 15 to 20 km, shows poor reflectors that probably represent strongly folded and faulted Precambrian and Palaeozoic rocks with igneous intrusions; it is cut by a few subplanar reflectors dipping at 20 to 30° that are interpreted as late Variscan thrusts. Most of these major thrusts in the middle crust appear to sole out at its base, which is thought to coincide with the brittle/ductile transition in rock behaviour. Zone 3, the lower crust, extends to the Moho at a depth of some 30 km, and displays short, flat, high-amplitude reflectors on seismic profiles. The upper part of Zone 3 may comprise crystalline basement rocks, and the lower part granulite gneisses. Interpretation of the offshore SWAT seismic reflection profiles (Figure 7) indicates that the threefold crustal zonation recognised in southern Britain also applies to the English Channel.

THE MOHO

On SWAT deep seismic sections in southern Britain the Moho appears flat at a moderately constant two-way travel time (TWTT) of about 10.5 seconds, corresponding to a depth of some 30 km (Chadwick, 1986; BIRPS and ECORS, 1986; Warner, 1987). Thick, low-velocity, post-Palaeozoic sediments in the uppermost crust should exert a time 'pushdown' on underlying reflectors. The absence of such a 'pushdown' at the level of the Moho suggests that it must actually rise under the post-Palaeozoic basins; that is, the crust thins under the basins, which are regionally isostatically compensated (Warner, 1987). Although the crust thins under post-Variscan basins, any such effect associated with earlier basins cannot be resolved due to Variscan and later extensional overprinting. The lower crust consequently shows no 'memory' of Variscan and Caledonian events (Meissner et al., 1986).

The reflection-determined depth of the Moho is in good agreement with that determined from seismic refraction (Matthews and Cheadle, 1986; Cheadle et al., 1987; Bois et al., 1989). Refraction experiments show the Moho beneath the Cornubian granite batholith at 27 to 30 km depth (Holder and Bott, 1971; Brooks et al., 1984), and the LISPB (Lithospheric Seismic Profile Britain) experiment suggested that the Moho shallows from some 35 km under Wales to less than 30 km in the central English Channel (Bamford et al., 1976). South-west of the Somme Fault in France (Figure 8), the depth to the Moho is generally 36 to 40 km, considerably deeper than beneath southern Britain (Bois et al., 1989). Beneath the English Channel the crust is therefore comparatively thin with a sharply defined Moho; Bamford and Prodehl (1977) consider such features to be characteristic of Variscan European crust. Initial interpretation of the ECORS deep-seismic reflection profile in northern France indicated

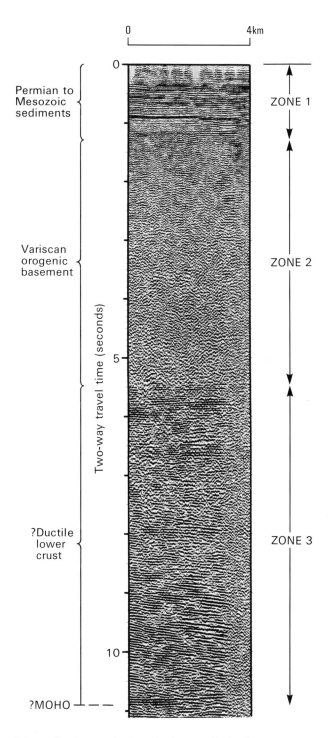

Figure 6 Deep-seismic reflection profile in the Wessex–Channel Basin, showing three-layer crust.

that the Moho was offset across the Wight–Bray Fault. However, recent wide-angle-reflection seismic surveys suggest that this is not the case (Hirn et al., 1987; Bois et al., 1989), so either the Wight–Bray Fault never cut the lower crust, or seismic layering within the lower crust postdates Variscan wrenching along the fault.

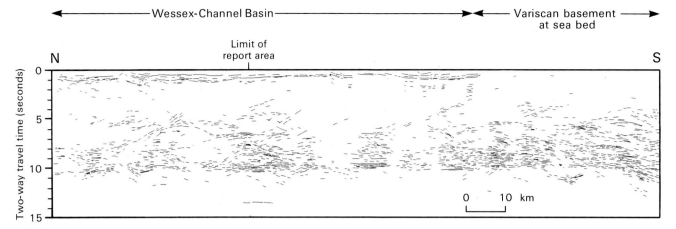

Figure 7   Line drawing of SWAT line 11.

ZONE 3, THE LOWER CRUST

This zone extends from 15 or 20 km to the Moho at about 30 km depth. It is characterised on seismic profiles by short, flat reflectors suggestive of some form of layering (Figures 6 and 7). In the south of the English Channel, the top and bottom of the lower crust sometimes correspond to bands of slightly stronger reflections (Matthews, 1986; Bois et al., 1989). On some SWAT lines, dipping reflectors similar to those in the middle crust extend downwards from the Moho, but displace neither it nor the lower crust. This lack of continuity between middle crustal and upper mantle dipping reflectors suggests that the lower crust is ductile (McGeary et al., 1987).

There is a general consensus that the Moho and the lamination in the lower crust of this area are no older than late Variscan in age (Meissner et al., 1987; Wenzel et al., 1987; Bois et al., 1989). This assumption is based on the relatively flat and shallow nature of the Moho, which shows no signs of roots to the Caledonian or Variscan orogens, and the absence of inferred Variscan thrusts within the lower crust. The primary cause of the layering in the lower crust may be compression, extension, or a thermal event, any of which could produce ductile shearing, metamorphism, or magmatism (Bois et al., 1987) resulting in horizontal interlayering of material with variable acoustic impedance. In central and southern Europe, the laminated lower crust was involved in strong deformation during the mid-Tertiary Alpine orogeny, showing that it existed by that time. It is possible that lower crustal layering developed towards the end of the Variscan orogeny by lithological differentiation due either to partial melting (Chadwick et al., 1989) or viscous-ordering processes (Trappe, 1990).

On the other hand, the crust beneath the British Isles has undergone significant Mesozoic thinning during the formation of sedimentary basins (Matthews, 1986; McGeary et al., 1987), so it is possible that the laminations indicate some form of extensional tectonic fabric of Mesozoic age. The nature and age of the laminated lower crust has excited worldwide interest in view of its possible linkage to Mesozoic extension and basin development (Dawson et al., 1986; Annales Geophysicae, 1987, pp.323–408; Mereu et al., 1989). Interpretations of the seismic layering invoke the presence of low-velocity, high-conductivity fluids such as water, brine, carbon dioxide, carbonic acid and methane. The fluids could have been introduced through subduction of sediments and other upper crustal rocks.

Granulites are considered to be representative of the lowest crustal rocks, and their metamorphism through interaction with water or brine would produce less-dense amphibolites.

Interlayered granulites and amphibolites with differing seismic velocities could then cause the reflections (Hall, 1986; Wenzel et al., 1987). However, investigations of mylonite zones produced by ductile shearing have latterly shown that they can produce strong reflections (Hurich et al., 1985; McDonough and Fountain, 1988); they may therefore also be commonly found in the lower crust.

ZONE 2, THE MIDDLE CRUST

The middle crust is seismically largely unreflective, and extends from 15 to 20 km depth up to either the post-Variscan sedimentary cover or, where such rocks are absent, to the sea bed. It corresponds to strongly deformed rocks of the Variscan foldbelt.

Dipping reflectors are common both offshore (Figure 7) and in southern England. They extend deep into the middle crust, and can be traced upwards to major Variscan thrusts cropping out in the Cornubian Massif (Holder and Leveridge, 1986a; Hillis and Day, 1987; Edwards et al., 1989). Williams and Brooks (1985) considered that SWAT profiles show the Variscan Front penetrating to at least 17 km depth, probably terminating at the top of the lower crust (Bois et al., 1988). SWAT profiles also show the Lizard–Dodman–Start Thrust (Figure 8), and Brewer (1984) interpreted a commercial line between Beachy Head and Dungeness as showing thrusts extending below 15 km without flattening out.

The ECORS deep-seismic line in north-east France (Cazes et al., 1986; Hirn et al., 1987; Pinet et al., 1987) revealed similar crustal features to those underlying southern Britain and the English Channel. The Variscan Front, or Faille du Midi (Figure 8), is listric near outcrop, and gently dipping at a depth of 5 to 10 km for some 100 km to the Somme Fault. Above it are Devonian and Carboniferous rocks of the Ardennes–Dinant Nappe, and below it the autochthonous foreland composed of undeformed Lower Palaeozoic and Precambrian rocks of the Caledonian Brabant Massif.

The Lizard–Dodman–Start Complex is best known west of the Start–Cotentin Line, where it forms the base of the lowest crystalline nappe in the area. The nappe consists in part of ophiolitic rocks obducted from the Rheic Ocean floor, and it overlies metamorphic rocks that may be of Late Palaeozoic age (Holder and Leveridge, 1986a; Evans, 1990). Bacon (1975) noted that a Bouguer gravity-anomaly high runs east from Start Point; although the total magnetic field (Figure 9) is smooth and relatively low over this feature, it may represent an eastward continuation of the Lizard–Dodman–Start Thrust Nappe.

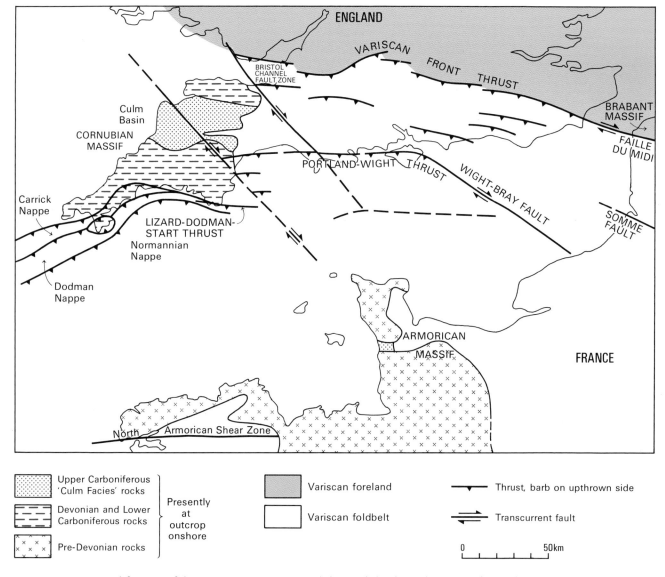

	Upper Carboniferous 'Culm Facies' rocks				Variscan foreland		Thrust, barb on upthrown side
	Devonian and Lower Carboniferous rocks	Presently at outcrop onshore			Variscan foldbelt		Transcurrent fault
	Pre-Devonian rocks						

0   50km

Figure 8 Structural features of the Variscan orogeny around the English Channel. In part after Holder and Leveridge (1986b).

Magnetic anomalies in the area (Figure 9) are largely due to basic igneous and metamorphic rocks within Zone 2, for the sedimentary rocks of Zone 1 are relatively weakly magnetised. Basal Permian volcanics produce very well-defined anomalies to the west of the Start–Cotentin Line, but these are absent in the study area. The Isle of Wight Arcuate Anomaly may be an extension of the Great Magnetic Anomaly of the Paris Basin (Terris and Bullerwell, 1965; Dingwall, 1971); its north-westerly trending portion runs to the south-west of the Wight–Bray Fault, before turning into a south-westerly direction to run into the Alderney–Ushant Anomaly (Avedik, 1975; Gerard, 1975; Lefort and Segoufin, 1978). The arcuate anomaly is probably due to basic igneous rocks intruded along fault zones (Autran et al., 1986; Gerard and Weber, 1971), although several interpretations of its age and structure have been proposed (Le Bourgne et al., 1971; Kellaway and Hancock, 1983).

ZONE 1, POST-VARISCAN SEDIMENTARY BASINS

This zone represents post-Variscan basin sediments, which are present over almost the whole report area except the extreme west, and are locally in excess of 4 km thick. On seis-

mic records the sediments produce strong, laterally continuous reflectors within a system of basins termed the Wessex–Channel Basin (Chapter 4). The main elements of this basin can be discerned from the Bouguer anomaly map shown in Figure 10. The Start–Cotentin Line, which forms the western limit of the report area, corresponds with a series of gravity highs, to the east of which there is a well-defined gravity province (Smith and Curry, 1975) bounded to its east by the Wight–Bray Fault. East of the Wight–Bray Fault, the anomalies trend slightly more west-north-west to east-south-east, reflecting Variscan structural control. The most prominent low anomalies are associated with the Tertiary Hampshire– Dieppe Basin, and the Tertiary Paris Basin. The Weald Basin gravity low passes offshore into the gravity high of the Weald–Artois Anticlinorium.

The offshore basins appear from gravity values to be isostatically compensated (Browne and Cooper, 1952); this is consistent with the evidence of seismic profiling, which indicates a compensating rise in the Moho beneath the basins (Chadwick, 1986). The Cornubian and Armorican massifs remained as structural highs during the formation of the post-Variscan basins because of the buoyancy and rigidity of the granites within them (Smith and Curry, 1975; Lake and Karner, 1987).

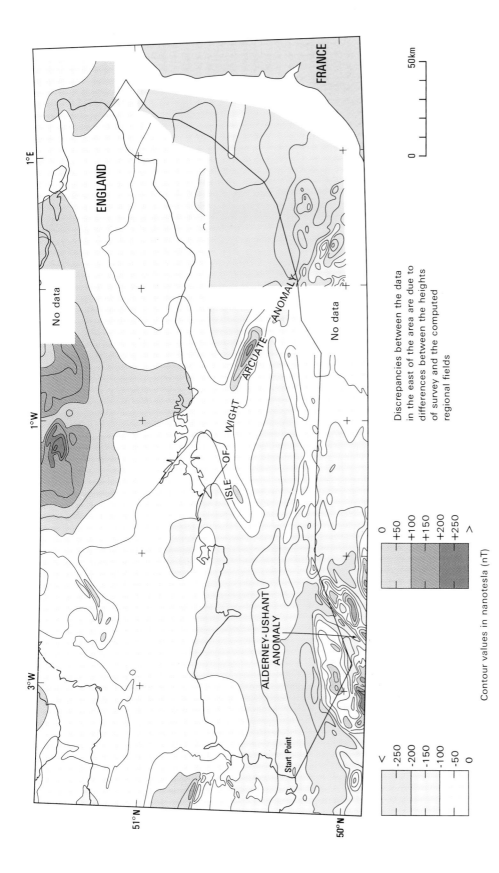

Figure 9 Aeromagnetic total-field anomaly map of the English Channel region. Compiled from published BGS maps.

Contour values in nanotesla (nT)

Discrepancies between the data
in the east of the area are due to
differences between the heights
of survey and the computed
regional fields

No data

No data

ENGLAND

FRANCE

ISLE OF WIGHT

ARCUATE ANOMALY

ALDERNEY-USHANT
ANOMALY

Start Point

1°E

1°W

3°W

51°N

50°N

50km

0

+50

+100

+150

+200

+250

>

<

-250

-200

-150

-100

-50

0

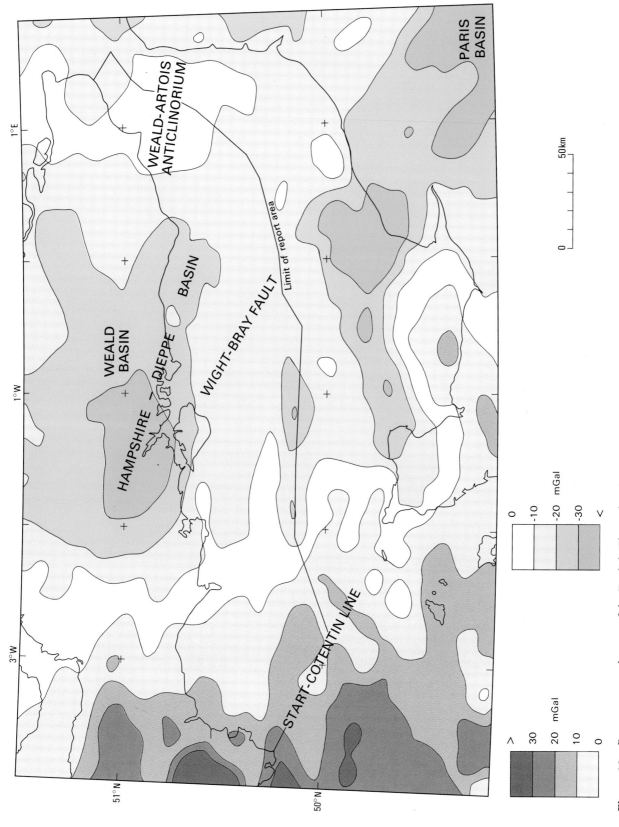

Figure 10 Bouguer anomaly map of the English Channel region.

12

3 Pre-Permian basement

Strata in the report area may be readily divided into rocks which predate the Variscan orogeny and those which postdate it. The former are the pre-Permian rocks that now make up a fractured basement of metamorphic, sedimentary and igneous rocks, whereas the latter fill sedimentary basins which formed on that basement.

Pre-Permian rocks are present beneath the entire English Channel, but crop out only as nearshore continuations of on-shore outcrops in Devon, Cornwall, Brittany, Normandy and The Boulonnais (Figure 2). In Devon and Cornwall to the west of the report area, the bulk of the outcropping strata are Devonian and Carboniferous sediments intruded by late Variscan granites. To the south of the report area, the Cotentin Peninsula is the northern tip of the Armorican Massif which extends southwards and westwards across Brittany; here there are rocks of all systems from Precambrian to Carboniferous. In the east, strata of Silurian to Carbon-iferous age are known from the Ferques Inlier of The Boulonnais (Figure 11).

Offshore wells have proved only Devonian strata at depth beneath the English Channel area, although older rocks may be present. Carboniferous rocks are interpreted to be present at depth in the east of the area as a continuation of the buried Kent Coalfield.

Geophysical anomalies indicate variable basement types in the western part of the report area (Day and Williams, 1970). In the north, the magnetic field is characterised by weak gradients, and low Bouguer gravity anomalies are present, indicating deep burial of magnetic basement extending from Cornubia. By contrast, in the south there are high-frequency magnetic anomalies which, to the south of the Ouessant–Alderney fault zone (Evans, 1990), correspond to the shal-lower magnetic basement of the offshore extension of the Armorican Massif (Lefort, 1979; Lefort and Segoufin, 1978).

Precambrian rocks are known in the Channel Islands, Normandy and Brittany. It is possible that Pentevrian rocks (Figure 3) at these localities continue at depth to connect with the Baltic Shield (Anderton et al., 1979), in which case they underlie the report area. Beneath Cornubia, Cope (1987) has proposed Precambrian quartz-mica schists or mica schists faulted against rhyolitic volcanic rocks. In the Cotentin Peninsula, a weathered Pentevrian surface is over-lain by Brioverian marine sediments and spilitic volcanics which were subjected to deformation, metamorphism and plutonism during the Cadomian orogeny. The Brioverian ig-neous activity continued into the Cambrian. It is not known whether Brioverian strata occur beneath the offshore area, and the same can be said of rocks of Early Palaeozoic age. However, the latter are known in both southern England and Cotentin, and so may be present at depth beneath the English Channel.

During the Early Palaeozoic, southern Britain lay to the south of the Iapetus and Tornquist oceans, which contracted as the continents of Laurentia, Baltica and Avalonia/ Gondwana converged to form the Caledonides. Conditions in the English Channel area at this time varied from conti-

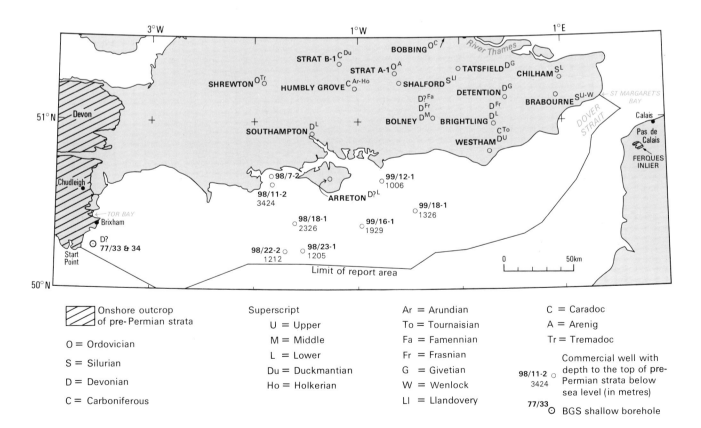

Figure 11 Positions of wells where pre-Permian strata have been proved at depth beneath southern England and the English Channel.

13

nental to shelf-marine, with major transgressions during Early Cambrian, Arenig (early Ordovician) and Llandovery (early Silurian) times.

During the Devonian, the report area lay on the north side of the Rheic or Proto-Tethys Ocean which separated the new continent of Laurasia to the north from that of Gondwana to the south. Gondwana moved north during the Devonian and Carboniferous, to close the Rheic Ocean. Collision continued from the late Viséan to the Namurian, causing the Variscan orogeny and contributing to the formation of the supercontinent of Pangaea (Ziegler, 1982). More specifically, the report area lay on the north side of an elongate back-arc basin, the Variscan Foredeep Basin, which extended from southern Ireland to Poland, and lay to the north of the Normannian High (Ziegler, 1982). The occurrence of ophiolite in the Lizard Complex (Evans, 1990) indicates that this basin was floored by oceanic crust. Holder and Leveridge (1986b) proposed that a southward-dipping subduction zone operated within the basin, while the Normannian High was the surface expression of a thrust nappe whose northward movement was driven by that of Gondwana.

As subduction proceeded and the Normannian and structurally lower nappes moved northward, the axis of the foredeep basin also moved northward, and marine sedimentation continued into the Carboniferous to produce the marine Culm facies of south-west England. As the nappe complex moved northward, it incorporated progressively younger sediments, so that the dates of metamorphism vary from 365–345 Ma (Late Devonian) in south Cornwall to 340–267 Ma (Early Carboniferous to Late Permian) in the core of the Carboniferous syncline in Devon (Evans, 1990).

The Variscan nappes are cut by a series of south-south-east-trending strike-slip faults (Evans, 1990). These may include the Wight–Bray Fault (Figure 8), which crosses the English Channel (Holder and Leveridge, 1986a; 1986b; Day, 1986). These authors proposed a 400 km dextral offset along this fault, for they consider that geophysical evidence indicates that the main structural zones of the German Variscides terminate against its eastern side, and that magnetic and gravity anomalies associated with the Variscan orogeny in south-west England terminate against its western side beneath the English Channel. There appears to be little evidence that this fault continues north-west from the Isle of Wight, hence this degree of lateral movement can only be accommodated if the fault were an active transcurrent fault at the time that subduction and northward nappe movement were occurring to the west.

Little is known of the Devonian and Carboniferous rocks believed to underlie the report area between the Wight–Bray Fault and the Faille du Midi (Figure 8). The Faille du Midi marks the Variscan Front, to the north of which Early Carboniferous marine-shelf sediments and Late Carboniferous paralic sediments (the Coal Measures of the Kent Coalfield) were formed on the craton north of the Rheic Ocean.

By the end of the Carboniferous Period, the Variscan orogenic zone had become a basement complex, broken by thrusts and transcurrent faults into a series of rigid blocks. These blocks, and movements along the fractures between them, controlled the development of later sedimentary basins in response to changing stress patterns.

PRECAMBRIAN

In Britain, the most southerly outcrops of undoubted Precambrian rocks are in south-west Wales, and none are known from boreholes south of the River Thames (Figure 11). The oldest rocks bordering the area are the Icart and Perelle gneisses of the Channel Islands, dated at 2620 ± 50 Ma (Adams, 1976). These have been ascribed to a metamorphic phase linked to the Icartian orogeny (Figure 3), as has a gneiss in the northern Cotentin Peninsula (Figure 1) between Cap de la Hague and Cherbourg (Pomerol, 1980).

On the Cotentin Peninsula, the weathered Pentevrian basement is composed largely of granitic and quartz-dioritic orthogneiss injected with granodioritic intrusions dated at around 1000 Ma (Pomerol, 1980). The Pentevrian basement is unconformably overlain by early Brioverian rocks. These are arkoses, greywackes, amphibolite-mica-schists and spilites that are in turn overlain by finer-grained, middle Brioverian schists and black cherts. Basal greywackes of the upper Brioverian rest unconformably on the middle Brioverian, and are overlain by schists. In the Channel Islands, the Brioverian Jersey Shale Formation (turbiditic mudstones, siltstones and greywackes) is succeeded by andesitic and acidic lavas and tuffs (Volcanic Group).

The Brioverian deposits were subjected to deformation, plutonism and metamorphism during the Cadomian orogeny, which continued from before 600 Ma to about 570 Ma. Associated with this orogeny was the intrusion of granites, granodiorites, diorites and gabbros, including the foliated l'Erée Adamellite of Guernsey at 660 ± 25 Ma (Bishop et al., 1975).

CAMBRIAN

No Cambrian rocks are known beneath southern England, but in the Channel Islands the Alderney Sandstone and the Rozel Conglomerate on Jersey (Figure 3) are believed to be early Cambrian alluvial-fan sediments (Doré, 1972). No later Cambrian strata are present. The Alderney Sandstone is almost 800 m thick and comprises red and yellow arkosic sandstones with sporadic siltstones.

In the Cotentin Peninsula, the early Cambrian is represented by red schistose grits of continental character, succeeded by an arenaceous formation deposited in a coastal environment. The middle Cambrian, dated by the trilobite *Paradoxides*, consists of green schists that were originally deposited during a marine transgression. These are overlain by red sandstones deposited during the succeeding regression. The late Cambrian is represented locally by a white sandstone. It is not known whether the lithologies preserved in Cotentin extend beneath the English Channel.

Intense igneous activity marked both the start and close of the Cambrian Period in the Armorican Massif and the Channel Islands; the Cobo Adamellite of Guernsey has been dated at 570 ± 15 Ma, and the granites on Jersey at 520 ± 4 and 490 ± 15 Ma (Anderton et al., 1979).

ORDOVICIAN

In England, the most southerly outcrop of rocks of clearly defined Ordovician age is at Tortworth in Gloucestershire, where over 1000 m of Tremadoc marine shales occur. However, a variety of Ordovician rocks have been proved at depth in boreholes beneath the Weald and farther west (Figure 11). At Shrewton, a thick sequence of Tremadoc siltstones with thin sandstone and mudstone bands has been proved, and lithologically similar strata crop out in the Belgian Ardennes to the east; it is therefore possible that they are continuous at depth beneath the Weald and the eastern

English Channel. The Strat A1 borehole proved quartzitic and glauconitic sandstones of Arenig age which are fine grained and micaceous with a calcite cement. At Bobbing, micaceous sandy shales with thin quartzitic sandstones of Caradoc age were drilled (Lister et al., 1969).

In the Armorican Massif, the variably thick (200–1000 m) Grès Armoricain orthoquartzite (Figure 3) marks the start of the Arenig transgression. It is overlain by Llanvirn and Llandeilo mudstones and sandstones, but sedimentation generally became sandier during Caradocian and Ashgillian times. Some limestones and basic submarine lavas and tuffs were deposited in the Ashgillian (Pomerol, 1980). The Llanvirnian Schistes à Calymènes (Figure 3) of northern France are part of the same province as contemporary Welsh strata, implying continuity of deposition across the English Channel.

SILURIAN

Silurian rocks have been drilled in several boreholes beneath the Weald and north Kent (Figure 11). At Shalford, Llandoverian mudstones were proved interbedded with sandstones and siltstones, and at Brabourne and Chilham, dark blue to grey and black graptolitic shales were penetrated; those at Chilham are of late Llandovery age, whereas those at Brabourne are late Llandovery to early Wenlock. In all three boreholes, the top few metres of the Silurian were stained red and purple, presumably as a result of later subaerial weathering. High dips in all three wells were imposed during the Caledonian and/or the Variscan orogeny.

On the Armorican Massif, most Llandoverian sediments are sandstones (Figure 3). However, on the Cotentin Peninsula, silty sandstones and black shales were deposited locally, and towards the east near Caen (Figure 1), there are Llandoverian shales and siltstones with fucoids. During

CARBONIFEROUS	SILESIAN	Westphalian	GRÈS et SCHISTES
		Namurian	Grey sandstone
	DINANTIAN	Viséan	CALCAIRES
		Tournaisian	DOLOMIE de HURE CALCSCHISTES de la VALLÉE HEUREUSE
DEVONIAN	UPPER	Famennian	GRÈS et PSAMMITES de FIENNES et ST. GODELEINE
			SCHISTES ROUGES d'HYDREQUENT
		Frasnian	CALCAIRE de FERQUES
			SCHISTES de BEAULIEU
	MIDDLE	Givetian	CALCAIRE de BLACOURT
			GRÈS et SCHISTES de CAFFIERS
	LOWER	Siegenian to Eifelian	
		Gedinnian	SCHISTES BARIOLES ROUGES et VERTS
SIL-URIAN		Ludlow	ARGILES SCHISTEUSES

Figure 12 Generalised Palaeozoic stratigraphy of north-eastern France. Based on outcrop in the Ferques Inlier and nearby boreholes.

Wenlock and Ludlow times, black shales and limestones were deposited over the massif; these are overlain by late Ludlovian micaceous siltstones with interbedded white sandstones.

Silurian strata have been proved beneath Devonian rocks in numerous boreholes in the Pas de Calais (Figures 11 and 12). These are lithologically similar to those in south-east England; they consist of black and sometimes yellow, slightly cleaved shales, and the presence of *Monograptus colonus* indicates an early Ludlovian age (Pruvost and Pringle, 1924). In the Ferques Inlier, Devonian rocks lie unconformably on untectonised Ludlovian black shales (Prevost, 1839).

In view of the preponderance of deep-water marine sediments of various ages in the Silurian of southern England, Armorica and The Boulonnais, it is likely that similar deposits were formed in the English Channel area, but none has been proved.

DEVONIAN

Strata of Devonian age crop out widely in and immediately off south-west England (Figure 2), as well as in the Ferques Inlier (Figures 11 and 12) and the Cotentin Peninsula. They have also been proved at depth beneath southern England, the English Channel and the Pas de Calais. Eight wells drilled in the central part of the English Channel have penetrated strata of presumed Devonian age at depths of 1006 to 3424 m (Figure 11), with the deepest lying beneath the Portland–Wight Basin to the west of the Isle of Wight.

No fossils have been found in offshore wells, and since there is little lithological variation, the Devonian rocks recovered cannot be classified. Well 98/11-2, the deepest drilled to date in the English Channel, recovered 16 m of grey, hard, moderately foliated pelite with thin, irregular, quartz veinlets. The thickest Devonian sequence recorded is the 302 m of metasediments in well 98/23-1, where the strata consist of generally pink, partly off-white or dark red phyllite that is tentatively referred to the Devonian. In well 99/12-1, 181 m of reddish grey, hard, fissured pelite with interbedded metaquartzite were drilled. Other wells bottomed in either pelites, phyllites or quartzites. In all the wells, the supposed Devonian is overlain unconformably by Permian or younger sediments.

Lower Devonian

During the Early Devonian the report area coincided with the Cornwall Basin (Ziegler, 1982), a part of the Variscan Foredeep Basin. To the north lay the Old Red Sandstone continent of Laurasia from which much sediment was derived. Two smaller landmasses to the south also provided sediment, the Normannian High which ran westward from the Channel Islands, and the Mid German High which extended eastward from just north of the Seine Estuary.

The oldest proven Devonian strata in south-west England are the Dartmouth Slates (Dineley, 1966), which consist of fluvial and deltaic sandstones, siltstones and mudstones that have a nonmarine fauna and flora indicating a Gedinnian to Siegenian age. These are believed to represent the southern limit of coastal-plain deposition on the flank of Laurasia (Anderton et al., 1979).

The Meadfoot Beds succeed the Dartmouth Slates conformably, and comprise finely alternating slates, siltstones and sandstones, with conglomerates and uncommon but persistent marine limestones. Coarse agglomerates and tuffs occur within these slates around Brixham (Edmonds et al., 1975).

The Staddon Grits succeed the Meadfoot Beds conformably but possibly diachronously; they consist of sandstones, intra-formational conglomerates, and thin limestones.

The rocks which crop out at Start Point are interbanded hornblende and chlorite schists, mica schists, and pink dolomitised limestones. They are faulted against Meadfoot Beds to the north, and since they show similar structures to that unit, they may also be Devonian strata once buried to greater depths and subsequently elevated by normal faulting (Coward and McClay, 1983; Edmonds et al., 1975).

Devonian rocks crop out offshore from Start Point to the north side of Tor Bay (Figure 2), extending offshore for up to about 8 km. To the east of Start Point, 3.9 m of mica and hornblende schists were proved in BGS boreholes 77/33 and 34 in an offshore occurrence of the Start Point metamorphic rocks (Figure 11). The remainder of the outcrop is likely to comprise mainly Lower Devonian rocks, with Middle and Upper Devonian strata around Torbay. Lithologies comparable with the Dartmouth Slates, Meadfoot Beds and Staddon Grits may be expected to extend offshore into the report area.

Several boreholes in the Southampton area (Figure 11) record Early Devonian continental sequences dominated by thick sandstones that are partly conglomeratic or interbedded with red shales and siltstones. Their total thickness exceeds 900 m, and ages of 390 to 380 Ma have been obtained at Arreton (N J P Smith, written communication, 1986). Very few Early Devonian strata are known in The Boulonnais, which lay on the Brabant Massif to the north of the Cornwall Basin (Ziegler, 1982); Gedinnian variegated red and green schists are known from boreholes, but no strata are preserved in the Ferques Inlier. However, Cotentin lay on the flanks of the Normannian High to the south of the basin, where inter-bedded sandstones and mudstones of Gedinnian age, and highly fossiliferous interbedded limestones and mudstones of Siegenian age, were deposited.

Middle Devonian

The Staddon Grits of Devon (Figure 3) are succeeded conformably by early Eifelian, black, fossiliferous shales and slates with thin limestones and some lavas and tuffs. Volcanism occurred frequently from Middle Devonian to Early Carboniferous times as the Cornwall Basin was affected by episodes of tectonism, generally yielding spilitic pillow lavas, tuffs and agglomerates. During the Givetian, very pure, massive or thinly bedded, pale grey limestones formed in a belt extending from Devon through the Isle of Wight to Belgium. These are well exposed on the north side of Tor Bay and at Chudleigh (Figure 11).

The Devonian succession of the Ferques Inlier (Wallace, 1968, 1969; Ager and Wallace, 1966) shows rapid changes from marine to lagoonal facies as the Devonian shoreline of the Brabant Massif moved back and forth. The Grès de Caffiers (Figure 12) is a continental formation of red and green sandstones with basal conglomerates which rests upon Ludlovian black shales. It is overlain by highly fossiliferous, black, shaly, backreef limestones of the Calcaire de Blacourt, that are also of Givetian age.

At the Detention borehole (Figure 11), limestones with corals and brachiopods are predominant in the Givetian sequence; these beds resemble the Calcaire de Blacourt and point to the lateral continuity of the limestones across the Dover Strait. At Tatsfield (Figure 11), interbedded micritic shales and limestones yielded Givetian palynomorphs (Mortimer and Chaloner, 1972). No Middle Devonian sediments are known from Normandy, but it is believed that

deeper-water shales were deposited in the southern part of the report area to the south of the limestone belt (Ziegler, 1982).

Upper Devonian

During the Late Devonian and Early Carboniferous, a north-ward marine transgression occurred towards Wales and central England, causing the mainly shallow-water limestones of south Devon to be overlain by deeper-water cephalopod limestones and ostracod shales. The succession deposited in Frasnian and Famennian times in south Devon and Cornwall is of very variable thickness (House, 1963) owing to the development of submarine highs and basins. Up to 1500 m of shales were deposited in the basins, with condensed sequences of pelagic limestones over the highs. Volcanic rocks are associated with the basinal sediments.

Conditions in The Boulonnais were similar to those in Devon, with the Calcaire de Blacourt succeeded conformably in the Frasnian by the Schistes de Beaulieu (red shales with lenses of dolomite and limestone) and grey and pink, highly fossiliferous limestones of the Calcaire de Ferques. The Famennian is represented by the Schistes Rouges d'Hydrequent (red shales with thin, impersistent sandstones) and the pure white sandstones of the Grès et Psammites de Fiennes et St Godeleine.

In the Brightling borehole (Figure 11), slickensided, brown, Frasnian mudstones with minor sandstones (Butler, 1981) are faulted against Mesozoic rocks. At Bolney, the Middle Devonian argillaceous sequence passes up into interbedded limestones and mudstones from which Butler (1981) recorded Frasnian fossils, although limestones near the top of the Devonian section may be equivalent to the Calcaire de Ferques. Butler (1981) also noted that quartzitic sandstones at the top of the Bolney section resemble the Grès et Psammites de Fiennes et St Godeleine of the Ferques Inlier, suggesting that these also may extend beneath the English Channel. At Westham, red shales and thin limestones that have yielded Late Devonian miospores apparently pass conformably into Tournaisian beds. In the eastern English Channel no drilling has taken place, but N J P Smith (1985) inferred Devonian strata rising to only 600 m depth below the western end of the Dover Strait.

On the Cotentin Peninsula the Middle Devonian is absent, and the Late Devonian succession starts with a basal conglomerate overlain by sandstones passing up into some 200 m of siltstones with sandstone lenses. Cotentin still lay on the flanks of the Normannian High to the south of the Cornwall Basin (Ziegler, 1982), and it may be assumed that thick, deep-water shales accumulated over most of the report area.

CARBONIFEROUS

Carboniferous rocks crop out both in the Culm Basin of Devon (Figure 8) and in the Ferques Inlier (Figures 11 and 12); they have also been proved at depth beneath south-east England and the Pas de Calais. They do not crop out offshore within the report area, and their offshore extent below the Mesozoic is problematic. The Kent Coalfield extends offshore, possibly as far as the coast of north-east France, and Dinantian strata are believed to extend offshore in the vicinity of Hastings (Dungeness-Boulogne and Thames Estuary Solid Geology sheets; N J P Smith, 1985). Farther west, N J P Smith (1985) shows undifferentiated Devonian/Carboniferous under most of the report area, but only

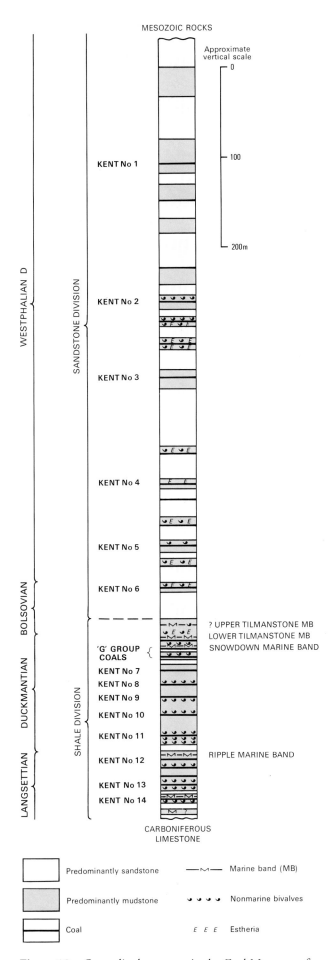

Figure 13 below the image:

MESOZOIC ROCKS

Approximate vertical scale

KENT No 1

KENT No 2

KENT No 3

KENT No 4

KENT No 5

KENT No 6

? UPPER TILMANSTONE MB
LOWER TILMANSTONE MB
SNOWDOWN MARINE BAND

'G' GROUP COALS

KENT No 7
KENT No 8
KENT No 9
KENT No 10
KENT No 11
KENT No 12

RIPPLE MARINE BAND

KENT No 13
KENT No 14

CARBONIFEROUS LIMESTONE

WESTPHALIAN D — BOLSOVIAN — DUCKMANTIAN — LANGSETTIAN

SANDSTONE DIVISION — SHALE DIVISION

Predominantly sandstone   —ᴹ— Marine band (MB)

Predominantly mudstone   ᵥ ᵥ ᵥ Nonmarine bivalves

Coal   E E E Estheria

Figure 13 Generalised sequence in the Coal Measures of east Kent. After Shephard-Thorn (1988).

Devonian has been proved. If any Carboniferous strata are present, they probably take the form of relatively small thrust slices or fault blocks within the Devonian. The Carboniferous outcrop in Devon takes the form of an east–west-orientated synclinorium, the axis of which lies well to the north of the report area; it is unlikely that this structure extends offshore.

Dinantian

The passage between the Devonian and Dinantian in Devon is conformable, for the deposition of deep-water mudstones with thin sandstones and limestones continued without interruption. Tuffs, agglomerates and lavas were extruded locally, and towards the close of the Dinantian, radiolarian cherts were deposited under quiet conditions in fairly deep water.

In the Ferques Inlier, the Devonian is similarly seen to pass up conformably into a Dinantian shelf facies. The black, calcareous Calcschistes de la Vallée Heureuse are seen only as a thrust slice, but are similar in facies to the Devonian shelf limestones. The lower part of the overlying limestone succession (Dolomie de Hure) is dolomitised, but the main part is characterised by algal accumulations which can be traced for considerable distances.

In southern England, Dinantian limestones have been proved in a number of boreholes beneath the Weald and the Kent Coalfield. Up to 300 m of bituminous, crystalline, oolitic and pyritous limestones with calcitic mudstones have been found. At Westham, 130 m of Tournaisian limestone unconformably overlie Upper Devonian at a depth of 1234 m, and at Humbly Grove to the north-west, an early Tournaisian to early Viséan age was obtained. Seismic profiles indicate that up to 900 m of Dinantian limestone extend beneath the Dover Strait (Cameron et al., 1992).

Silesian

During the Namurian, the southern part of the report area became land as the Variscan nappes advanced northward, while the northern part of the area, along with Devon, south-east England and The Boulonnais lay within the Variscan Foredeep Basin (Ziegler, 1982). Sediment was derived both from the Normannian High and the North Armorican block to the south, and the Welsh and Brabant massifs to the north. In Devon, a thick sequence of shales with thin turbiditic sandstones was laid down to form the Crackington Formation. No Namurian rocks are known in south-east England due to pre-Westphalian folding and erosion, whereas grey Namurian sandstones do crop out in the Ferques Inlier, although most of the sequence is missing because of Variscan thrusting.

During the Westphalian, the nappes had moved northward such that deposition was restricted to a belt running from north Devon through Kent and the Dover Strait to The Boulonnais. The Westphalian does not crop out at Ferques, but has been proved in boreholes where the Grès et Schistes include thin coal seams and carbonaceous sandstones.

The Kent Coalfield takes the form of an elongate west-north-west-trending synclinal basin (Shephard-Thorn, 1988) that extends beneath the English Channel towards France (Gallois, 1965). The deepest known part is at St Margaret's Bay (Figure 11), where Westphalian rocks overlie the Dinantian unconformably. Westphalian rocks offshore may be more than 1600 m thick (Cameron et al., 1992), but the maximum proven thickness onshore is 884 m. This consists of mudstones, siltstones, sandstones, seatearths and coals (Figure 13) laid down in an intermittently subsiding basin. Marine bands in the succession enable correlation with other areas. The sequence is divided into two major lithological groups: the Shale Division consists of 213 m of mudstones with subordinate sandstones, including eight main coal seams and at least four marine bands. The overlying Sandstone Division comprises around 670 m of sandstones and sandy shales with six main coal seams.

To the west of the Kent Coalfield in the Strat B1 borehole (Figure 11), shales and sandstones with thin coals underlain by a dolerite sill are of Duckmantian (Westphalian B) age. Farther north, the Coal Measures are mainly Westphalian D (Allsop et al., 1982). Both in the Kent Coalfield and to the west, geochemical maturity indicates that a considerable thickness of younger strata, most likely of Carboniferous age, was deposited but removed prior to the Jurassic transgression. This is characteristic of Westphalian basins lying immediately north of the Variscan Front.

4   Post-Variscan structural evolution

Following the Variscan orogeny, thick sedimentary sequences of Permian to Tertiary age were laid down in the report area in a system of basins collectively termed the Wessex–Channel Basin (Penn et al., 1987). This system incorporates the onshore sedimentary basins of southern England and counterpart offshore basins in the central and eastern parts of the English Channel. Recent work on the Wessex–Channel Basin (Stoneley, 1982; Whittaker, 1985; Chadwick, 1986; Lake and Karner, 1987) shows a system of partially inverted extensional sub-basins (Figure 14) whose principal structural features are illustrated in Figure 15. Major subplanar normal faults with predominantly southerly downthrows lie *en-échelon* in roughly east–west-trending fault zones; these delineate the constituent structural elements of the basin. A system of asymmetric graben and half-graben represented by the Pewsey, Weald, Dorset, Portland–Wight and Central English Channel basins, is separated by the structurally high areas of the London Platform, Hampshire–Dieppe High and Central English Channel High (Figure 14a). The structural highs are extensional features and are markedly asymmetrical, forming the updip portions of asymmetric basins to the north (Figure 15).

Subsequent to crustal extension, compressive tectonic stresses in latest Cretaceous and Tertiary times caused crustal shortening, resulting in partial reversal of the major extensional faults, and minor inversion of the constituent basins. Consequently, reverse faults and monoclines are closely associated with earlier normal faults, and inversional anticlines are superimposed upon earlier basins (Figure 14b).

The present morphology of the basin (Figure 16) largely reflects the dominant extensional processes. Maximum sediment thicknesses are found in the Portland–Wight Basin where, in spite of later inversion, over 4000 m of strata are found. Other major depocentres include the Central English Channel Basin and the Dorset Basin, with over 3000 m of preserved sediments. The most important structure within the Wessex–Channel Basin is the Lyme Bay–Portland–Wight–Bray fault system (Figure 14) that separates the Portland–Wight Basin from the much thinner sediments of the Hampshire–Dieppe High. The fault system now has a normal displacement which in places approaches 1500 m (Figures 15 and 16), although prior to the reversal which accompanied basin inversion, it was considerably greater.

STRUCTURAL AND PLATE-TECTONIC SETTING

Prior to development of the Wessex–Channel Basin, the structural framework of the region was formed in Devonian and Carboniferous times. Convergence of the Gondwanan and Laurasian continental masses led to development of the Variscan orogenic belt and formation of the Pangaean supercontinent. On deep-seismic reflection profiles (Figures 6 and 7), the resulting strongly tectonised Cambrian to Carboniferous rocks form a largely unreflective seismic unit (Zone 2). Variscan deformation was characterised by the development of major thrust zones and intense folding (Figure 8), which can be mapped both at outcrop and in the subsurface (Chadwick et al., 1983; Leveridge et al., 1984; Donato, 1988). The thrust zones trend roughly east–west, dip to the south at angles of between about 20 and 30°, and cut the Variscan basement to depths of about 15 to 20 km (Cazes and Torreilles, 1988). At greater depths the thrusts pass into seismically layered lower crust (Zone 3) and become indistinct, their discrete shear displacements perhaps coalescing into more pervasive, ductile, forms of strain. Contemporaneous with, or forming shortly after the thrusts, a system of widely spaced, subvertical, dextral, north-westerly trending transcurrent faults can be seen in the exposed basement massifs of south-west England (Figure 8). It is likely that the direction of Variscan convergence was dominantly south-east to north-west, parallel to the transcurrent faults, imparting a dextral transpressional component of displacement to many of the east–west-trending thrusts.

The end-Carboniferous plate-tectonic reconstruction of part of Pangaea illustrated in Figure 17a shows the approximate relative positions of the present-day circum-North Atlantic continents and the Variscan Orogenic Belt. Figure 17b illustrates a reconstruction for mid-Cretaceous times subsequent to the extensional phases of basin development and immediately prior to the onset of sea-floor spreading in the North Atlantic region. Relative continental motion from Permian to Early Cretaceous times can thus be assessed by comparing the two reconstructions. Except for the far southwest of the North Atlantic region, where sea-floor spreading commenced earlier, these relative motions can be explained by continental lithospheric extension of Pangaea, though local areas of extreme stretching may have experienced minor sea-floor spreading. From Permian to mid-Cretaceous times, 350 km of roughly east–west continental extension between Europe and Canada was associated with widespread basin subsidence on the north-west European and east Canadian continental shelves, including the development of the Wessex–Channel Basin. Additionally, in Late Jurassic and Early Cretaceous times, a lesser component of roughly north–south extension accompanied formation of the Bay of Biscay as Iberia rotated anticlockwise. This latter extension vector probably strongly influenced Late Jurassic and Early Cretaceous subsidence patterns in the Wessex–Channel Basin.

MECHANISMS OF LITHOSPHERIC EXTENSION AND COMPRESSION

The mechanism by which continental lithosphere extends is the subject of much current debate. The simplest model (McKenzie, 1978) proposes a lithosphere composed of a brittle upper layer and a ductile lower layer which extends by pure shear to produce a symmetrical lithospheric cross-section. Alternatively, the uniform-sense, simple-shear model of Wernicke (1985) suggests that extension is concentrated along a deeply penetrating, low-angle shear zone. Thinning in the upper lithosphere is laterally offset along the shear zone from thinning in the lower lithosphere, to produce a markedly asymmetrical lithospheric cross-section. It is likely that the Wessex–Channel Basin developed by a mechanism intermediate between these two extreme models. Bulk lithospheric extension was probably dominantly pure shear, but low-angle shear zones in the strongest parts of the lithosphere, that is

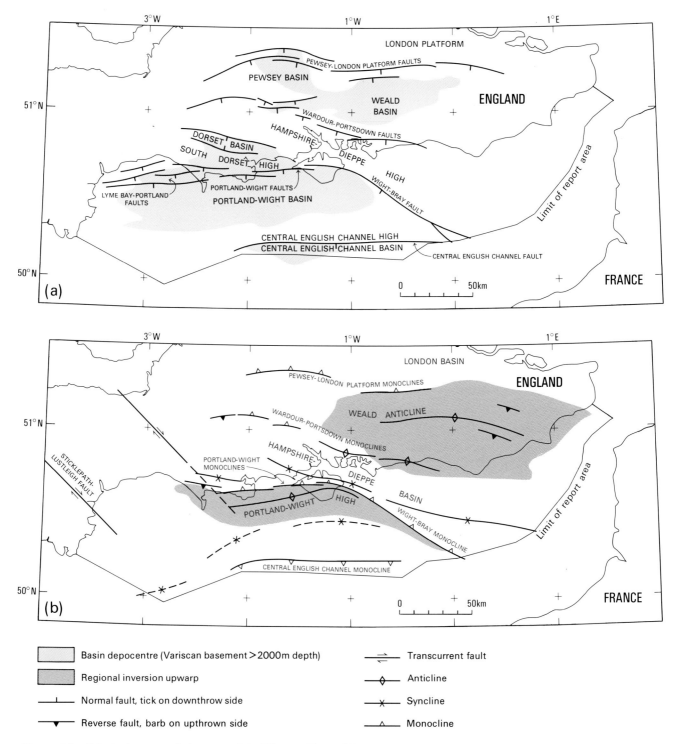

Figure 14 Principal structural elements of the Wessex–Channel Basin.
a) Extensional (Permian to Early Cretaceous) features. b) Compressional (Tertiary) features.

the middle to upper crust and possibly the upper mantle, imparted localised heterogeneities (cf. Klemperer, 1988).

The formation of sedimentary basins by heterogeneous pure-shear extension is illustrated schematically in Figure 18a. Brittle middle to upper crust extends by normal displacement along a low-angle fracture zone that is commonly a reactivated pre-existing structure such as a major thrust, and the hanging-wall block collapses into a system of normal faults. At greater depth, where the temperature is higher, pure-shear strain becomes more important as the lower crust extends in a dominantly ductile manner. The uppermost mantle with its refractory ultramafic composition is relatively strong and brittle, and probably deforms in a manner similar to the upper

crust by extension along discrete shear-zones, which again may be reactivated pre-existing compressional structures. The lower lithosphere probably extends and thins by pure-shear in a manner similar to the lower crust. Elevated lithospheric isotherms give rise to a positive thermal anomaly which isostatically buffers the amount of initial, faulted, basin subsidence. The region of maximum lithospheric thinning depends upon the distribution of the upper mantle shear zones, and does not necessarily directly underlie the region of maximum crustal thinning.

Upon cessation of active extension (Figure 18b), the elevated isotherms relax slowly back to their pre-extension position over an interval of several tens of millions of years.

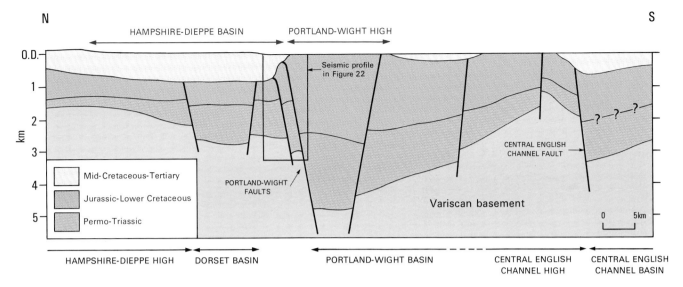

Figure 15 Simplified geological cross-section through the Wessex–Channel Basin. Extensional (Permian to Early Cretaceous) structural features anotated in black, compressional (Tertiary) features in red. See Figure 16 for location.

This gradual cooling and rethickening of the lithospheric plate produces a regional, flexural subsidence whose rate decreases exponentially with time. Deposition during this phase of thermal-relaxation subsidence is characterised by a lack of extensional faulting, with sediments commonly overlapping the margins of the earlier-faulted basins.

In the Wessex–Channel Basin, flexural thermal subsidence was gradually replaced by a period of lithospheric compression, which produced a minor amount of crustal shortening, partial reversal of the main fault zones, and inversion of the sedimentary basins (Figure 18c). Inversion structures are of two types; regional upwarps associated with crustal thickening and pure-shear basin shortening, and localised flexures produced by reversal of the basin-controlling normal faults.

DEVELOPMENT OF THE WESSEX–CHANNEL BASIN

The gross structural architecture of the Wessex–Channel Basin is essentially the product of extensional stress fields acting upon the structurally heterogeneous Variscan basement. The major low-angle Variscan thrust zones were particularly prone to reactivation during crustal extension, and important basin-controlling planar normal faults developed in their hanging-wall blocks. Thus, the major east–west-trending zones of normal faults follow the underlying thrusts (compare Figures 8 and 14). It is important to emphasise that with lithospheric extension vectors varying from east–west during the early stretching of Pangaea to north–south as the Bay of

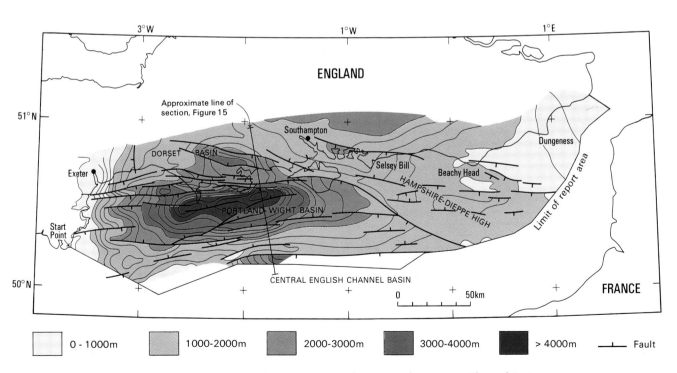

Figure 16 Structure contour map of the base of post-Variscan sediments in the Wessex–Channel Basin.

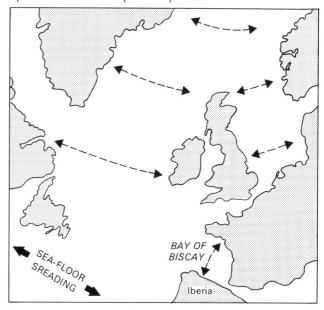

a) End Carboniferous (290 Ma)

PANGAEA

VARISCAN FRONT

b) Mid-Cretaceous (105 Ma)

SEA-FLOOR SPREADING

BAY OF BISCAY

Iberia

Figure 17 Plate-tectonic reconstructions of the North Atlantic region prior to the onset of North Atlantic sea-floor spreading. Dashed arrows indicate approximate resultant Permian to Early Cretaceous extension vectors. Modified from Chadwick et al. (1990).

Biscay was formed, the major normal faults suffered predominantly oblique (transtensional) overall displacements.

The structural history of the Wessex–Channel Basin can be divided into three stages:

i) Permo-Triassic.   During Early Permian and Early Triassic times, crustal extension led to the development of fault-bounded basins. Late Permian and Late Triassic times were characterised by post-extension, thermal subsidence.

ii) Jurassic to Early Cretaceous.   Extension in Early Jurassic times gave way to regional thermal subsidence with only minor pulses of extension. Renewed extension in the Late Jurassic and more particularly during Early Cretaceous times, led to the rapid subsidence of localised faulted basins, with erosion of intervening horsts.

iii) Mid-Cretaceous to Tertiary.   By mid-Cretaceous times, active extension had ceased as sea-floor spreading began in the North Atlantic region. Regional thermal subsidence dominated the area through the Late Cretaceous, but the increasing effects of compressive stress fields led to progressive basin inversion which culminated in mid-Tertiary times.

These three tectonic stages can be summarised by a series of isopach maps (Figures 19, 20 and 21). Taken in sequence, they show how the structural characteristics of the basins have changed with time.

Permo-Triassic

Basin subsidence began in Early Permian times, as evidenced by the exposed western edge of the Dorset Basin where a thick sequence of continental redbed sediments containing volcanic rocks dated at c.280 to 290 Ma (see Warrington and Scrivener, 1990) are preserved in the Crediton Trough and near Exeter (Figure 19). Elsewhere, the subsurface distribution of Permian strata is not well known, though deep borehole information indicates marked thickness changes indicative of an early graben system (Whittaker, 1975). However, the predominantly argillaceous nature of the Permian sequence suggests that for much of the interval, subsidence was

regional, with little contemporaneous fault activity. Later, during Early Triassic times, renewed crustal extension led to a strongly rejuvenated fault-scarp topography and the deposition of coarsely arenaceous sediments. Major faults active at this time include the Lyme Bay–Portland and Central English Channel faults with over 1000 m and up to 800 m of syndepositional throw respectively (Figures 14, 15 and 19). To the south of these faults, the Portland–Wight Basin and the Central English Channel Basin developed as deep asymmetric graben. In Late Triassic times, fault activity gradually declined, surface topography diminished, and argillaceous and evaporitic sediments were deposited.

Permo-Triassic subsidence was concentrated in the western part of the Wessex–Channel Basin, with up to 3000 m of sediment preserved in the western part of the Portland–Wight Basin, and up to 2000 m in the Dorset and Central English Channel basins. Farther east, the Hampshire–Dieppe High and the Weald Basin suffered little subsidence and no significant syndepositional faulting; the eastern part of the Portland–Wight–Bray fault system was virtually dormant, and only thin outliers of Permo-Triassic strata are preserved.

Jurassic and Early Cretaceous

Jurassic and Early Cretaceous subsidence of the Wessex–Channel Basin is summarised by the isopach map of preserved sediments (Figure 20). Towards the end of Triassic times, continued erosion and regional subsidence resulted in a change from continental conditions to a shallow-marine environment in which a relatively uniform, cyclical sequence of argillaceous and carbonate rocks was deposited. Renewed crustal extension in the Early Jurassic led to important normal faulting and a change in depositional patterns as the loci of maximum subsidence shifted eastwards. In the Portland–Wight Basin, the hitherto dormant Wight–Bray Fault became active as the depocentre migrated eastwards. Locally, in the western part of the basin above the Permo-Triassic depocentre (Figure 19), listric normal faults developed, detaching in the thick Triassic salt sequence. These listric faults are

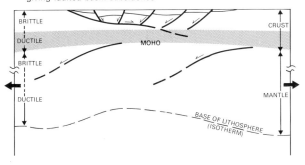

a) Active extension of lithospere by heterogeneous pure shear, giving faulted basin subsidence

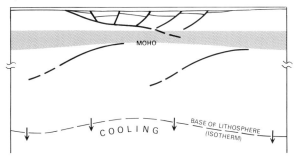

b) Post-extension thermal relaxation with flexural basin subsidence

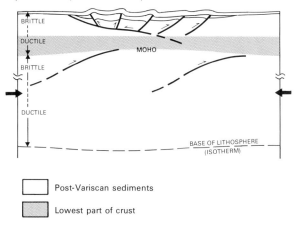

c) Active compression of lithosphere with basin inversion.

☐ Post-Variscan sediments

▨ Lowest part of crust

Figure 18 Schematic illustration of lithospheric extension and compression.

in marked contrast to the dominantly subplanar normal faulting observed elsewhere. Farther north, subsidence began in the Weald Basin as the Pewsey–London Platform Faults became active (Figure 14).

By Middle to Late Jurassic times (Callovian–Oxfordian), a tectonic regime of regional thermal subsidence had become established, with only minor contemporaneous fault activity that increased gradually with time. The Oxford Clay is a uniform marine argillaceous unit that overlapped earlier formations, overstepping northwards and westwards, probably on to Variscan basement massifs.

Late Jurassic (Kimmeridgian) times saw a renewal of crustal extension, with the Weald and Portland–Wight basins subsiding rapidly along the London Platform and Portland–Wight–Bray fault systems. The Jurassic trend towards an increased area of deposition continued, and it is probable that the Kimmeridge Clay overlapped all earlier Mesozoic formations to onlap against the greatly diminished emergent Variscan basement massifs.

Towards the close of the Jurassic, a marked fall in relative sea level led to a shrinkage of the depositional area and re-emergence of the structural highs. This trend continued into the Early Cretaceous. Rapid crustal extension accompanied by major normal faulting allowed thick clastic sequences to accumulate in the restricted Weald and eastern Portland–Wight basins, where sedimentation was probably continuous. In contrast, surrounding areas were uplifted and severely eroded. This extreme structural demarcation was accomplished by considerable movement along the major fault zones. For example, cumulative Jurassic and Early Cretaceous displacement on the Portland–Wight Faults in places exceeds 1500 m (Figure 20). Erosion was particularly severe in the western part of the area, where thick sequences of Permo-Triassic and Jurassic strata were removed to uncover Variscan basement rocks. Similar, though less severe uplift affected the London Platform, where Jurassic strata were removed to reveal Palaeozoic basement. The Hampshire–Dieppe and the Central English Channel highs were also eroded, in places down to the level of Middle Jurassic strata. This important period of erosion lasted from end-Jurassic to end-Barremian times, and resulted in the late-Cimmerian Unconformity, a depositional hiatus of regional significance on the north-west European continental shelf (Rawson and Riley, 1982). Two mechanisms of uplift, acting in unison, appear to have been responsible for the unconformity; local footwall uplift associated with isostatic recovery during crustal extension (Barr, 1987) was superimposed upon a regional uptilt to the west. The latter may have been due to thermal upwarp associated with the onset of North Atlantic opening (Lake and Karner, 1987).

The late-Cimmerian Unconformity is a good example of a post-rift unconformity associated with the transition from extensional to post-extensional phases of basin evolution. It is a particularly prominent stratigraphical boundary because a variety of formations lie beneath it, and it is overlain by generally unfaulted strata. Similar unconformities were probably associated with earlier extensional episodes in the Wessex–Channel Basin, most notably in Permo-Triassic times, but these have been cut by later extensional faults, and since they lie within rather lithologically uniform sequences, are less easily recognised.

Mid-Cretaceous to Recent

By mid-Cretaceous (Aptian) times, crustal extension in the North Atlantic region was giving way to active sea-floor spreading. In the report area, this transition heralded a new tectonic regime of regional thermal subsidence with a virtual absence of normal faulting and an enormous increase of depositional area. Isopachs of preserved mid-Cretaceous and younger sediments (Figure 21) are severely affected by later inversion, which in places removed several hundred metres of strata, and do not clearly illustrate original depositional trends. The paucity of normal faulting is in marked contrast to earlier basin development. Mid-Cretaceous strata overlapped the late-Cimmerian erosion surface, overstepping westwards (cf. Figure 18b) on to Jurassic and Permo-Triassic beds, and northwards on to the basement rocks of the London Platform, part of the London–Brabant Massif.

By Late Cretaceous times, continued regional subsidence and an associated high relative sea level led to submergence of most of the British landmass. Cessation of terrigenous sediment supply allowed deposition of the pure carbonate Chalk sequence, which onlapped westwards on to the Cornubian Massif. Though there was little active faulting, subsidence patterns continued to show evidence of subsurface structural control, albeit in subdued form. The Weald and eastern

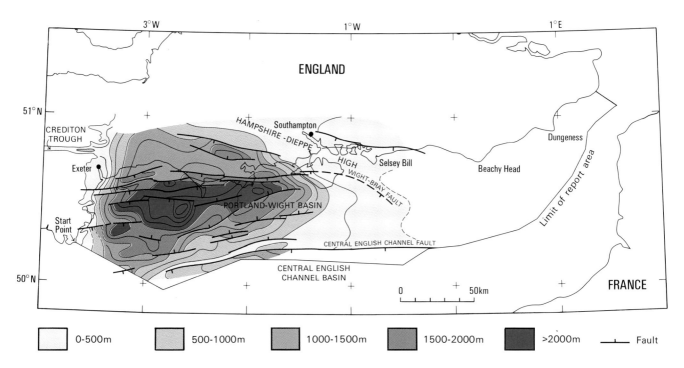

Figure 19 Isopachs of Permo-Triassic strata.

Portland–Wight basins, which had undergone recent extension, continued to subside rapidly as their young sedimentary fills compacted (Chadwick, 1986). Conversely, the structural highs which had suffered severe late-Cimmerian erosion were covered by thinner, more compacted sedimentary sequences, and subsided more slowly. In the western part of the Wessex–Channel Basin, movements on steep north-westerly trending Variscan transcurrent faults helped to accommodate regional subsidence, and influenced local thickness trends (Drummond, 1970). It was at this time, prior to structural inversion, that the Wessex–Channel Basin reached its greatest depth, with over 5000 m of sediment in the deeper parts of the Portland–Wight Basin.

The end of Cretaceous times was marked by an erosional episode which heralded important tectonic changes in the Wessex–Channel Basin. Crustal extension and basin subsidence, which had been dominant for over 200 million years, gave way in Tertiary times to an episode of crustal compression and basin inversion (Whittaker, 1985; Lake and Karner, 1987).

Residual thermal subsidence inherited from the Early Cretaceous extensional episodes continued into early and mid-Tertiary times, and considerable thicknesses of shallow-marine and freshwater clastic sediments accumulated, with still some evidence of structural control by north-west-trending basement features. However, an increasingly dominant

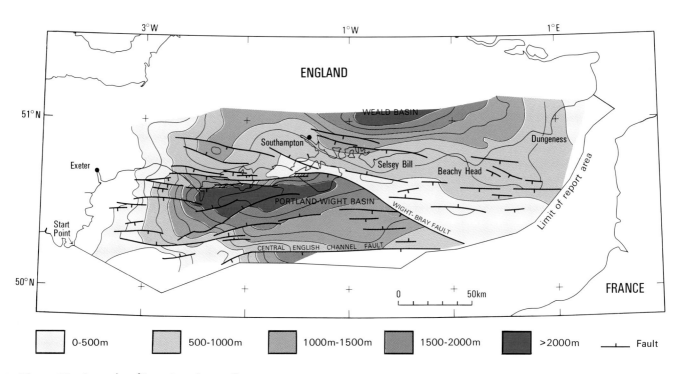

Figure 20 Isopachs of Jurassic to Lower Cretaceous strata.

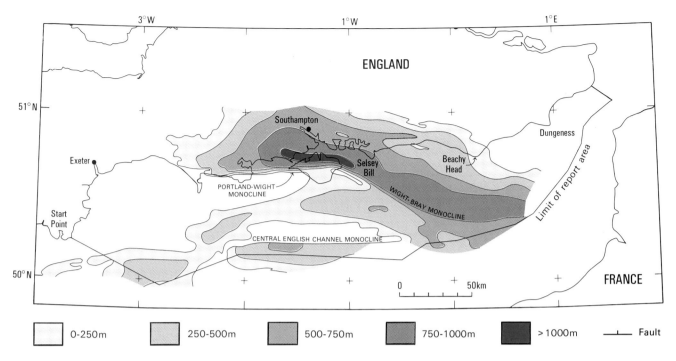

Figure 21   Isopachs of middle Cretaceous to Tertiary strata.

influence was that of basin inversion, which dictated patterns of subsidence markedly different from those of the Mesozoic Era. The preservation of Tertiary strata in the synclines of the London and Hampshire–Dieppe basins (Figure 14b) is a consequence of this inversion.

The principal inversion structures of the Wessex–Channel Basin exemplify perfectly the principles of structural inversion, as they lie directly upon earlier extensional features of opposite structural polarity (Cooper and Williams, 1989). The Weald Anticline and Portland–Wight High overlie the Weald Basin and the Portland–Wight Basin respectively, and the London and Hampshire–Dieppe basins overlie the London Platform and Hampshire–Dieppe High respectively (Figure 14).

The time of onset of basin inversion is difficult to establish precisely, but is critical in determining whether the London and Hampshire–Dieppe basins are purely synclinal features formed after deposition of the Tertiary strata, or whether they were true synsedimentary basins. Evidence of very early minor inversion movements lies within the Chalk sequence; analysis of backstripped subsidence curves (Chadwick in Whittaker, 1985) indicates that during Late Cretaceous times, basement beneath the London Platform started to subside more rapidly than that beneath the Weald Basin, thereby forming structural precursors to the London Basin and Weald Anticline. Sedimentological studies (Plint, 1982; Edwards and Freshney, 1987a) also indicate that inversion influenced depositional trends very early in the Tertiary when embryonic forms of the Weald Anticline, Portland–Wight High and the London and Hampshire–Dieppe basins developed, the latter becoming important depocentres.

An alternative view (e.g. King, 1981) is that throughout early Tertiary times the Weald Anticline and Portland–Wight High had not yet become topographically significant, and were covered with sediments only slightly thinner than those in the London and Hampshire–Dieppe basins. If this were the case, then the present disposition of Tertiary strata is largely the consequence of postdepositional inversion during the Miocene.

The balance of evidence indicates that minor episodes of inversion affected the Wessex–Channel Basin from Late Cretaceous times onwards, coeval with the 'Laramide' inversions of northern Europe (Ziegler, 1981), but that major inversion did not take place until Miocene times, associated with 'Helvetic' Alpine and Pyrenean orogenic events.

The inversion structures of the Wessex–Channel Basin fall into two related categories:

Firstly there are regional upwarps such as the Weald Anticline and the Portland–Wight High (Figures 14b and 15), which comprise major flexures with axial uplifts of more than 1000 m. These features appear to be associated with regional pure-shear basin shortening, and it is noteworthy that the greatest uplifts occur in basins which contain thick Lower Cretaceous sequences. It may be that these young, uncompacted and relatively weak sediments were particularly prone to compressive shortening and consequent uplift. Conversely, basins containing older, more competent sediments, such as the Dorset and western Portland–Wight basins, were less affected by shortening and uplift.

The second type of inversion structure comprises linear east–west-trending zones of faulted flexures which are related directly to the reversal of underlying basin-controlling normal faults. These flexure zones are, from north to south, the Pewsey–London Platform monoclines, the Wardour–Portsdown monoclines and anticlines and the Portland–Wight–Bray monoclinal structures (Figure 14). Similar though smaller structures elsewhere can be related to more localised fault reactivation, for example reverse faults are exposed at the surface within the Weald Anticline.

The detailed geometry of the inversion structures is illustrated by the geological cross-section in Figure 15, and by a seismic-reflection profile which crosses the Portland–Wight structure (Figure 22). The north-facing Portland–Wight monoclines separate the Portland–Wight High to the south from the Hampshire–Dieppe Basin to the north. They lie directly above the Portland–Wight normal faults and were clearly formed by reversal of those structures during compressional reactivation. Net vertical displacement across the Portland–Wight structure changes from down-to-the-north

25

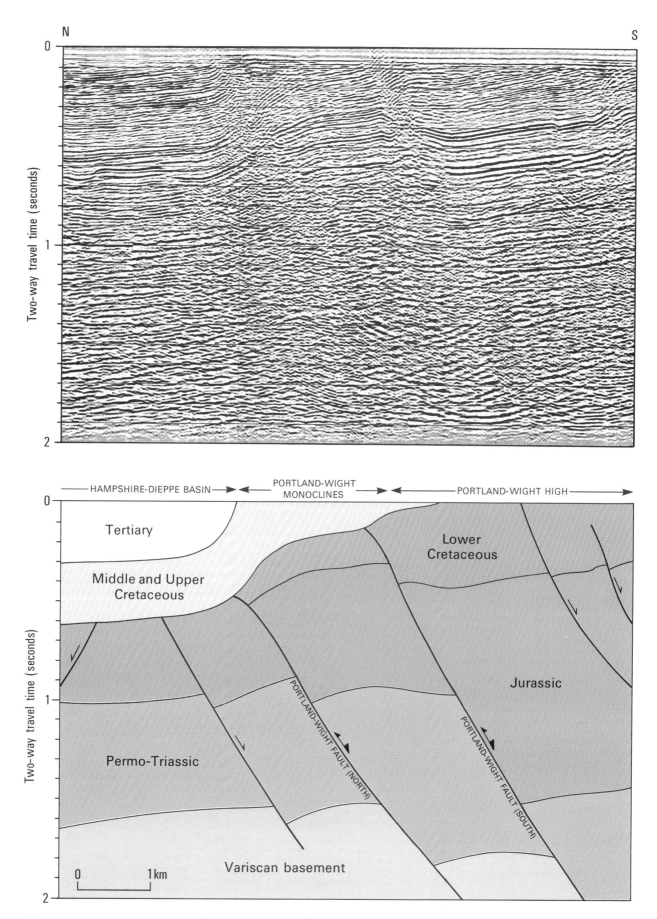

Figure 22 Seismic-reflection profile across the Portland–Wight structures in Bournemouth Bay, illustrating reversal of the Portland–Wight faults and related inversion features. See Figures 15 and 16 for location.

at shallow levels where the initially flat-lying mid-Cretaceous and younger strata are strongly flexured, to down-to-the-south at deeper structural levels where the original normal displacement of Permo-Triassic and Jurassic strata greatly exceeds the subsequent reverse throw.

The role of the Central English Channel fault system during basin inversion is enigmatic; it does not appear to have suffered significant reversal, for the sense of throw on both the Tertiary monocline and the underlying Mesozoic normal fault is down-to-the-south (Figures 20 and 21). The reason for this apparent lack of involvement with the basin inversion is unclear.

Following basin inversion, which ended in mid-Tertiary times, the surface of much of the Wessex–Channel Basin has probably stayed close to sea level. Considerable erosion of its western part may have continued as a result of regional eastward tilting and uplift of Cornubia.

5 Permian and Triassic

Permian and Triassic strata are widely distributed offshore in the western part of the area, but only come to crop in the extreme west (Figure 2). Several Permo-Triassic lithostratigraphical divisions (Figure 23) are known within the nearshore outcrop (Figure 24), with the basal Permian breccias resting unconformably on Devonian and Carboniferous rocks. Nearby offshore inliers take the form of anticlines in which only the Mercia Mudstone Group is known to crop out. At depth, over 3100 m of Permo-Triassic strata are present in the Portland–Wight Basin (Figure 19), although the greatest thickness proved by drilling is 1969 m in well 98/11-2 (Figure 5 and 25).

Compressive uplift associated with the end of the Variscan orogeny during the Late Carboniferous was followed by a period of lithospheric extension during which thick sediments accumulated in restricted basins bounded by contemporaneous growth faults. The Dorset Basin (Whittaker, 1985) extended westwards from Dorset into east Devon (Figure 16), and continued offshore to the east as the Portland–Wight Basin, which is bounded by faults that may be re-activated Variscan thrusts (Chadwick et al., 1983). Volcanic activity was associated with rapid subsidence and active normal faulting during the Early Permian; this is represented inland in the Dorset Basin by the Exeter Volcanic Series (Knill, 1969; Cornwell et al., 1990), but no volcanicity is known either at the coast or within the offshore sediments of the report area. However, aeromagnetic anomalies to the west of the Start–Cotentin Ridge have been attributed to Permian volcanics (Day, 1986).

Deposition of Permian breccias (Figure 23) was restricted to down-faulted basins, and was dominated by alluvial and aeolian processes fed by widespread erosion of the Variscan uplands. Alluvial-fan breccias accumulated against fault scarps and became finer grained distally, interfingering with aeolian sandstones that were possibly winnowed from the alluvial fans (Laming, 1966). The climate was hot and semiarid, with prevalent easterly and north-easterly wind directions indicated by structures within the aeolian sandstones. These observations support palaeomagnetic evidence that the area lay within the northern trade-wind belt (Anderton et al., 1979).

At the close of the Permian, the area comprised a desert peneplain with sedimentation having largely infilled topographic hollows on the block-faulted basement. There followed a period of thermal-relaxation subsidence that led to an increased area of deposition and 'steer's head' overlap (Whittaker, 1985). The Aylesbeare Mudstone Formation at the base of the Triassic thus overlies both Permian sediments and Variscan basement. It was deposited in a floodplain alluvial complex of low-energy fluvial and lacustrine environments in desert basins with internal centripetal drainage. In the east Devon outcrop, palaeocurrent directions are towards the north-east.

Whittaker (1985) considered that renewed lithospheric extension later in the Early Triassic rejuvenated the tilted fault-block, rift-valley topography and led to renewed erosion and the deposition of conglomerates in south-west England. However, Smith and Edwards (in press) suggest that the conglomerates, the Budleigh Salterton Pebble Beds, represent a phase of low subsidence rates and tectonic quiescence in the Wessex Basin. The pebble beds (Figure 23) rest with minor unconformity on the Aylesbeare Mudstone Formation, and clasts of south-westerly Cornubian and Armorican derivation in them imply a considerable distance of travel. Deposition took place on a braid plain or an externally drained, fluvially dominated alluvial fan (Smith, 1990; Smith and Edwards, in press).

The conglomerates are succeeded above an aeolian deflation surface (Henson, 1970; Edwards and Smith, 1989) by the Otter Sandstone Formation, which oversteps eastward to rest upon either the Aylesbeare Mudstone Formation or Variscan basement. The sandstones are composed of upward-fining cycles, with erosional and conglomeratic bases, and siltstones or mudstone at the top, commonly with dessication cracks. These fluvial units were probably formed by seasonal rivers in a hot climate, possibly less arid than that of the Permian.

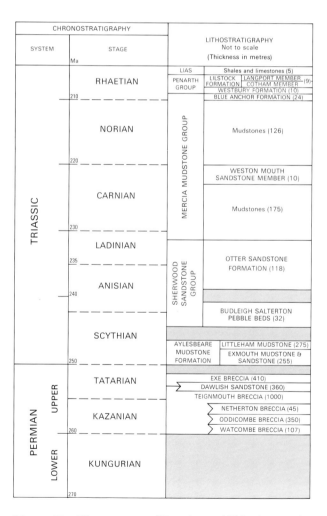

Figure 23 The sequence of Permian and Triassic strata in the east Devon coastal outcrop. Thickness shown in metres. Modified after Warrington and Scrivener (1990), Warrington et al. (1980), Smith et al. (1974) and Selwood et al. (1984).

28

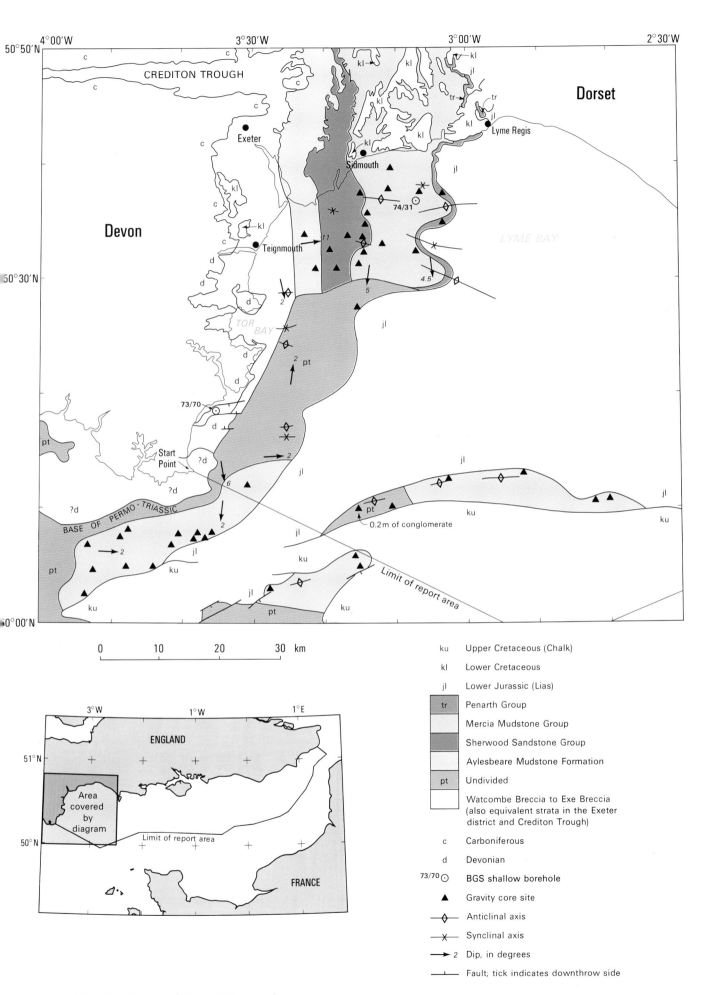

Figure 24 Distribution of Permo-Triassic sedimentary groups at outcrop.

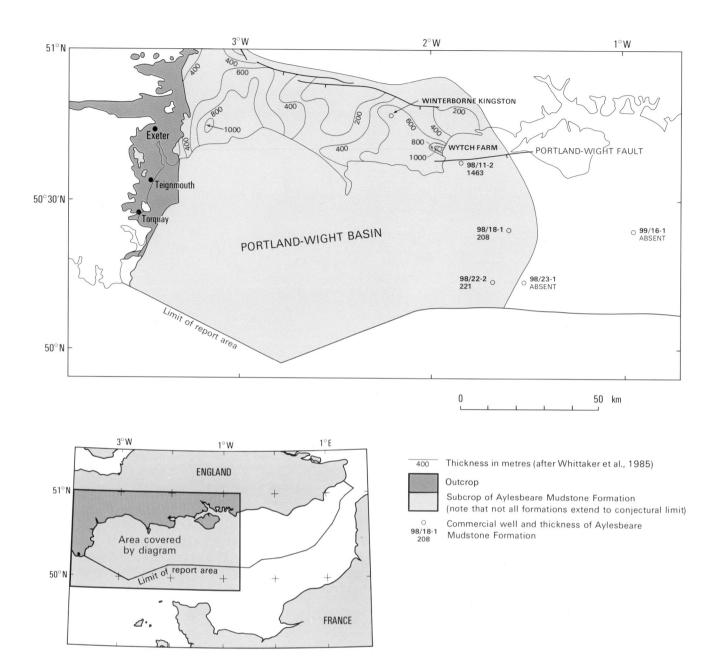

Figure 25 Distribution of strata ranging from the Watcombe Breccia to the Aylesbeare Mudstone Formation.

The top of the Sherwood Sandstone Group throughout England is diachronous, for fine-grained sediments succeeded later in the south of England than in the north, indicating an overall south to north palaeoslope. The overlying Mercia Mudstone Group is primarily an argillaceous sequence dominated by red mudstones and evaporites (Warrington, 1974). The sediments probably formed on an alluvial peneplain with ephemeral playa lakes (Arthurton, 1980; Simms and Ruffel, 1990). The base of the group youngs southwards from a late Scythian age in northern England to Ladinian in the English Channel area. In the east it may be even younger where it oversteps the Sherwood Sandstone Group to rest upon Variscan basement. Active normal faulting continued along basin margins, producing local breccias and conglomerates. However, the dominance of fine-grained material, the great thickness of the group, its widespread extent, and overstepping relationship, combine to suggest subdued topography with subsidence largely attributed to thermal relaxation effects following a mid-Triassic extensional phase (Whittaker, 1985). An arid or semiarid climate is indicated by the pres-

ence of sheeted bedrock and exfoliated pebbles in marginal areas, by thick evaporite sequences, and by the paucity of kaolinite in the sediments, which suggests that chemical weathering was minimal in source areas (Anderton et al., 1979). The widespread and fossiliferous Weston Mouth Sandstone Member in Devon represents a short-lived deltaic or fluvial phase (Ruffel, 1990; Simms and Ruffel 1990).

The grey and greenish dolomitic mudstones of the Blue Anchor Formation represent supratidal and intertidal sabkha environments that existed during the initial stages of the Rhaetian marine transgression (Warrington and Whittaker, 1984). By this time most of England was a peneplain, and as sea levels rose, the area south and south-west of the London Platform was rapidly inundated from the west. The Penarth Group comprises the marine Westbury Formation and Langport Member, separated by the Cotham Member which includes supratidal to lagoonal deposits (Warrington, 1981) that reflect a widespread but short-lived regressive phase. Tectonic activity in the English Channel area during the Rhaetian appears to have been slight.

Above the Langport Member, the basal, fully marine shales and limestones of the Lias that occur below the level of appearance of the earliest Jurassic ammonite *Psiloceras planorbis* are considered to be of Rhaetian age. However, since these cannot be distinguished offshore from the overlying Jurassic strata, they are here considered along with the Jurassic.

In the following account, the limited offshore detail available makes it necessary to draw heavily on onshore data; the coastal section of east Devon is based on Edmonds et al., (1975), Selwood et al., (1984), Hamblin (1969) and Henson (1971). Boreholes most extensively used are Winterborne Kingston (Rhys et al., 1982), Wytch Farm (Colter and Havard, 1981), Arreton (Falcon and Kent, 1960), Middleton 1 (unpublished), Portsdown (Taitt and Kent, 1958), Henfield 1 (Taitt and Kent, 1958; Young and Lake, 1988), Grove Hill 1 (Lake et al., 1987) and Brabourne (Smart et al., 1966).

UPPER PERMIAN BRECCIAS

In the Devon coastal sequence, the earliest strata are the breccias and sandstone of the Marldon Group (Laming, 1966), which are restricted to the Torquay area. The formations from the Watcombe Breccia to the Exe Breccia (Figure 23) constitute locally derived, alluvial-fan breccias and aeolian sands. They show predominantly eastward palaeocurrent directions (Durrance and Laming, 1982; Selwood et al., 1984), indicating sources in the area of present-day Dartmoor. Henson (1973) interpreted the Teignmouth Breccia, Dawlish Sandstone and Exe Breccia as a piedmont complex of mid-fan breccias and fan-base sands. The breccias were deposited by stream floods and streams, with sheet floods in fan-head and mid-fan areas (Hamblin, 1969; Henson, 1971). The Dawlish Sandstone is a fan-base deposit of aeolian and fluvial origin that migrated up-fan over the breccias during a period of increased aridity (Selwood et al., 1984).

Warrington and Scrivener (1988; 1990) record a palynomorph assemblage of Late Permian (Kazanian to Tatarian) age in the Whipton Formation which underlies the Teignmouth Breccia at Exeter (Bristow and Scrivener, 1984). However, the base of the breccia sequence may become progressively older southwards from Exeter (Durrance and Laming, 1982), so that part of the Teignmouth Breccia in Tor Bay may possibly predate the Exeter palynomorph assemblage. However, it is still likely that the whole sequence up to the Exe Breccia is of Late Permian age.

The Teignmouth Breccia comprises upward-fining, planar-bedded units with erosional bases, and has a matrix of haematite-stained silty sand and sandy silt. Megaclasts include Devonian and Carboniferous sandstones, slates and cherts, as well as penecontemporaneous sandstones and basaltic lavas and a variety of intrusive and extrusive igneous rocks.

The Watcombe, Oddicombe and Netherton breccias are restricted to the coastal zone south of Teignmouth. The Watcombe and Netherton breccias have a sandy clay matrix that supports fine-grained slate and sandstone intraclasts, with subordinate coarser clasts of sandstone, limestone and porphyry. The Oddicombe Breccia is characterised by clasts of Devonian limestone up to 1.5 m across, with subordinate sandstone, slate and quartz-feldspar porphyry; Laming (1966) deduced from a study of rounding of the limestone clasts that transport was eastwards into the basin. Similar limestone-dominated breccias in the Marldon Group of the Torquay area have been named the Tor Bay, Paignton and Chelston breccias (Laming, 1966).

The Dawlish Sandstone interdigitates westwards with the Teignmouth Breccia and eastwards with the Exe Breccia. It includes fluvial units up to 2 m thick made up of cross-bedded or planar-bedded, medium- to fine-grained, silty, quartzose sandstone. Upward-fining breccia lenses up to 4 m thick contain megaclasts similar to, but smaller than, those in the Teignmouth Breccia; these pass up into planar-bedded sandstones. Sets of aeolian sandstone up to 5 m thick are recognised by large-scale dune bedding and by an absence of gravel clasts and mica. The Exe Breccia resembles the Teignmouth Breccia, except that the clasts are smaller, less than 0.15 m across.

The eastward extent of the alluvial-fan and aeolian formations is not known, but is unlikely to be great as the breccias form wedges infilling restricted cuvettes adjacent to source areas. Henson (1972) shows the Teignmouth Breccia and Dawlish Sandstone thinning eastward to the River Exe. However, since all formations except the Watcombe and Netherton breccias crop out in coastal cliffs, it is reasonable to suppose that they continue offshore. Borehole 73/70, well to the south of the onshore outcrop (Figure 24), recovered red-brown breccia of uncertain affinity which has coarse, angular clasts of quartz and sandstone in a mudstone matrix; this breccia is overlain by red-brown sandstone.

Breccias recorded at Wytch Farm and in wells 98/18-1 and 98/22-2 (Figure 25) may approximate in age to those of east Devon. However, in view of their coarseness so far from the Dartmoor Massif, and the presence of a high proportion of quartz, quartzite, marble and schist pebbles not known in Devon, they must have formed in one or more different cuvettes. At Wytch Farm, less than 60 m of Wytch Farm Breccia rest upon Devonian phyllites; it comprises angular clasts of pale, grey-green mudstone and well-foliated, pale grey phyllite with quartz pebbles and very little matrix. No breccias occur beneath the Aylesbeare Mudstone Formation in well 98/11-2, but 161 m rest upon Variscan basement in well 98/18-1, and 221 m in 98/22-2. The former drilled angular to rounded schist and marble clasts in a red-brown clay matrix, and the latter recovered angular clasts of quartzite, dark brown claystone and dark grey mica schist up to 100 mm long in a matrix of fine- to coarse-grained sandstone with a few beds of red-brown claystone. Fining-upward sequences up to 1 m thick are recorded in both wells.

AYLESBEARE MUDSTONE FORMATION

The Aylesbeare Mudstone Formation has traditionally been regarded as Late Permian in age (Selwood et al., 1984; Smith et al., 1974), following the arbitrary adoption of the base of the Budleigh Salterton Pebble Beds as the base of the Triassic. However Henson (1970; 1973), on sedimentological grounds, took the base of the Triassic at the base of the Aylesbeare Mudstone Formation, whereas Warrington and Scrivener (1990) constrain the system boundary within the sequence separating the Dawlish Sandstone and the Otter Sandstone (Figure 23).

The Aylesbeare Mudstone Formation (Bristow and Scrivener, 1984) includes the Exmouth Mudstone and Sandstone and Littleham Mudstone (Henson, 1970; Warrington et al., 1980; Bristow and Scrivener, 1984). The Exmouth Mudstone and Sandstone comprises reddish brown mudstones with interbedded red and green, cross-bedded sandstones. Five rhythms are present on the east Devon coast,

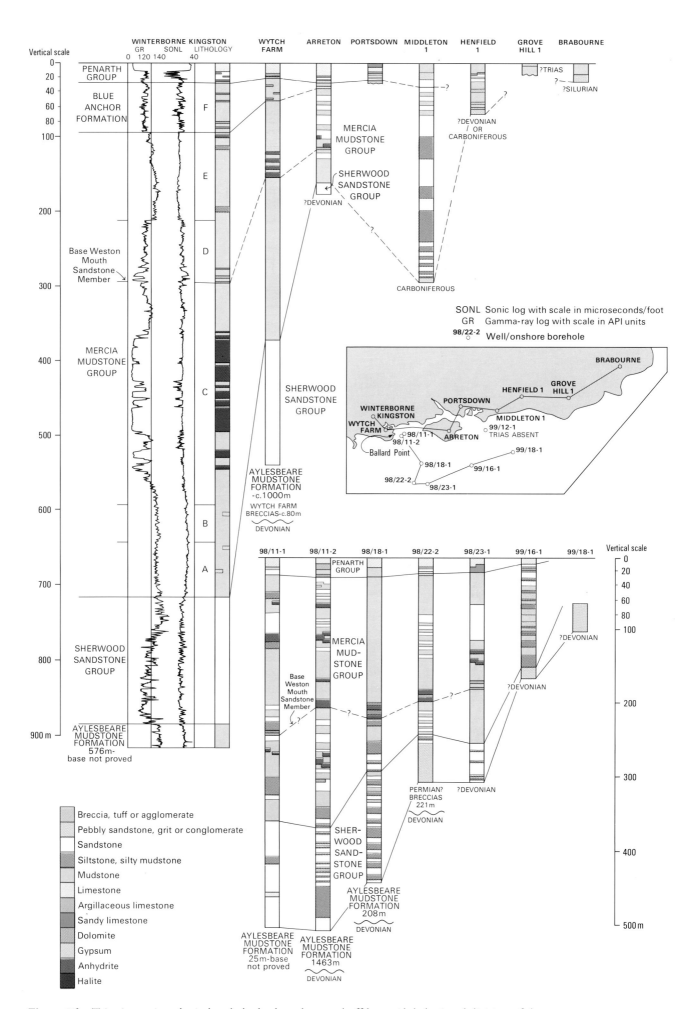

Figure 26   Triassic stratigraphy in boreholes both onshore and offshore. Alphabetic subdivision of the Mercia Mudstone Group after Lott et al. (1982).

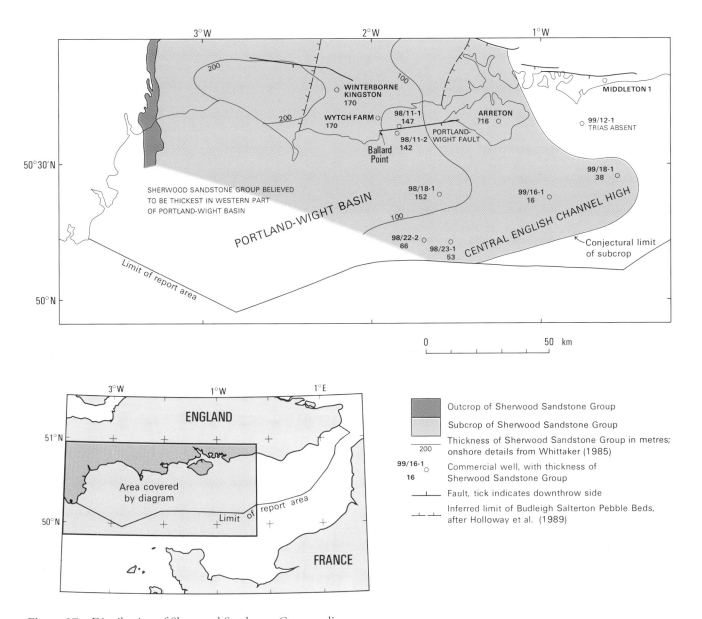

Figure 27 Distribution of Sherwood Sandstone Group sediments.

with sandstones grading up into mudstones through poorly sorted, sandy siltstones; mudstone-pellet conglomerates occur at the erosive base of some of the rhythms.

The Littleham Mudstone comprises almost structureless reddish brown mudstones in which grains of quartz and a few of feldspar occur in a haematite-stained silt and clay matrix. There are persistent intercalations of olive-green silty sandstone that are planar bedded or show small-scale cross-bedding. Uraniferous and vanadiferous concretions up to 200 mm across occur low in the member (Harrison, 1975; Durrance and George, 1976).

The Aylesbeare Mudstone Formation has been interpreted by Laming (1966) and Henson (1970) as a floodplain alluvial complex. The thick sandstones are formed from channel sands, whereas the thin sandstones represent crevasse splays and levees, and the mudstones are vertical-accretion overbank deposits. The clay-mineral assemblage comprises illite, kaolinite and chlorite with swelling chlorite (Henson, 1973), which accords with that of fluviolacustrine environments. Palaeocurrent analysis of the channel sandstones (Henson, 1971) shows a pattern characteristic of braided channels, with a flow direction from the south-west.

Two BGS gravity cores from within the Aylesbeare Mudstone Formation outcrop (Figure 24) proved red-brown,

silty, micaceous mudstones with some green mottling. Farther east, the Aylesbeare Mudstone is recorded at depth in wells both onshore and offshore. At Winterborne Kingston (Figure 25), red-brown and purple-brown silty mudstones and siltstones with traces of anhydrite were penetrated for 576 m without the base being reached. At Wytch Farm, about 1000 m of strata, mostly similar to those at Winterborne Kingston, were logged as Aylesbeare Mudstone Formation. However, from about 550 m to 760 m below the top there is a unit of conglomerates, largely composed of slate clasts, that fines upwards into claystones; a period of tectonic activity is implied, with erosion of a relatively local source. In geophysical logs, the Aylesbeare Mudstone Formation is characterised by uniformly high velocities and intermediate gamma-ray values.

Offshore, the Aylesbeare Mudstone Formation in well 98/11-2 comprises 1463 m of claystones with minor sandstones, amorphous anhydrite and dolomites. The claystones are red-brown, blocky, silty, micaceous and slightly calcareous; the sandstones are white, fine to medium grained, moderately sorted and argillaceous. In well 98/18-1, 47 m of similar claystones and siltstones were recorded. Equivalent strata are absent from most onshore and offshore wells farther to the east and south, which in view of the great thickness in well 98/11-2 may reflect an unconformity beneath the Sherwood Sandstone Group rather than an original thinning of the strata. This interpretation is supported by an angular discordance of 20° between the Aylesbeare Mudstone Formation and Sherwood Sandstone Group at Wytch Farm.

SHERWOOD SANDSTONE GROUP

The Sherwood Sandstone Group of the Devon coastal section is divided into the Budleigh Salterton Pebble Beds and the thicker Otter Sandstone Formation (Figure 23). Cobbles, boulders and pebbles make up about 80 per cent of the former, in a matrix of gravel and silty sand. The larger clasts decrease in size upwards, and beds of cross-bedded sandstone are common in the top third of the formation. Metaquartzites up to 0.45 m in diameter are the dominant clasts; they are petrographically comparable with the Grès Armoricain of Brittany and the Carne Quartzite of south Cornwall (Selwood et al., 1984). Other clasts include tourmalinised sandstones and schorl from the aureole rocks of the Cornubian granites, and porphyries and rhyolites resembling those of Cornwall. The Budleigh Salterton Pebble Beds are believed to have been deposited by southerly derived streamfloods in channels on a braid plain or a fluvially dominated alluvial fan (Henson, 1971; Smith, 1990).

The Otter Sandstone Formation succeeds the Budleigh Salterton Pebble Beds unconformably; locally there is a layer of ventifacts at its base. The formation comprises cross-bedded, micaceous, brown sandstones with beds of calcite-cemented conglomerate and scattered mudstone lenses. Sedimentary rhythms are present, with conglomerates passing up into sandstone showing large-scale cross-bedding that becomes smaller scale upwards. Lower in the formation, planar-bedded, coarse-grained sandstone and silty, fine- to medium-grained sandstones predominate. Muscovite concentrated on bedding planes makes the mudstones and fine-grained sandstones fissile. The Otter Sandstone Formation is largely of fluvial origin, having been deposited in low-sinuosity braided streams which flowed from the south (Henson, 1971); aeolian dunes were produced by reworking of exposed channel bars. The formation has yielded vertebrate remains that indicate a Middle Triassic (Anisian) age (Walker, 1969; Paton, 1974; Spencer and Isaac, 1983; Milner et al., 1990).

Offshore outcrop of the Budleigh Salterton Pebble Beds is unproven, but BGS gravity cores (Figure 24) have recovered soft red sandstones of the Otter Sandstone Formation. The Sherwood Sandstone Group is believed to be thickest in the western part of the Portland–Wight Basin (Figure 19), but this has not been tested by drilling. At both Winterborne Kingston and Wytch Farm (Figure 26) to the north of this basin, the Sherwood Sandstone Group comprises about 170 m of variably cemented, fine- to coarse-grained, red-brown arkosic sandstone grading to claystone in a series of upward-fining rhythms. No basal conglomerate was recorded. Lott and Strong (in Rhys et al., 1982) described upward-fining rhythms between 1 and 3 m thick that are comparable with present-day floodplain deposits formed under semiarid conditions. Morton (in Rhys et al., 1982) concluded that the heavy-mineral suite indicates derivation from the Armorican Massif.

At the Wytch Farm Oilfield, porous sandstones of the Sherwood Sandstone Group form the more productive of two reservoirs, oil having migrated across the Purbeck–Wight Faults from downthrown Jurassic source rocks. The porosity and permeability of the sandstones vary, but both are high in some thin beds (Penn et al., 1987) as a result of an original anhydrite cement preventing compaction during burial, and then dissolving to restore the original porosity and permeability, which were further enhanced by dissolution of feldspar grains (Milodowski et al., 1986). Dranfield et al. (1987) considered the main barriers to permeability to be discontinuous shale bands; they modelled the porosity and permeability of the lithofacies as resulting from braided-stream, sheet-flood and playa sedimentation. The lower and middle parts of the group are dominated by proximal channel sandstones, whereas the upper part shows a more complex medial to distal sequence of sheet-flood and playa-margin sediments.

To the north-east of the main basin, the Sherwood Sandstone Group thins rapidly; it appears to be only 16 m thick at Arreton (Holloway et al., 1989), and to be absent from Middleton and well 99/12-1. At Arreton, fine- to medium-grained sandstone and coarse quartz fragments are provisionally assigned to the Budleigh Salterton Pebble Beds. Wells off Ballard Point (Figure 27), in the vicinity of the Portland–Wight Faults, show around 140 m of Sherwood Sandstone Group, comprising pale, red-brown or white, fine- to coarse-grained sandstones with minor red siltstone beds, as well as a limestone bed in well 98/11-1. Well 98/18-1, towards the south-eastern flank of the Portland–Wight Basin, recorded 152 m of identical sandstones, with a limestone bed near the top and native copper and malachite mineralisation lower down. Geophysical logs (Figures 26, and 28) display a very 'spiky' gamma-ray log and relatively low, rather serrated resistivity and sonic log traces.

Wells on the southern and eastern flanks of the Portland–Wight Basin record a thin, conglomeratic Sherwood Sandstone Group sequence (Figure 27). On geophysical logs, the conglomerates are characterised by lower, more even, gamma-ray values, and higher velocities than the sandstones. In well 98/22-2 on the Central English Channel High, a conglomerate with quartz pebbles up to 55 mm in diameter grades up into some 10 m of fine- to medium-grained, poorly sorted sandstone. Some thin red claystone beds were noted, and oil shows were recorded (Penn et al., 1987). In well 98/23-1 there are pale, red-brown sandstones with fine to coarse, subangular, poorly sorted grains in anhydritic and siliceous cement. The sequence includes bands of conglomerate containing pebbles and boulders of claystone, metaquartzite and sandstone up to 30 cm in diameter. The top of the sequence is a red-brown argillaceous siltstone grading up to the Mercia Mudstone Group. A thinner (16 m) sequence of conglomeratic sandstone was recorded below the Mercia Mudstone Group in well 99/16-1. In well 99/18-1 the only representative of the Triassic is 38 m of white, orange and brown calcareous sandstone with conglomerate bands towards the base that contain fragments of phyllite, quartzite and limestone; this is assigned to the Sherwood Sandstone Group. The presence of thin conglomeratic sandstones in these four wells suggests that the group dies out not far to the south, along an east-north-east-trending line (Figure 27).

MERCIA MUDSTONE GROUP

The Mercia Mudstone Group, formerly the Keuper Marl (Warrington et al., 1980), has the greatest area of offshore outcrop of any Permo-Triassic group (Figure 24 and 29). It exceeds 700 m in thickness onshore, and oversteps the Sherwood Sandstone Group to the east, but it is absent from the two most easterly offshore wells (Figure 29).

An arid climate persisted from Ladinian to Norian times, and red terrigenous mudstones were laid down over much of

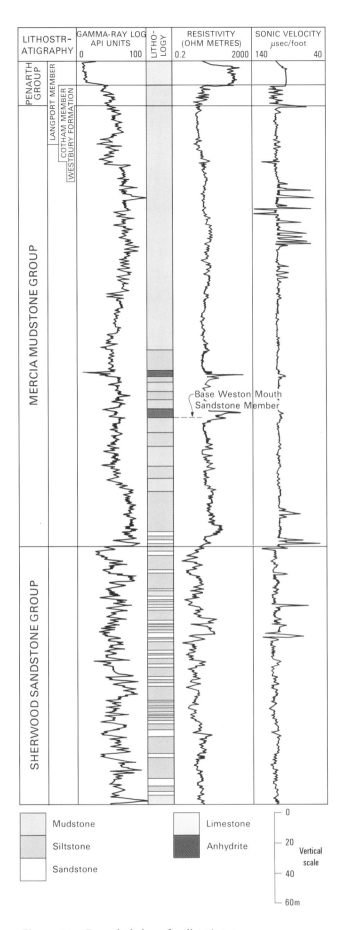

Figure 28 Downhole log of well 98/18-1.

England, although in areas marginal to contemporary highs these pass into breccias and conglomerates. Some normal faulting continued during deposition of the Mercia Mudstone Group, delineating areas of high ground from depositional basins, but the dominance of fine-grained sediments in most areas indicates widespread subdued topography. The mudstones are generally red, with some green-grey reduction mottling; they are silty, locally calcareous (marls), and contain thin sandstones. Jeans (1978) distinguished two clay-mineral assemblages: a matrix assemblage of detrital origin, and another which crystallised within the mudstones during diagenesis. The mudstones are gypsiferous and anhydritic, and towards the depocentres they contain halite (Lott et al., 1982). Halite is known at Winterborne Kingston, and although none is recorded in offshore wells, it is believed to occur in the offshore sequence towards the depocentre west of the existing wells (Figure 29).

The mudstone sequence onshore is divided by the grey dolomitic mudstones and sandstones of the Weston Mouth Sandstone Member (Warrington et al., 1980), which may correlate with the Arden Sandstone of the Midlands. Jeans (1978) and Fisher (1972) distinguished two arenaceous members, but Warrington and Scrivener (1980) found only one 11 m-thick unit of intercalated sandstones in the Lyme Regis borehole (Figure 29), which lies only 5 km from the coastal outcrop. Furthermore, only one such unit is recognised on borehole logs from east Devon and west Dorset (Lott et al., 1982). The mudstone sequence below the Weston Mouth Sandstone Member in Devon has yielded Carnian palynomorph assemblages from about 135 m above the base of the Mercia Mudstone Group up to the top of the Weston Mouth Sandstone Member (Warrington, 1971). Succeeding mudstones have yielded an impoverished assemblage which may be Norian (Fisher, 1972).

The Blue Anchor Formation, formerly the Tea Green Marl and Grey Marl (Warrington et al., 1980; Warrington and Whittaker, 1984), occurs at the top of the Mercia Mudstone Group and comprises green, calcareous shales and mudstones passing up into grey marls. It has yielded Rhaetian palynomorph assemblages in south-east Devon (Stevenson and Warrington, 1971; Orbell, 1973), and represents the first phase of the Rhaetian marine transgression (Warrington, 1981; Warrington and Whittaker, 1984). The sediments resemble modern sabkha deposits formed in supratidal and low-energy intertidal environments. Nodules of porphyroblastic gypsum are common in the structureless, supratidal sediments, but halite is absent.

Outcrop of the Mercia Mudstone Group was proved offshore at Lyme Bay in borehole 74/31 (Figure 24), which yielded red-brown mudstone with grey-green mottling and thin layers of fibrous gypsum. Similar mudstones were proved in eight gravity cores nearby, and by a further 23 gravity cores in three areas of outcrop farther south (Figure 24). No earlier Permo-Triassic formations are proved in these latter areas, although one gravity core recorded 0.2 m of conglomerate. In the nearshore outcrop off Start Point, there is no evidence that the Mercia Mudstone Group is faulted against the Devonian, so either it rests directly on the Devonian or the intervening Permo-Triassic formations are very thin.

Lott et al. (1982) subdivided the Mercia Mudstone Group of Winterborne Kingston and other wells in south-west England into six lithostratigraphical units on the basis of geophysical-log character (Figure 26). The lowest unit, unit A, comprises red-brown silty mudstones and siltstones with harder, better-cemented bands and a little anhydrite or gypsum. Unit B is a comparatively uniform, soft, red-brown mudstone sequence, whereas unit C is made up of red-brown, silty mudstones and siltstones with intercalated dolomites and much interbedded halite. Unit D is formed of hard dolomitic siltstones and mudstones with locally abundant anhydrite or gypsum; a prominent dolomite/sulphate-rich development at the base of this unit is correlated with the Weston Mouth Sandstone Member. Unit E comprises red-brown silty mudstones with traces of anhydrite or gypsum, and unit F, the Blue Anchor Formation, consists of red-brown and grey-green silty mudstones and siltstones with variable dolomite cement.

At Wytch Farm, the Blue Anchor Formation comprises about 30 m of medium-grey claystone with thin limestones; an anhydrite marker at the base of unit D is correlated with the Weston Mouth Sandstone Member. At Arreton, the Blue Anchor Formation is represented by varicoloured marls and shales with beds of microcrystalline limestone, and the dolomite bed some 90 m below the top of the group is believed to be the equivalent of the Weston Mouth Sandstone Member (Figure 26). The Mercia Mudstone Group at Middleton 1 is rather thicker than at Arreton, but similarly includes beds of white and red sandstone throughout; in both cases, these sands may result from erosion of the ridge upon which offshore wells 99/12-1 and 99/18-1 reveal the Mercia Mudstone Group to be absent (Figure 29). Eastwards from Middleton, the group thins rapidly, and at Henfield 1 a reduced sequence (66 m) is believed to include both the Mercia Mudstone, Penarth and lowest Lias groups. The strata here and at Brabourne include breccias and conglomerates containing ?Carboniferous limestone fragments.

Wells off Ballard Point (Figure 26), in the vicinity of the Portland–Wight Faults, recorded Mercia Mudstone Group thicknesses comparable with those at Wytch Farm. Most of these sediments are red-brown, blocky, moderately calcareous mudstones and siltstones that are locally pale green-grey and include some white, amorphous or fibrous anhydrite. Sandstone beds become important low in the sequence; these are pale grey, fine to medium grained, poorly to well sorted and calcareous. Dolomitic limestones may correlate with those at the base of unit D at Winterborne Kingston, and thus with the Weston Mouth Sandstone Member. The Blue Anchor Formation is composed of grey or green-grey dolomitic claystones that on well logs record high velocity, high resistivity, and low gamma radiation.

Successively thinner sequences of Mercia Mudstone Group are recorded on the south-east flank of the Portland–Wight Basin in wells 98/18-1 and 98/22-2. Sandstone beds occur near the base, and prominent developments of anhydrite may correlate with the Weston Mouth Sandstone Member; the Blue Anchor Formation consists of grey claystones and pale grey microcrystalline limestones. Farther to the east, towards the basin margin in wells 98/23-1 and 99/16-1, the sand content increases and the beds become pebbly. The group is appreciably thinner in well 99/16-1, suggesting an approach to an upland source area in the east, and is absent in 99/18-1. A 49 m-thick sandstone in well 98/23-1 is clean, medium grained, angular and poorly sorted, although towards its base it is argillaceous and micaceous as it grades up from the underlying, moderately calcareous, micaceous, red-brown siltstones. The claystones overlying the sandstone are dominantly pale green, with red, purple and brown interbeds; they may represent the Blue Anchor Formation as they include minor patches of anhydrite and stringers of dolomitic limestone. It is not clear whether the Weston Mouth Sandstone Member is represented in well 98/23-1 by the thick sandstone or by the dolomite bands lower in the sequence.

PENARTH GROUP

The Penarth Group, formerly the Rhaetic (Warrington et al., 1980), is the thin deposit of a widespread marine transgression. Triassic erosion had reduced most of England to a subdued topography, and a relatively small rise in sea level resulted in the inundation of most of the land area. At the coast in the south-west of England, where the 19 m-thick Penarth Group overlies the Mercia Mudstone Group with a slight nonsequence, it is divided into the Westbury and Lilstock formations (Figure 23). The relatively low sonic velocities and high gamma-ray values of the Westbury Formation and Cotham Member differentiate them from the succeeding Langport Member with its higher velocities and lower gamma-ray values (Figures 26 and 28).

The Westbury Formation comprises black, pyritous and calcareous shales with thin nodular limestones. There are sandstones near the base, which is marked by a distinctive bone bed. The fauna is dominated by bivalves, together with some other taxa, indicating a marine environment. The Lilstock Formation is divided into a lower Cotham Member, and an upper Langport Member that includes the White Lias Limestone. The Cotham Member comprises grey, green and brown mudstones and algal limestones; it represents a variable suite of fresh to brackish, supratidal, shallow-water, or marine environments (Kelling and Moshrif, 1977; Poole, 1978). The Langport Member is fully marine, with interbedded grey and white microcrystalline limestones and laminated shales.

The offshore outcrop of the Penarth Group in Lyme Bay (Figure 24) has been proved by two BGS gravity cores. The more northerly of these yielded black, hard, fissile shale of the Westbury Formation, whereas the other recovered cream-coloured limestone and marl of the Cotham Member. No Penarth Group sediment has been recorded from the areas of Triassic outcrop shown farther south, where the discovery of red mudstones in gravity cores adjacent to the Lias outcrop may indicate a nonsequence between the Mercia Mudstone Group and the Lias.

In boreholes from Winterborne Kingston to Portsdown (Figure 26), the Westbury Formation is relatively thick (up to 15 m), and at its base is greenish grey, thinly bedded sandstone with shaly partings. This passes up into medium-grey to black, pyritic shale and siltstone overlain by up to 2.7 m of the Cotham Member comprising grey and green argillaceous limestone with anhydritic or pyritic mudstone. The Langport Member is up to 14 m thick and consists of pale, massive, fine-grained limestones with dark, pyritic shale wisps and stylolites. East of Portsdown, the standard Penarth Group sequence is not found, and the age of the strata underlying the earliest proven Lias is in doubt; the Westbury Formation at Middleton 1 may be represented by red shale overlying purple-red, fine-grained sandstone. At Henfield 1, Rhaeto-Liassic plant remains are recorded at 1508 m, possibly near the top of the Trias, and at Grove Hill 1, off-white calcutites, chert and mottled marls of unproven age were penetrated. The group appears to be absent at Brabourne.

Where the Mercia Mudstone Group is proved offshore in the Portland–Wight Basin, the Penarth Group is found lying conformably between that group and the Lias. It has a relatively constant thickness of 20 to 25 m, but thins to the east in well 99/16-1. In the west, the Westbury Formation and Cotham Member are dominantly subfissile mudstones, locally pyritic and calcareous. Interbedded sandstones are fine grained, argillaceous and generally calcareous, whereas interbedded limestones are blocky, argillaceous and microcrystalline. The Langport Member comprises blocky, microcrys-

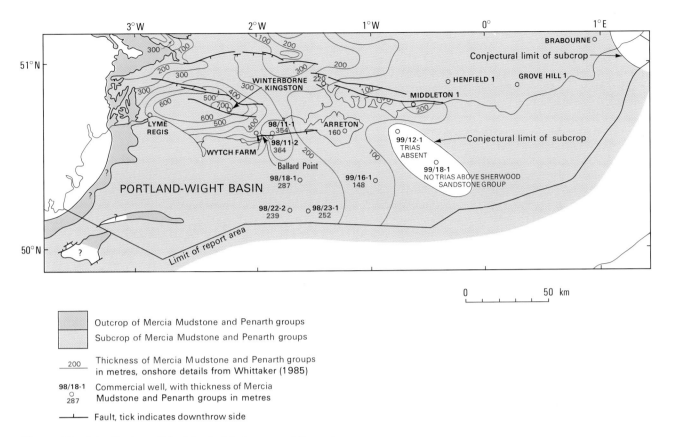

Figure 29 Distribution of the Mercia Mudstone and Penarth groups.

talline limestone that is locally argillaceous and pyritic, but noticeably paler and less argillaceous than the overlying Lias limestone.

On the eastern flank of the Portland–Wight Basin, the only recorded Langport Member limestones are in wells 98/23-1 and 99/16-1. The absence of Westbury and Cotham lithologies may indicate that the Rhaetian transgression, which came from the west, did not extend this far east until Langport Member times, and did not reach the region of wells 99/12-1 and 99/18-1 until the Jurassic.

6 Jurassic

Jurassic strata occur widely in the report area, and crop out in the west and east (Figure 30). In the west, the submarine outcrops of Lower, Middle, and Upper Jurassic strata are almost continuous from the Dorset coast to Normandy. In the east, latest Upper Jurassic strata come to outcrop in the core of the Weald Anticline, and in The Boulonnais and its offshore extension. Triassic strata in the region normally pass up conformably into Jurassic successions, and the latter are usually overlain unconformably by Lower Cretaceous sediments which generally overstep them on to basin-framing Palaeozoic massifs. Locally, however, as in the Weald Anticline and the Portland–Wight High, they pass conformably into lowest Cretaceous strata.

The English Channel lies oblique to the main structural grain of the Wessex–Channel Basin (Figure 30), so that the geology of the poorly explored offshore area may be predicted by extrapolating the results of onshore exploration along strike. The regional Jurassic succession is described by comparing its variation within three structurally controlled belts of deposition: the Portland–Wight Basin and its counterparts which extend into Normandy, the Hampshire–Dieppe High and its extension into Dorset, and the Weald Basin.

These basins (Whittaker, 1985) are asymmetric, being bounded on their northern and north-eastern flanks by Jurassic syndepositional faults. The faults show variable growth along their lengths, and grew at different rates at different times, so that the Jurassic succession shows considerable thickness variation within the basins, as well as between adjacent basins and highs. Generally, Early Jurassic crustal extension reactivated pre-existing normal faults to create the belts of basins and highs. This was succeeded by Mid-Jurassic flexural subsidence which resulted in sediment drape over these earlier Jurassic structures. The latter were in turn rejuvenated by Late Jurassic extension.

The Jurassic succession predominantly comprises a cyclically deposited sequence of variably calcareous shales and mudstones, with subordinate calcareous sandstones and limestones. Almost all of the succession yields abundant, wholly marine macro- and microfaunas, as well as a marine microflora. From time to time, slow relative subsidence of some of the highs was such that marginal to sublittoral facies were deposited locally in marginal-marine to brackish waters. The widespread lateral persistence of extremely thin beds is a major feature of the Jurassic rocks, and further testifies to deposition in shallow-shelf seas on a fundamentally stable platform. Regional study shows this epeiric shelf to have extended to most of north-west Europe, and to have flanked a proto-North Atlantic Ocean (Arkell, 1956; Chadwick et al., 1989) at a palaeolatitude of approximately 35°N (Smith et al., 1981), at a time when tropical seas extended farther north than at present (Hallam, 1981).

The characteristic upward-shallowing sedimentary cycles occur hierarchically on a scale of a few metres involving individual beds, to hundreds of metres in major lithostratigraphical groups. They have been long recognised (Arkell, 1956; Hallam, 1964) and known to underpin small-scale, local, as well as large-scale, regional correlation. In about the last twenty years, BGS cored drilling has demonstrated that even small-scale variation can be traced from basin to basin. The larger-scale cycles closely reflect the principal three-fold British subdivision of the Jurassic System. Thus, the lower and upper,

predominantly argillaceous sequences are separated by a median sequence characterised by more calcareous beds (Arkell, 1933; Mégnien, 1980). In such a widespread, stable, marine shelf, the ubiquitous nektonic ammonites prove to be outstanding stratigraphical indicators, and form the principal basis for regional correlation (Cope et al., 1980a; 1980b).

The larger-scale sedimentary cycles have lately been interpreted by Vail et al. (1977) and Haq et al. (1987) in terms of coastal advance and retreat; they assume that these changes, occurring similarly in disparate sedimentary basins, reflect eustatic variation of sea level. The sequence boundaries of such cycles thus have a two-fold chronostratigraphical significance; first of all in being chronostratigraphical boundaries themselves, and secondly in reflecting changes in environment which directly affect ammonite distribution.

The Jurassic rocks of the report area are subdivided into Lower, Middle and Upper (including Callovian) Series. The Lower Jurassic corresponds approximately to Lower, Middle and Upper Lias; the Middle Jurassic is approximately coextensive with the Inferior Oolite and Great Oolite groups. The Upper Jurassic approximates to the Kellaways Beds, Oxford Clay, Corallian Beds, Kimmeridge Clay, Portland Beds and Purbeck Beds. These strata are also widely known in northern France (Arkell, 1956), and these subdivisions correspond almost exactly to those used by Arkell (1933) in his great regional synthesis. Recent studies have shown that the beds can be traced precisely from surface to subsurface by means of their characteristic geophysical-log signatures (Whittaker et al., 1985), providing a means of extrapolating the successions offshore.

LIAS

The Lias was deposited almost entirely during Early Jurassic time, for the base of the Jurassic System (*sensu* Cope et al., 1980a) lies within a few metres of the base of the Lias in those areas where it passes conformably upwards from the Penarth Group. Lithologically it comprises predominantly calcareous, locally ferruginous or bituminous mudstones and shales which are commonly pyritic. These are rhythmically and cyclically interbedded with each other and with thin, variably argillaceous, micritic or porcellanous limestones. At certain levels, thin beds of siltstone and sandstone are present, the latter sometimes sufficiently prominent to form a discrete member or formation.

Shelly macrofossils are common, together with a calcareous microflora and microfauna of coccoliths, foraminifera and ostracods. Dinoflagellate cysts are an important constituent of the palaeoflora, and there is normally an abundant ichnofauna.

The rock types commonly occur in sedimentary cycles, ranging from a few metres to tens of metres in thickness. The complete cycle, most obvious at the smallest scale, opens with a basal shale which commonly rests sharply on the subjacent strata. The shale characteristically contains a limited fauna,

Figure 30   Distribution of Jurassic strata in and around the report area.

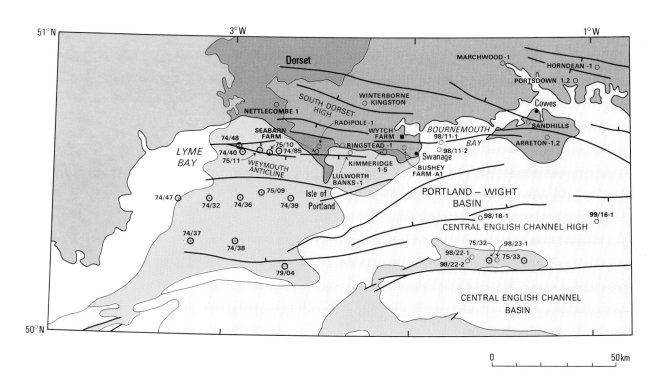

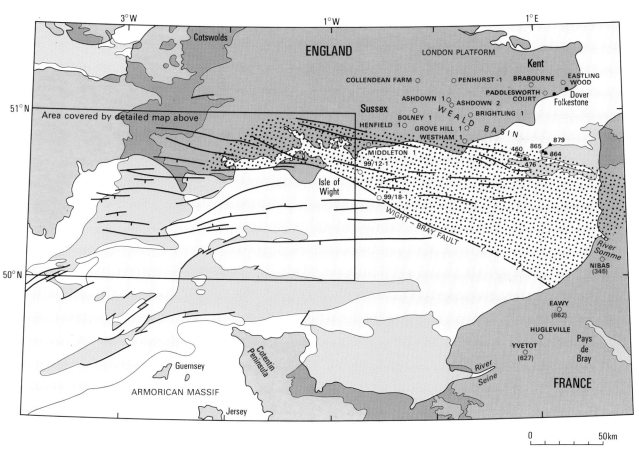

Legend

Outcrop of Jurassic rocks	
Subcrop of Jurassic rocks	
Approximate limit of Hampshire-Dieppe High	
Fault	

98/18-1 ⊙	Commercial well/borehole
■	Oilfield
75/32 ⊙	BGS shallow borehole
460 ▲	BGS shallow core
YVETOT ⊙	French borehole with thickness of total Jurassic

and where bituminous, consists of thin alternations of carbonaceous and clay laminae, with fine calcite stringers parallel with, and at various angles to, the bedding.

The shale passes up to, or may locally exhibit a *Chondrites*-mottled boundary with, blocky, calcareous mudstones containing a benthonic fauna, generally of burrowing bivalves. The mudstones, in turn, usually pass rapidly to argillaceous limestones. More coarsely siliciclastic rocks, if present, tend to occur in upward passage from the mudstones. They show bioturbation, and may have calcareous nodules and lenses or be chamosite bearing, before passing abruptly into limestones.

The origin of these cycles has been researched over a long period of time (Hallam, 1975), and it is clear that they correspond to the parasequences of Haq et al. (1987). Their contained faunas, especially ichnofaunas (Sellwood, 1970; 1972) help explain their mode of formation. The basal shales indicate an initial increase in water depth accompanied by sediment starvation with, in the case of the bituminous beds, relatively anaerobic bottom conditions. Subsequent pulses of sedimentation and decreasing water depth, accompanied by more-aerobic bottom conditions, gave rise to the mudstone component of the cycle. Thereafter, sediment starvation with still-decreasing water depths resulted in the development of limestones, though local increase in coarse-grained, clastic input led to sandstone formation. Subsequent rapid increase in water depth led to the break in sequence characterising the onset of the succeeding cycle.

Lower Lias

The Lower Lias is magnificently exposed on the Dorset coast, where it comprises alternating medium to dark grey, locally silty and calcareous mudstones with interbeds of thin, pale to medium grey, hard, microcrystalline, variably argillaceous limestone. The lowest few metres lie within the Triassic System, but otherwise the Lower Lias spans the Hettangian and Sinemurian stages and the lower part of the Pliensbachian Stage. The sequence is predominantly calcareous below and argillaceous above, but the variable proportion of limestone to mudstone throughout allows the recognition of five subdivisions which may be identified by characteristic geophysical-log profiles (Figure 31; Whittaker et al., 1985).

The lowest subdivision, the Blue Lias, is famed for its closely spaced alternations of limestone and mudstone which give rise to extremely serrated geophysical-log signatures with an overall sinusoidal shape to the curves. The succeeding Shales-with-Beef consists of alternating calcareous mudstones and shales; the former tend to dominate in the lower part, and the latter in the upper, giving rise to moderately serrated geophysical-log signatures marked on average by relatively low sonic velocities, and moderate gamma-ray values which decrease towards the top.

The overlying Black Ven Marl consists predominantly of shales, and shows high gamma-ray values and low sonic velocity, although impersistent limestones give rise to sporadic sonic-log 'spikes' and corresponding low gamma-ray values. There is a trend to overall upward decrease in gamma-ray values, commonly capped by increased values at the top; this gives rise to a characteristic asymmetric profile.

The Belemnite Marl consists of alternating beds of paler grey, calcareous, silty mudstones and darker bluish grey, less-calcareous mudstones. These alternations give rise to poorly serrated geophysical-log curves with overall lower gamma-ray values and higher sonic velocity than the underlying unit. Well-marked sonic 'spikes' and corresponding low gamma-ray values are due to impersistent limestones. The Green Ammonite Beds consist of pale grey, poorly calcareous mudstones which tend to become silty and micaceous in their upper part. They usually ex-

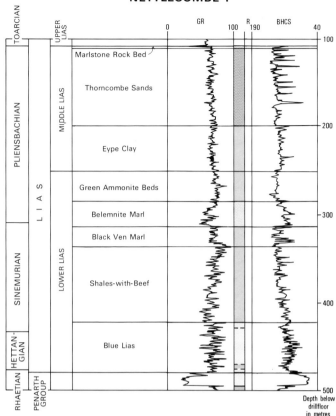

NETTLECOMBE 1

GR — Gamma-ray log with scale in API units

BHCS — Borehole compensated sonic log with scale in microseconds/foot

R — Shaded area indicates core recovery (no core recovered in this part of the borehole)

Figure 31 The Lower and Middle Lias sections at Nettlecombe 1. For location see Figure 30; for key to lithology see Figure 32.

hibit a poorly serrated geophysical-log signature of moderate to high gamma-ray values and low sonic velocity.

SOUTH OF THE HAMPSHIRE–DIEPPE HIGH

The succession along the Dorset coast lies on the Hampshire–Dieppe High immediately to the north of the Portland–Wight Basin, but the sequences within the western part of this basin appear to be virtually identical (Warrington and Owens, 1977; Darton et al., 1981). To the east, drilling of the Weymouth Anticline, near to the northerly bounding fault of the basin, suggests that all subdivisions of the Lower Lias are present in some 350 m drilled. When traced eastwards along the basin strike, the thickness increases to about 600 m in Kimmeridge Bay, before thinning farther east where some 274 m were proved just south of the Wight–Bray Fault at Arreton. Here the succession is thinner both towards the Central English Channel High in wells 98/18-1 and 98/22-2, and towards the Wight–Bray Fault in well 99/16-1 (Figures 30 and 32). In all three wells, the overall reduced thickness of the Lower Lias (155 to 163 m towards the Central English Channel High, and 113 m towards the Wight–Bray Fault) results from the absence of the Green Ammonite Beds and, locally, most or all of the Belemnite Marl, probably as a result of Pliensbachian erosion.

South of the Central English Channel High the succession thickens, but details are not known except at outcrop on the coast of Normandy. Here it is complicated by the development of marginal facies where the sea encroached against the

Armorican Massif (Arkell, 1956), but it is sufficiently recognisable as to betray its original continuity with the Central English Channel Basin.

When traced eastwards in the concealed ground along the French coast the Lower Lias becomes thinner, mainly due to pre-Pliensbachian overlap which has led to the complete absence of Sinemurian and Hettangian strata. The latter reappear north-east of the Seine, where the Lower Lias thickens north-eastwards from 24 m at Yvetot to over 105 m in the Eawy borehole (Figure 30). The structural relationship of this depositional basin to that south of the Central English Channel High is not defined, but it similarly lies to the south-west of the Wight–Bray Fault.

HAMPSHIRE–DIEPPE HIGH

The 154 m-thick Dorset coast sections of the Lower Lias (Melville and Freshney, 1982) lie upon this high to the north of the Portland–Wight Basin. When traced along strike to the east, the Lower Lias thins to some 116 m in the Wytch Farm Oilfield, but maintains the same facies and subdivisions (Bristow et al., 1991). It thickens to some 145 m in the fault block to the south of Wytch Farm, as proved the Bushey Farm-A1 borehole, and reaches substantially greater thickness farther south.

Farther east, wells in Bournemouth Bay pass through the northerly bounding faults of the basin. In well 98/11-1, the Lower Lias is 87 m thick and of Dorset facies, and it thickens to some 155 m in well 98/11-2. The thinnest drilled sequence of Lower Lias is 12 m at Sandhills 1, immediately to the north of the Wight–Bray Fault on the Isle of Wight, where subdivisions cannot be recognised (Figure 32). Following the line of the Wight–Bray Fault, the Lower Lias is absent altogether in mid-Channel at well 99/12-1 (Penn, 1985), apparently as a result of erosion, although it is likely that the Lower Lias would have been thin, as in well 99/18-1. Little is known of it along the marine section of this belt of attenuation, but in northern France (Mégnien, 1980) it is known to be comparably thin.

The belt of attenuated Jurassic strata referred to as the Hampshire–Dieppe High has an overall asymmetric profile. In general the Lower Lias thickens northwards and north-eastwards away from the southern rim of extreme attenuation, but it does so irregularly, for it locally thickens into smaller fault-bounded basins to a maximum proved thickness of over 300 m at Winterborne Kingston (Rhys et al., 1982) within the Dorset Basin.

Similar, but less dramatic thickening occurs north of the Isle of Wight, towards the Wardour–Portsdown Faults (Whittaker, 1985). The throw of these faults however diminishes eastwards, and some 148 m of Lower Lias have been proved at Henfield 1 (Taitt and Kent, 1958; Young and Lake, 1988). Here, the basal marls of probable Rhaetian to Sinemurian age, though at least partially marine in origin and equivalent to the Blue Lias, are of such nearshore facies that they invite comparison with the way in which the onset of fully marine, shelf sedimentation was delayed until within Early Jurassic time on the northern flanks of the Armorican Massif.

In the eastern part of the Hampshire–Dieppe High, basal early Sinemurian redbeds at Grove Hill 1 (Lake et al., 1987), and probably Henfield 1 (Young and Lake, 1988), are further evidence that it was not as rapidly submerged beneath Early Jurassic waters as was its western part, and hence parts of the eastern English Channel may have been emergent in earliest Jurassic time. In northern France, some 10 m of typically Liassic marls and sandstones, thought to be late Sinemurian in age, lie directly upon Palaeozoic rocks in the Nibas borehole (Mégnien, 1980). As such, they may represent the local equivalent of a late Sinemurian transgressive pulse seen in Normandy, and be a French counterpart of the Early Jurassic onlap hinted at by the Sussex succession.

WEALD BASIN

On the upthrown side of the Wardour–Portsdown Faults, and farther into the Weald Basin, the Lower Lias is generally argillaceous and the typical subdivisions are readily identifiable. Some 274 m of Lower Lias in the Bolney 1 borehole at the centre of the Weald Basin (Figure 32) rest on the Penarth Group, and comprise a full complement of subdivisions, though carrying sandy levels in its basal 50 m (Gallois and Worssam, in press). When traced eastwards, substantially along the basin strike, the succession thins and is 220 m thick at Ashdown 2 (Bristow and Bazley, 1972), where the basal Lias and subjacent strata indicate delay in the onset of fully marine, inner-shelf sedimentation, as on the Hampshire–Dieppe High to the immediate south.

When traced farther eastwards, parallel to the Sussex coast, the Lower Lias thins rapidly as lower beds are overlapped on to the London Platform (Lamplugh et al., 1923; Lamplugh and Kitchin, 1911). At Brabourne there is a thin, early Pliensbachian, basal argillaceous sandstone with rounded pebbles derived from the underlying Palaeozoic basement. These beds thin to 12 m near Folkestone and about 2 m at Dover, with only the uppermost parts preserved above a basement bed (Shephard-Thorn, 1988). At Paddlesworth Court (Figure 32), a thin Lias sequence is preserved beneath Middle Jurassic rocks.

In The Boulonnais, Lower Lias is known from shallow boreholes along a narrow coastal strip (Pruvost and Pringle, 1924) where a few metres of clay and marlstone lie on Palaeozoic basement in a manner recalling the Kent Coalfield succession (Mégnien, 1980). It may be that the greater part of the Lower Lias beneath the marine area, particularly that beneath French waters, will comprise highest Lower Lias, and as the beds are traced towards England, successively lower strata will appear beneath them. It may also be deduced that, accompanying this basinward thickening, the basal facies may increase in thickness, and earliest Jurassic strata comprise an upper part of more-marine aspect, and a lower part of less-marine aspect akin to that proved along the East Sussex coast.

Middle Lias

The Middle Lias is exposed in the cliffs of the Dorset coast, where the succession is of late Pliensbachian age and comprises some 120 m of silty, micaceous clays which become increasingly sandy near the top. The geophysical-log signature in the Nettlecombe 1 borehole shows relatively constant gamma-ray and sonic values, but with slightly decreasing gamma-ray, and increasing sonic values as the succession is climbed (Figure 31). The Eype Clay comprises bluish grey, calcareous mudstones and clays containing nodules of ironstone, and argillaceous limestones interbedded with sporadic, micaceous sandstones; the basal ten or so metres are interbedded with thin, calcareous sandstones. The hard, calcareous and sandy beds give rise to marked sonic spikes and corresponding low gamma-ray values. The Eype Clay passes up into 22 to 30 m of micaceous and ferruginous sandy clays and marls with nodules and bands of fissile sandstone, the Down Cliff Sands (Figure 33), which are capped by a thin, hard, ferruginous, sandy limestone, the Margaritatus Bed.

The sequence is essentially repeated in the overlying beds. Thin, blue clays with high gamma-ray motif pass upwards to the pale brown and yellow, argillaceous Thorncombe Sands, in which layers of well-cemented, calcareous doggers give high sonic and low gamma-ray spikes. The Thorncombe Sands, up to 26 m in thickness on the Dorset coast, are capped by a few centimetres of reddish brown to greenish grey, fine-grained, iron-shot, locally conglomeratic, highly

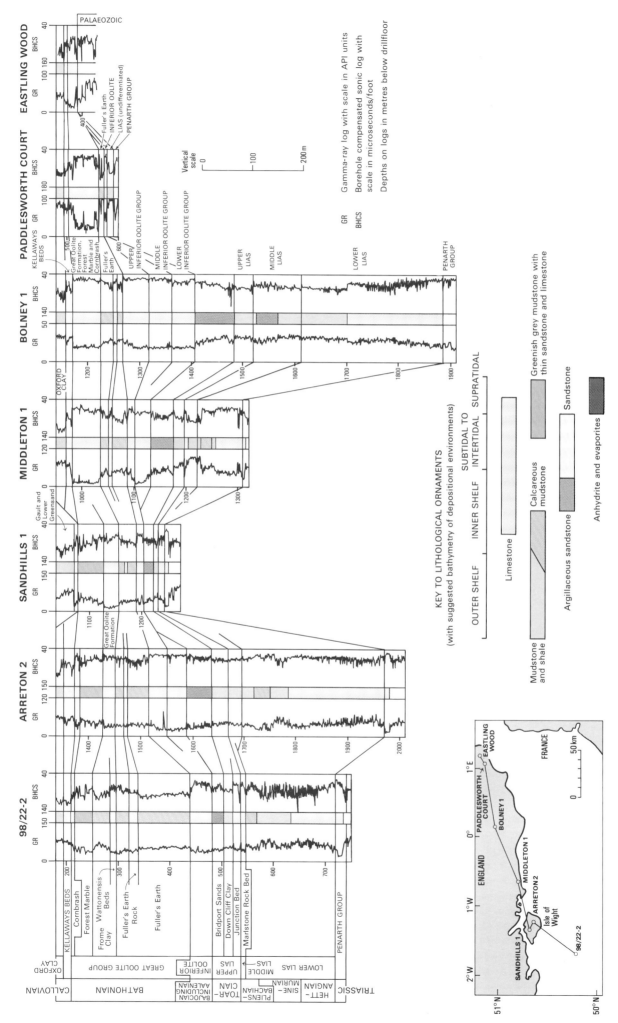

Figure 32 Correlation of Lower and Middle Jurassic rocks from the Portland–Wight Basin to the Weald Basin.

42

fossiliferous limestone termed the Marlstone Rock Bed, which gives a prominent sonic spike. The latter is commonly anastomosed to an overlying, thin, but quite different limestone such that both condensed sequences have been united in the single name, the Junction Bed.

SOUTH OF THE HAMPSHIRE–DIEPPE HIGH

The silty clays characteristic of the lower part of the Middle Lias have been proved offshore to the south of the coastal sections (Warrington and Owens, 1977). The banded nature of the younger sandy parts of the sequence gives rise to good seismic reflections on shallow-seismic profiles acquired in Lyme Bay (Darton et al., 1981). The entire sequence has been proved along strike to the east in the Radipole-1 borehole (Figure 33), where some 170 m are present, and a substantial part of the lower Thorncombe Sands is very argillaceous. A similar sequence is present at Kimmeridge Bay, where compared with Radipole, it would appear that a reduction in thickness is almost entirely due to eastward thinning of this lower, argillaceous part of the Thorncombe Sands. Even more dramatic attenuation has taken place farther east at Arreton, where only some 27 m of strata can be assigned to the Middle Lias, of which the upper 16 m are in the sandy facies.

Offshore towards the centre of the English Channel, only pale grey, micritic, microcrystalline limestones are present resting on eroded Lower Lias; they are 12 m thick in well 98/18-1, 8 m in well 98/22-2 (Figure 32), and 3 m in well 99/16-1. In Normandy, a comparable thickness of condensed upper Pliensbachian, micritic, sandy limestone with ferruginous ooliths rests with widespread unconformity on eroded Lower Lias, and

where it comes locally against eroded islets of older strata, it has littoral facies. As the Middle Lias is traced north-eastwards across northern France by means of boreholes, a pale grey, calcareous, glauconitic sandstone (the Banc du Roc) is underlain by black to grey, calcareous, sandy, pyritic mudstones (Mégnien, 1980). These increase in thickness towards the line of the Wight–Bray Fault to 30 m at Eawy (Figure 30), where the entire sequence has a typical Middle Lias geophysical-log profile.

HAMPSHIRE–DIEPPE HIGH

The 120 m or so of Middle Lias of the coastal exposures represent a reduction in thickness of some 30 per cent when compared with beds within the Portland–Wight Basin immediately to the south. Comparable reduction takes place from Kimmeridge Bay to Wytch Farm. Offshore in Bournemouth Bay on the southern margin of the high, the Middle Lias is almost entirely developed in the older, silty mudstones facies, and its top is hard to identify other than as a thin, argillaceous limestone underlying Upper Lias clays (Bristow et al., 1991). The sequence thins from 108 m in well 98/11-2 to 81m in well 98/11-1 farther to the north, and thins further to the 52 m-thick succession in the Bushey Farm fault-block immediately to the north of the fault bounding the Dorset Basin (Figure 14).

On the Isle of Wight, only a metre of limestone, probably equivalent to the Marlstone Rock Bed, is present at Sandhills 1 (Figure 32). Farther along strike to the south-east it disappears altogether, and may be absent offshore along much of the south-west rim of the Hampshire–Dieppe High.

In Dorset, the Middle Lias thickens gradually northwards into the Dorset Basin to be around 140 m thick at Winterborne Kingston (Rhys et al., 1982). A similar northward thickening on the high takes place farther east; at Cowes, the Middle Lias is composed of only a few metres of Marlstone Rock Bed, but to the north-east the sequence thickens by the inclusion of subjacent mudstones. Such a succession characterises the entire landward flank of the Hampshire–Dieppe High, and probably offshore also.

WEALD BASIN

Immediately north of the Wardour–Portsdown Faults, the Middle Lias of Horndean-1 is some 65 m thick and is in typical sequence, with characteristic geophysical-log character. The succession is comparable to the 95 m or so drilled at Bolney (Figure 32; Gallois and Worssam, in press) near the centre of the Weald Basin. To the east, the Middle Lias thins to around 60 m at Ashdown 2 (Bristow and Bazley, 1972). Interbedded limestones are persistent as the succession thins on to the London Platform, and comprise almost the entire 4 to 6 m of Middle Lias of the Dover area (Lamplugh and Kitchin, 1911; Lamplugh et al., 1923; Shephard-Thorn, 1988).

Since the Middle Lias of The Boulonnais is comparable to these condensed sequences of Kent (Pruvost and Pringle, 1924; Mégnien, 1980), it is likely that much of the intervening offshore area is underlain by similar strata. Indeed, given the apparent symmetry of Middle Lias overlap from the Weald Basin to the Hampshire–Dieppe High to the south-west and the London Platform to the east, it is probable that the Middle Lias of most of the eastern English Channel comprises thin, sandy limestones and argillaceous sandstones, sporadically preserved round the feather-edge of the basin.

Upper Lias

The youngest part of the Upper Lias is excellently exposed in the cliffs of the Dorset coast, though not in continuous succession as the earlier beds are greatly condensed. The whole succession coincides with the Toarcian Stage, apart from a

RADIPOLE - 1

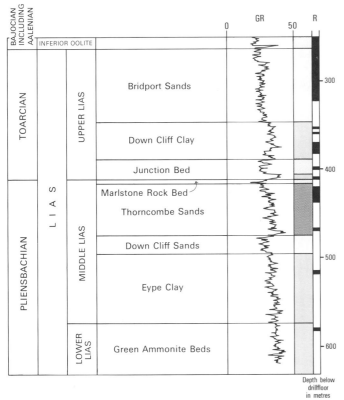

GR Gamma-ray log with scale in API units

R Shaded area indicates core recovery

Figure 33 A typical Middle and Upper Lias section in the Radipole-1 borehole. For location see Figure 30; for key to lithology see Figure 32.

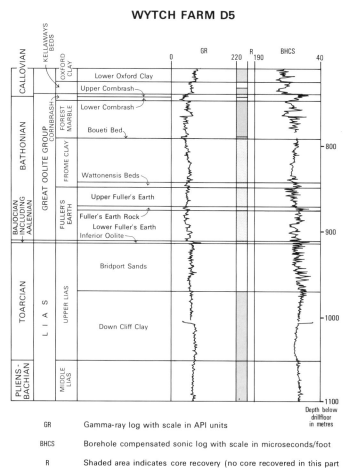

WYTCH FARM D5

| GR | R | BHCS |
| 0   220 | 190 | 40 |

Depth below
drillfloor
in metres

GR   Gamma-ray log with scale in API units

BHCS   Borehole compensated sonic log with scale in microseconds/foot

R   Shaded area indicates core recovery (no core recovered in this part of the borehole)

Figure 34 The Upper Lias and Middle Jurassic at Wytch Farm Oilfield well D5. For location see Figure 30; for key to lithology see Figure 32.

few metres at the top which extend into the Bajocian (including the Aalenian) Stage.

At the base, the fine-grained lithographical limestone of the Junction Bed generally gives rise to a cylindrical log signature characterised by low gamma-ray values (Figure 33) and corresponding high sonic velocity. It is a condensed deposit, rarely more than 1.5 m thick in west Dorset (Wilson et al., 1958), which contains representatives of all six Toarcian ammonite zones.

The main mass of the exposed Upper Lias was deposited within the latter half of the latest zone. The finely serrated log profiles typical of the bluish grey, micaceous mudstones of the Down Cliff Clay have high gamma-ray values and low sonic velocity at their base. There is an upward decrease in gamma-ray values as the formation passes up to the Bridport Sands. The latter are very fine-grained sandstones that give a highly serrated log signature caused by the rapid alternation of variably argillaceous, soft and hard, calcite-cemented beds (Figure 34). Gamma-ray values are only moderately low since the formation is feldspathic. Thus the asymmetry of the profiles accurately reflects the overall upward-shoaling nature of the sequence (Whittaker et al., 1985), which crudely repeats that of the Middle Lias.

SOUTH OF THE HAMPSHIRE–DIEPPE HIGH

Shallow offshore drilling to the south of Dorset, such as BGS borehole 74/36 (Figure 30), has shown that the Junction Bed of the west Dorset coast passes into a sequence of mudstones and argillaceous limestones towards the centre of the Portland–Wight Basin (BGS Portland Solid Geology sheet;

Warrington and Owens, 1977). However, nearer to the northern margin of the basin in south-west Dorset at Radipole-1 (Figure 33), some 14 m of argillaceous limestone that corresponds to the Junction Bed is overlain by 42 m of Down Cliff Clay and 85 m of Bridport Sands. There, the Upper Lias is, at just over 140 m, some 100 m thicker than in the Bridport area, but along strike at Kimmeridge 5 (Figure 30) it is over 195 m thick.

Still farther east in Bournemouth Bay, over 170 m of Upper Lias were proved in well 98/11-2, where 112 m of Bridport Sands overlie 60 m of Down Cliff Clay with no obvious equivalent to the Junction Bed. The similarity of the succession to that at Kimmeridge suggests that the main northerly bounding fault to the basin during the deposition of these beds lay to the north of well 98/11-2.

The Upper Lias also thins gradually southwards across the basin, being some 127 m thick in well 98/18-1, around 79 m on the Central English Channel High in well 98/22-2, and 61 m in well 99/16-1 near the eastern margin. In general, it maintains its stratigraphical character but is more calcareous and argillaceous in its upper part. There is usually a prominent basal mudstone around 2 m thick overlain by well-developed, fine-grained argillaceous limestones 6 to 13 m thick with a characteristic upper Junction Bed geophysical-log signature in well 98/22-2 (Figure 32). The Down Cliff Clay is similarly distinctive and recognisable, attaining a thickness of 72 m in well 98/18-1, but thinning to 20 m in well 98/22-2 and to 13 m in well 99/16-1. The geophysical signature shows the characteristic upward transition to the deeply serrated profiles typical of the Bridport Sands, but the lithology is one of alternating argillaceous limestone and calcareous mudstone in wells 98/18-1 and 99/16-1. In well 98/22-2 to the south, the hard beds are calcareous siltstones. A prominent feature throughout this southern part of the basin is the occurrence of a median, more-argillaceous level, in places over 10 m thick.

The Upper Lias of Normandy is less than 10 m thick, and contains in its basal part various condensed deposits that have yielded ammonites which show them to be the correlatives of the upper Junction Bed of Dorset. The highest few metres of the succession are calcareous mudstones. Overall, this thin Upper Lias pinches out to the south against the residual topography of the Armorican Massif (Mégnien, 1980). To the north-east, the succession is comparable, ranging from 20 m at Yvetot to 28 m at Eawy.

Thus the continuity of relatively deep-water sedimentation in a starved basin, as indicated by the upper Junction Bed, extended across the entire basin area during most of Toarcian time. In later Toarcian times, an outer-shelf mud regime was established, but was restricted to southernmost parts and passed northwards into an area characterised by inner-shelf muds, and possibly even subtidal sand bodies.

HAMPSHIRE–DIEPPE HIGH

The Upper Lias thickens substantially eastwards along the South Dorset High and is over 140 m thick at the Wytch Farm Oilfield where the Bridport Sands, the upper of two oil-bearing reservoirs, is over 60 m thick, and lies on almost 80 m of Down Cliff Clay, with no obvious development of the Junction Bed (Figure 34). To the east beneath Bournemouth Bay, well 98/11-1 penetrated a thinner Upper Lias consisting of 79 m of sandstone overlying 46 m of clay, again with no prominent representative of the upper Junction Bed. There is dramatic attenuation on the Isle of Wight, where at Sandhills 1 only some 21 m of sandstone overlie about 7 m of mudstone (Figure 32). The Upper Lias thickens northwards from this belt of attenuation, and initially retains its Dorset character; it is 187 m thick at Winterborne Kingston (Rhys et al., 1982). Seismic evidence indicates that along the south-western margin of the Hampshire–Dieppe High, the Lias disappears beneath Middle Jurassic overstep. A comparable northward thickening appears to take place where the Upper Lias is traced into the Weald Basin (Figure 32).

On the French coast there are mostly lower Toarcian, Upper Lias silty clays, with levels rich in ferruginous ooliths, that thicken to some 30 m to the south-east (Mégnien, 1980). Thus the Upper Lias of the easterly part of the Hampshire–Dieppe High may be composed largely of that part of the sequence which is condensed or missing to the south-west.

WEALD BASIN

North of the Wardour–Portsdown Faults, the Upper Lias thickens rapidly into the Weald Basin. The 46 m of Upper Lias in Grove Hill 1 (Figure 30) is an upward-coarsening sequence, similar to the 62 m at Henfield and 71 m drilled at Brightling (Taitt and Kent, 1958; Young and Lake, 1988). Although apparently similar to the Dorset sequence, here the Lower Toarcian is by comparison expanded, and the Upper Toarcian sequence condensed. It is some 110 m thick in Horndean-1, where the predominantly silty mudstone succession may have a poorly developed representative of the Junction Bed at its base. These mudstones locally grade to very fine-grained sandstone near the top, and 17 m of interbedded, very fine-grained sandstone and siltstone cap the sequence. A similarly upward-coarsening Upper Lias sequence of almost identical thickness was proved at Bolney (Figure 32), along the basin axis to the east (Gallois and Worssam, in press).

The Upper Lias thins dramatically on to the London Platform in Kent (Lamplugh and Kitchin, 1911), with 16 m of shaly clay recorded at Folkestone (Lamplugh et al., 1923). It probably extends into the eastern English Channel, but is apparently absent beneath unconformable Middle Jurassic strata in The Boulonnais (Mégnien, 1980), and it is likely to be missing over the Weald Basin and flanking highs beneath French waters.

MIDDLE JURASSIC

As used here, the Middle Jurassic Series comprises the Bajocian (including Aalenian) and Bathonian stages, and is almost exactly coextensive with the Inferior Oolite and Great Oolite groups. Despite a considerable range in lithology, the overall unity and distinctiveness of these beds, and the contrast with Lower and Upper Jurassic sediments, is well expressed in the name given to their French correlatives, the Dogger calcaire (Mégnien, 1980). Within the report area, the sediments are overwhelmingly the products of carbonate platform sedimentation within a subtropical region starved of clastic, terrigenous detritus.

The carbonates may have formed upon or around a bar or mound, or simply upon a ramp flanking low-lying land areas such as the London Platform and Armorican Massif. They are well developed as such in the Cotswolds (Figure 30), but the limestones of south Dorset may have formed as condensed deposits on a more distant, offshore, submarine swell or undulating shelf. Quartz-sand deposition is local and rare, so that grain size in these beds usually refers to the detrital carbonate fraction, even where argillaceous sediments predominate. The latter are invariably calcareous as a result of their deposition flanking the offshore margin of the platform from which much of the detrital carbonate fraction is assumed to have been derived.

The limestones are generally yellow weathering, but grey or blue when fresh, and range from fine-grained argillaceous limestones to variably shelly, oolite grainstones, packstones and wackestones that may be locally iron-shot. Hardground surfaces are many, and commonly bound major lithostratigraphical units. Microfauna and microflora are not in abundance, presumably owing to the destructive energy associated with many of the depositional environments, as well as to diagenesis. Contained macrofossils, such as corals, bivalves, brachiopods, bryozoans, echinoids, and ichnofauna are closely related to lithology. By comparison with modern analogues, these associations have been used to identify lagoonal, behind-barrier, barrier, and fore-barrier depositional environments (Green and Donovan, 1969; Mégnien, 1980).

The argillaceous sediments range from pale grey, silty, very calcareous mudstones through calcareous, blocky mudstones and less-calcareous, darker grey, slightly silty, poorly bedded mudstones to very dark grey, shaly mudstones. Microfossils are common throughout, and as with the limestones, there is a close relationship of fauna to lithology (Penn et al., 1979).

Cyclic sequences abound in both limestone and mudstone facies, and may indicate relative deepening or shallowing of water and consequent migration of facies. These cycles occur at several scales, and their bounding nonsequences, commonly marked by hardgrounds or firmgrounds, are important surfaces in stratigraphical correlation, particularly since the close relationship between facies and fauna may make correlation between mudstone and limestone facies difficult. The major cycles underpin the stratigraphical subdivisions and classification of the rocks of the series (Arkell, 1956; Penn et al., 1979; Mégnien, 1980; Rhys et al., 1982).

Inferior Oolite

The Inferior Oolite exposed in Dorset is exceptionally thin, comprising only 3 to 6 m of bioclastic limestones with a dominantly packstone texture. The succession is condensed; it shows the entire Bajocian (including the Aalenian) and the lowest Bathonian (Wilson et al., 1958). The beds give indication of having been deposited beneath waters only tens of metres deep, on a submarine swell or a slightly undulating shelf (Gatrall et al., 1972).

Classic studies (Buckman, 1893, 1910; Arkell, 1933) show that the nonsequences separating the Lower, Middle and Upper Inferior Oolite are of regional importance, for the formations which they bound tend to behave stratigraphically independently (Whittaker, 1985).

The Lower Inferior Oolite consists of thin, pale grey to brown, microcrystalline limestones that are sporadically sandy at the base and contain locally abundant limonite ooliths and pisoliths. The Middle Inferior Oolite comprises bluish or brownish, microcrystalline limestones which are coarsely iron-shot in their middle and lower parts, and has characteristic, disrupted, stromatolite-lined burrow-fills of pseudoconglomeratic aspect. The Upper Inferior Oolite consists of pale grey to yellow, microcrystalline limestones with sporadic ooliths. The succession is locally argillaceous, and rubbly at the top.

The geophysical-log signature is characterised by low gamma-ray values and high sonic velocity (Figures 32 and 35). The curves tend to be poorly serrated and individual limestones are difficult to recognise except where prominent interbedded mudstones or peculiar mineralogy, such as may be associated with condensed or hardground levels, give rise to gamma-ray peaks (Whittaker et al., 1985).

SOUTH OF THE HAMPSHIRE–DIEPPE HIGH

The limestones of the Inferior Oolite form a positive feature on the sea bed in Lyme Bay; this characteristic, together with the sharp decrease in sonic velocity which marks its upper

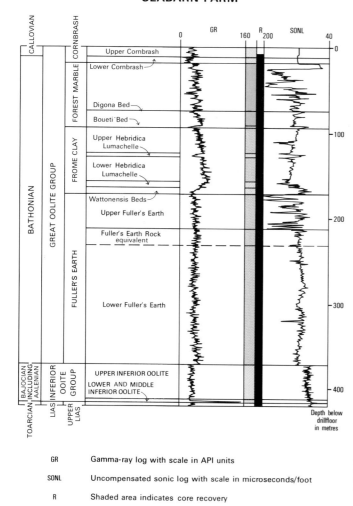

GR — Gamma-ray log with scale in API units

SONL — Uncompensated sonic log with scale in microseconds/foot

R — Shaded area indicates core recovery

Figure 35 A typical Middle Jurassic section at Seabarn Farm. For location see Figure 30; for key to lithology see Figure 32.

surface, enabled Darton et al. (1979) to map its occurrence off the Dorset coast. Drilling has proved a full sequence in typical south Dorset facies which, at almost 20 m, is substantially thicker than on the coast (Penn et al., 1980). Along the basin strike to the east at the Seabarn Farm borehole, the Inferior Oolite was proved to consist of a condensed, basal limestone containing derived and phosphatised fragments of Lower and Middle Inferior Oolite, overlain by 45 m of thin-bedded, calcareous siltstone, containing an abundant late Bajocian fauna (Whittaker et al., 1985). The very high gamma-ray peak and velocity spike marking the basal bed is widespread and distinctive (Figures 33 and 35).

This distinctive sequence is found in all the boreholes in the Weymouth Anticline, as well as in the Lulworth Banks 1 well and at Kimmeridge Bay. Its easterly extent is unknown, but in the north-eastern corner of the basin some 70 m of more-argillaceous Inferior Oolite were proved at Arreton 2. The succession thins to the south of the basin, where there are 11 to 25 m of similar overall character that are particularly argillaceous in the Upper Inferior Oolite (Figure 32).

The sequence in Normandy comprises a succession of condensed limestones very similar to those of south Dorset (Arkell, 1956), and thins irregularly southwards against residual basement topography. The succession thickens gradually eastwards to over 60 m beneath the area of the Seine, and to some 106 m at Eawy closer to the Wight–Bray Fault, where there are well-developed mudstone interbeds as well as oolitic

limestones in the upper part. There is thus some comparison with the sequence developed within the Portland–Wight Basin, and it may be that a similar increase in thickness, with a comparable facies sequence, occurs as the Normandy succession is traced northwards into the Central English Channel Basin.

HAMPSHIRE–DIEPPE HIGH

The condensed sequence of south Dorset is even thinner to the east at Wytch Farm, where only a metre or so (Figure 34) of condensed, pseudoconglomeratic, hardground limestone gives rise to marked gamma-ray and sonic-velocity peaks (Bristow et al., 1991). This extremely attenuated succession occurs over a wide area, although it is slightly thicker in Bournemouth Bay. The succession is present on the Isle of Wight at Sandhills, but farther south-east the Inferior Oolite is known to be absent on the upthrow side of the Wight– Bray Fault.

When traced to the north, the Inferior Oolite thickens into the Dorset Basin at Winterborne Kingston, such that all three subdivisions are present in a south Dorset facies expanded by the development of dark grey, interbedded, shell-grit mudstones and sandy, commonly glauconitic limestones in the Middle Inferior Oolite.

Farther east (Figure 32), the sequence similarly thickens northwards (Thomas and Holliday, 1982; Young and Lake 1988) and attains some 118 m at Portsdown (Taitt and Kent, 1958) by the rapid development of sandy, ferruginous, and generally poorly oolitic limestones of the Lower and Middle Inferior Oolite. These are succeeded by relatively thin Upper Inferior Oolite which bears great similarity to that of the Cotswolds, and comprises oolitic, commonly grainstone, limestones overlain by rubbly, argillaceous limestones which thicken northwards more gradually.

It appears, therefore, that the northern margin of the Hampshire–Dieppe High is characterised by an Inferior Oolite of partly carbonate-platform facies which thins southwards, such that the lower subdivisions are unlikely to be present beneath the English Channel.

In northern France, the Inferior Oolite is some 50 m thick in well-developed Cotswold facies comparable to that of the Sussex coast. Though thinner than to the west of the Wight–Bray Fault, there is little evidence of the extreme attenuation encountered in southern England. Thus it may be presumed that beneath the English Channel, much of the Hampshire–Dieppe High comprises a westward-thinning Inferior Oolite which may be absent next to the Wight–Bray Fault, and indeed over a large area to the east of it.

WEALD BASIN

Some 130 to 170 m of Inferior Oolite are present in the central Weald (Figures 32 and 36) in typical carbonate-platform Cotswold facies (Gallois and Worssam, in press). These become somewhat thinner eastwards to 125 m around Ashdown (Bristow and Bazley, 1972), and then thin more dramatically eastwards on to the London Platform in Kent, where only the Upper Inferior Oolite is present. It comprises a calcareous sand with sporadic, derived, lignitic material, and contains a basal, phosphatised pebble bed resting on Lias to the west, as at Paddlesworth Court, but on Palaeozoic strata to the east (Figure 32).

Similar overlap is seen in The Boulonnais, where some 30 m of strata in a broadly similar succession rest on Lias to the south, but on Devonian and Carboniferous strata to the north. The similarity of The Boulonnais with Kent suggests that beneath the entire intervening English Channel the Inferior Oolite is thin, being probably mostly Upper Inferior Oolite with a well-developed basal sandy facies. This represents a north-easterly extension of the Hampshire–Dieppe High succession with little or no expression of any Weald Basin.

Great Oolite Group

On the northern margin of the Wessex–Channel Basin, the sequence in ascending order is Fuller's Earth, Great Oolite Formation, Forest Marble and Cornbrash. The group is approximately coextensive with the Bathonian Stage, whose base lies within the top few metres of the Upper Inferior Oolite, and whose upper limit is drawn at the base of the Callovian Upper Cornbrash. The Dorset coast succession differs in that the Frome Clay laterally replaces the Great Oolite Formation, so demonstrating the most striking feature of the group, which is that the shelf-mud deposits of the south and south-west Wessex–Channel Basin generally pass laterally north and north-eastwards into carbonate-platform deposits (Martin, 1967; Green and Donovan, 1969; Whittaker, 1985). Comparable changes take place within the Paris Basin, where the carbonate facies is developed towards both Armorica and the London Platform (Mégnien, 1980).

The major lithostratigraphical boundaries coincide with prominent, widespread stratigraphical breaks that subdivide the succession into four upward-shoaling sequences. The Cornbrash begins the succeeding, predominantly Callovian, sequence (Penn et al., 1979; Rhys et al., 1982). Within each sequence, the transition from shelf-mud deposits to carbonate deposits is quite sharp, but takes place progressively farther into the area of mud deposition as the succession is climbed (Whittaker, 1985), so that within the Wessex–Channel Basin the entire Great Oolite is a major upward-shoaling sequence, as in the Paris Basin (Mégnien, 1980).

The higher formations, as well as representing the most widespread development of shallowest-water facies, are the most laterally widespread and persistent (Whittaker, 1985), showing that sediment supply, albeit largely carbonate-gener-

ated within the basin, outstripped the increased water depths indicated by progressive coastal onlap. This complex, cyclic sequence of migrating facies belts was superimposed obliquely upon a basin frame which repeatedly showed its earlier Jurassic inheritance, so that the four sequences are developed to different degrees and in different successions of facies within the major structural units of the Wessex–Channel Basin.

SOUTH OF THE HAMPSHIRE–DIEPPE HIGH

The Great Oolite is not fully exposed in Dorset but has been proved by the Seabarn Farm borehole (Figure 35). There, the Fuller's Earth rests sharply on a nodular condensed bed of Upper Inferior Oolite and comprises 200 m of interbedded, pale and medium grey mudstone with sporadic carbonaceous material and prominent shell beds in the upper part; this gives rise to mildly serrated gamma-ray and sonic curves corresponding to alternating blocky and fissile mudstones, and more-prominent values corresponding to the more-calcareous beds at the top.

The succeeding 80 m of Frome Clay contain a basal few metres of alternating argillaceous limestone and shell-grit mudstone, the Wattonensis Beds, which produce strongly serrated log profiles. These are succeeded by high gamma-ray values and low sonic velocity of the overlying black shales, with very characteristic overall upward-decreasing, poorly serrated gamma-ray and sonic curves as the sequence becomes increasingly calcareous to the top. There are prominent oyster lumachelles which punctuate the log profiles with low gamma-ray, high sonic-velocity spikes.

The base of the succeeding Forest Marble is marked by a prominent brachiopod-bearing shell bed, the Boueti Bed. The remaining 70 m comprise chiefly grey and greyish green, calcareous mudstone with thin bioclastic limestones and shell beds. The Forest Marble gives rise to higher gamma-ray and lower sonic-velocity log responses from the mudstones, punctuated by sonic spikes and gamma-ray lows corresponding to the shell beds and thin sandstones. Some 5 m of Lower Cornbrash rest with burrowed contact on the Forest Marble and consist of pale grey, fine-grained, argillaceous limestone with muddy wisps and laminae. Over 12 m of Upper Cornbrash consist of alternating limestones and dark grey, poorly fissile, calcareous mudstones. These alternating limestones and mudstones give rise to a highly serrated log signature (Figure 34); in sufficiently thick sequences, Lower Cornbrash can be separated from Upper Cornbrash because its poorly developed mudstone interbeds give rise to a less-deeply serrated log profile.

BGS boreholes offshore to the west (Dingwall and Lott, 1979) have proved the Upper Fuller's Earth/Frome Clay sequence, and suggest that the Wattonensis Beds thicken by the development of the mudstones and thinning of the limestones. To the east, along the entire northern margin of the basin, the succession is similar in facies, but is much thinner at Arreton, where both the Lower and Upper Fuller's Earth contain a predominance of argillaceous limestones (Figure 32). The Frome Clay similarly passes laterally into oolitic grainstones, whereas the Forest Marble and Cornbrash retain their character.

In the southern part of the basin (Figure 30), BGS sampling (BGS Portland Solid Geology sheet; Dingwall and Lott, 1979) and wells have proved the group to be up to 224 m thick, and in the typical mudstone facies. In the eastern part in well 99/16-1, the group thins to 177 m, and the Frome Clay is barely recognisable as it is represented by a succession of alternating argillaceous limestones and mudstones.

From Normandy to the Pays de Bray, the Great Oolite Group displays a uniform facies, passing upwards from

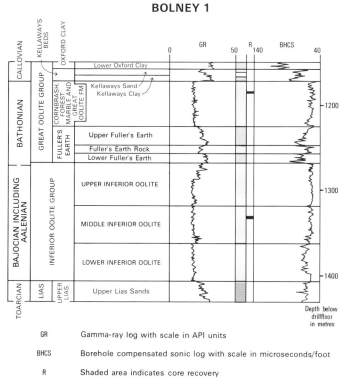

Figure 36   The Middle Jurassic section in the Bolney 1 borehole. For location see Figure 30; for key to lithology see Figure 32.

Fuller's Earth, through a sequence of argillaceous limestones, to oolitic grainstones. Lateral facies changes comparable to those in England appear to be present (Arkell, 1956; Mégnien, 1980). The mudstone facies however forms a discrete belt lying between the platform carbonates of Armorica and the Pays de Bray, and it may be presumed that this belt passes seawards (Mégnien, 1980) where it occupies the deeper parts of the basin in French waters immediately south of the Central English Channel High.

HAMPSHIRE–DIEPPE HIGH

A standard Great Oolite Group sequence, with minor variations, is present at about 170 m thickness in the Wytch Farm Oilfield (Figure 34; Bristow et al., 1991). This thickens to some 202 m at Bushey Farm (Figure 30), and retains its character as it thickens southwards into the Portland–Wight Basin. It similarly retains its facies sequence farther east where it thickens from well 98/11-1 to well 98/11-2 (Figure 30).

The group is thinner (c.130 m) in the northern part of the Isle of Wight, where the Frome Clay is completely replaced by a comparable thickness of argillaceous, shelly limestones (Figure 32). Along strike offshore in well 99/18-1, the Fuller's Earth thickens, but the Great Oolite Formation thins to 23 m beneath a slightly attenuated Forest Marble.

The Wytch Farm succession thickens northwards to Winterborne Kingston (Rhys et al., 1982), but the Isle of Wight succession thickens only slightly to Portsdown (Taitt and Kent, 1958). However, as within the Portland–Wight Basin, major facies change takes place when beds are traced eastwards along strike; the dominantly mudstone facies in Dorset and the south-west passes eastwards into a dominantly carbonate-platform facies.

Comparable relationships are suggested in northern France, so that the offshore portion of the Hampshire– Dieppe High probably comprises a thin Great Oolite Group, although the upper part may not be present everywhere because of Early to mid-Cretaceous erosion. Drilling evidence suggests generally that regional internal overlap of lower Fuller's Earth by higher Fuller's Earth towards the western margin of the high is likely, as is local overstep by the Great Oolite Formation. It is probable too that the upper parts of the latter thin towards the west beneath probable Forest Marble overstep.

WEALD BASIN

North of the Wardour–Portsdown Faults, the Great Oolite Group thickens into the western Weald Basin. In the Horndean-1 borehole, all three members of some 50 m of Fuller's Earth are present, but the most important feature is the substantial thickening of the Great Oolite Formation to over 100 m beneath about 18 m of Forest Marble and 7 m of Cornbrash. The oolites are of considerable economic significance since they and their correlatives along strike constitute an important hydrocarbon reservoir (McLimans and Videtich, 1987).

Eastwards along its axis, the basin shallows and the Great Oolite Group thins to 96 m at Bolney (Figures 32 and 36; Gallois and Worssam, in press), and 75 m at Ashdown (Bristow and Bazley, 1972) where argillaceous limestones are developed at the top of the Fuller's Earth. The succession is even thinner in Kent (Lamplugh et al., 1923; Arkell, 1933), where some 50 m rests on Inferior Oolite to the west, but upon successively older rocks to the east. The Fuller's Earth may be present as thin, calcareous shales to the west, where it is overlain by sandy limestones ascribed to the Great Oolite Formation, which farther to the east at Eastling Wood (Figures 32 and 37) rests upon basal sands. The main body of limestone is white, finely oolitic and shelly; it is overlain by typical Forest Marble mudstones and

limestones of constant thickness (56 m) and characteristic, widespread Cornbrash, which may be up to 8 m thick.

The sequence in The Boulonnais is identical to that in east Kent (Pruvost and Pringle, 1923; Arkell, 1933; Mégnien, 1980), and it may be predicted with some confidence that this succession exists beneath the eastern waters of the district, with the same eastwards internal thinning and overlap as it oversteps successively older rocks of the London Platform. It is also reasonable to assume that it will continue to increase in thickness to the south-west, mainly by the inclusion of the Fuller's Earth, until it passes into the sequence typical of the north-eastern flank of the Hampshire–Dieppe High.

UPPER JURASSIC

The Upper Jurassic Series is here used to include the Callovian, Oxfordian, Kimmeridgian and Portlandian stages, and is coextensive with the Upper Cornbrash, Kellaways Beds, Oxford Clay, Corallian Beds, Kimmeridge Clay, Portland Beds and the larger part of the Purbeck Beds. The range in lithology is the widest of all the Jurassic series, with a substantial thickness of argillaceous and calcareous facies, and also evaporitic strata. Both the argillaceous lithology and the widespread lateral extent of the major rock types contrasts with the Middle Jurassic.

The majority of beds are richly fossiliferous, containing a macrofauna dominated by ammonites and bivalves. The latter occupy many of the palaeoecological niches formerly held by brachiopods. Upper Jurassic bivalve-dominated benthic communities can be identified closely with their modern analogues (Duff, 1975; Oschmann, 1988; Wignall, 1990).

There is a close relationship between lithology and fauna, and the widespread lateral persistence of rock types means there is a close concordance between lithostratigraphical and biostratigraphical successions, enabling the widespread lateral persistence of small- and large-scale cycles of sedimentation to be recognised. Typically, the cycles have a basal, silty component which passes up to organic-rich shales and mudstones, which are in turn overlain by more calcareous mudstones. At the top, sandstones and limestones may be developed. Such cycles are commonly interpreted as indicating rapid subsidence followed by more gradual shallowing, with the arenaceous input perhaps indicating locally derived sediment supply exceeding subsidence.

At the largest scale, cycle components correspond approximately to formations and/or members. Thus the Kellaways Sand and basal silty beds of the Lower Oxford Clay are succeeded by the organic-rich parts of the Lower Oxford Clay and overlain by the calcareous mudstones of the higher parts of the formation. The sandstones and limestones of the succeeding Corallian Beds apparently represent the continuation of this cycle, but these beds are complicated by the development of an argillaceous facies, which is widespread in the subsurface. A final large-scale cycle may be seen in the way in which silty beds at the base of the Kimmeridge Clay are succeeded by its oil-shale-rich median portion, and the more calcareous mudstone of the Upper Kimmeridge Clay. This cycle is completed by the Portland Sand and Portland Limestone, followed by the evaporitic and lagoonal sediments of the Purbeck Beds.

Kellaways Beds and Oxford Clay

Although coming extensively to outcrop in the Weymouth Anticline, these beds are poorly exposed. At the base, the Kellaways Clay passes rapidly up from the Cornbrash, and

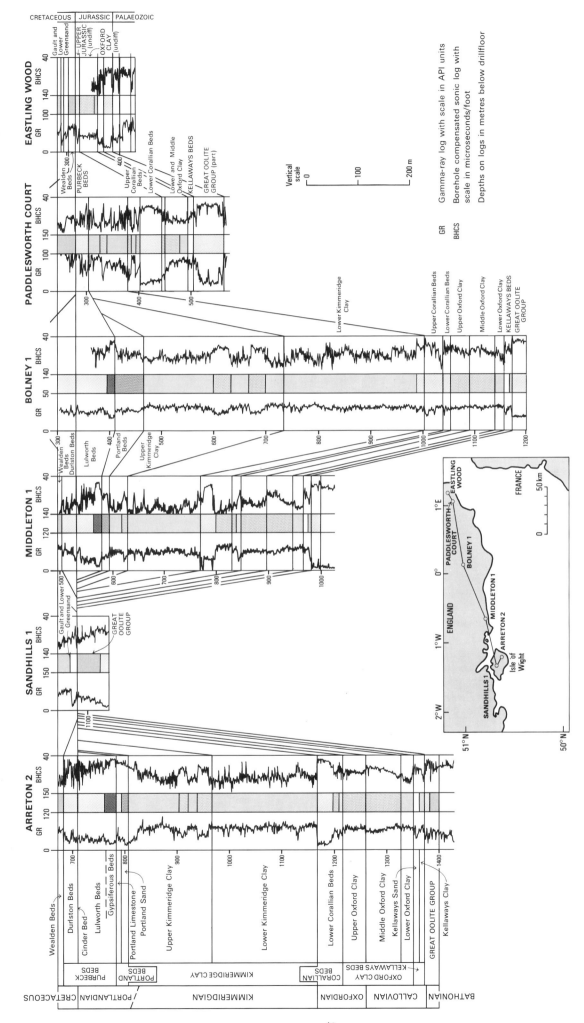

Figure 37 Correlation of Upper Jurassic sediments from the Portland–Wight Basin to the Weald Basin. For key to lithology see Figure 32.

49

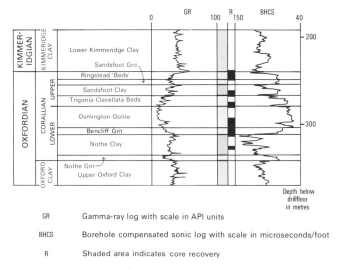

KIMMERIDGE 3

KIMMER-IDGIAN	KIMMERIDGE CLAY	Lower Kimmeridge Clay
		Sandsfoot Grit
OXFORDIAN	CORALLIAN — UPPER	Ringstead 'Beds'
		Sandsfoot Clay
		Trigonia Clavellata Beds
	CORALLIAN — LOWER	Osmington Oolite
		Bencliff Grit
		Nothe Clay
	OXFORD CLAY	Nothe Grit
		Upper Oxford Clay

GR 0 — 100   R 150   BHCS 40

— 200
— 300

Depth below drillfloor in metres

GR   Gamma-ray log with scale in API units

BHCS   Borehole compensated sonic log with scale in microseconds/foot

R   Shaded area indicates core recovery

Figure 38   The Corallian Beds in the Kimmeridge 3 borehole. For location see Figure 30; for key to lithology see Figure 32.

comprises pale to dark grey, slightly silty and micaceous, calcareous mudstones. High gamma-ray values and low sonic velocities characterise the Kellaways Clay (Figure 37), but the former gradually decrease, and the latter increase, as the succession becomes interbedded with fine-grained, sporadically shelly sandstones of the Kellaways Sand. Hard, calcareous doggers give rise to prominent sonic spikes, one of which may delineate the top of the formation and complete the overall funnel shape of the signature. The subfissile mudstones of the overlying Oxford Clay give rise to a finely serrated log signature of high gamma-ray values and low sonic velocity, characterised by discrete 'spikiness' where silty and calcareous levels are developed. The varying proportions of calcareous silt and mudstone enable the various members to be delineated; in particular, carbonaceous mudstones in the Lower Oxford Clay may usually be detected by prominent gamma-ray highs some way above the base, and the contrast between the siltstones and cementstones of the upper part of the Middle Oxford Clay, and the basal mudstones of the Upper Oxford Clay, gives rise to a rapid upward increase in overall gamma-ray values and decrease in sonic velocity. The Callovian–Oxfordian boundary may be readily identified since it is coincident with this lithological change. Thereafter, the beds become increasingly calcareous, with thin, silty limestones prominent at the top of the formation.

SOUTH OF THE HAMPSHIRE–DIEPPE HIGH

The succession is constant along the northern margin of the basin, and is known from boreholes at Lulworth Banks and Kimmeridge to be about 200 m thick. In Bournemouth Bay, the faulted succession is comparable with that to the south of Wytch Farm, and to the 155 m of similar Kellaways Beds and Oxford Clay drilled at Arreton (Figure 37). Evidence of more gradual thinning to the south of the basin axis is seen in the 175 m of these beds proved in well 98/18-1 and 150 m in well 99/16-1. The beds come to outcrop on the Central English Channel High (BGS Portland Solid Geology sheet), where their thickness is unknown.

The succession exposed in the cliffs of France south-west of the Seine has overall similarity with the English sequence (Arkell, 1956). The sequence ranges from 150 to 160 m in thickness, increasing towards the Wight–Bray Fault. Thus over the entire marine area, the Kellaways Beds and Oxford Clay succession is remarkably uniform, thickening gradually

towards the northerly and north-easterly growth faults to be of maximum thickness just south of the Dorset coast.

HAMPSHIRE–DIEPPE HIGH

The succession appears to maintain its character throughout this region, but rarely attains the thicknesses present in the Portland–Wight Basin. To the north of Kimmeridge, it thins to some 150 m, and attains only 118 m at Wytch Farm. On the northernmost part of the Isle of Wight, there is a full and easily identified succession thickening towards the Wardour–Portsdown Faults (Figure 37). However, the Kellaways Beds and Oxford Clay are absent in the central part of the island, and along the southern edge of the Hampshire–Dieppe High over much of the marine area (Penn, 1985). Where the beds are preserved locally, as in well 99/18-1, they are thin (67 m) and lack the higher parts of the Oxford Clay beneath Corallian Beds. Along the north-east coast of France (Mégnien, 1980), only 90 to 115 m of these beds are proved in boreholes north-east of the Wight–Bray Fault, and they thin rapidly north of the Somme, where much of the upper part of the Oxford Clay is missing.

WEALD BASIN

The succession also maintains its character and subdivisions throughout the Weald Basin. To the north of the Wardour–Portsdown Faults, it is over 140 m thick and thins gradually eastwards along the basin axis to 106 m at Collendean Farm (Gallois and Worssam, in press) and to 106 m at Ashdown (Bristow and Bazley, 1972). To the south, it thins to less than 70 m at Westham where the Kellaways Beds may be poorly developed (Lake et al., 1987). Farther east in Kent, the Kellaways Beds are present as a ferruginous and glauconitic sandstone up to 15.6 m thick in a succession totalling just over 55 m at Dover (Shephard-Thorn, 1988). The Oxford Clay is persistently developed.

The exposures in The Boulonnais enable all the familiar English subdivisions of the Oxford Clay to be recognised, although the Kellaways Beds are represented by a thin, basal, ferruginous marl. The succession attains a thickness of over 70 m, but is reduced to zero by the overstepping Lower Cretaceous strata to the north, east and south (Pruvost and Pringle, 1924; Arkell, 1956; Mégnien, 1980). The offshore succession is likely to be limited in the east, but to the south-west it may expand rapidly to some 40 to 60 m and comprise a thin Kellaways Beds overlain by Oxford Clay before it attenuates against the Hampshire–Dieppe High.

Corallian Beds

The low-lying ground of the Weymouth Anticline is ringed by the dissected scarps of the Corallian Beds, which also form low ridges and coastal cliffs to the east where the succession is some 70 m thick (Arkell, 1947). At the base, lying with sharp contact upon the Upper Oxford Clay, are grey, fossiliferous, concretionary sandstones with locally a sandy, bivalve-rich limestone. These Nothe Grits are overlain by pale to dark grey, very calcareous, sporadically carbonaceous, shell-fragmental mudstones of the Nothe Clay, which pass up to grey, medium- to coarse-grained, sporadically argillaceous, cross-bedded sandstones of the Bencliff Grit. The geophysical-log character of these beds in the Kimmeridge 3 borehole (Figure 38) shows finely serrated curves of high gamma-ray values and low sonic velocity that correspond to an argillaceous sequence; these are punctuated by sporadic sonic spikes and gamma-ray lows due to more calcareous or sandy strata. The log traces show an upward-coarsening motif as the sequence becomes sandier and passes to the white or cream limestones and pale grey mudstones of the Osmington Oolite, which is characterised by poorly serrated curves of low gamma-ray values and high sonic velocity.

The overlying strata give rise to deeply serrated log profiles which show a characteristic bell shape as the bivalve-rich limestones of the Trigonia Clavellata Beds pass up to the Sandsfoot Clay. However, there is some upward reversal of this trend as the Sandsfoot Grit succeeds the Sandsfoot Clay in a sequence which repeats that shown in the lower beds. The Ringstead Waxy Clay and the succeeding, partly coralliferous, marls and limestones of the Ringstead Coral Beds are always sufficiently argillaceous to ensure that the overall log profile of the upper Corallian Beds is bell shaped. For descriptive purposes it is convenient to refer informally to the two main subvisions as lower and upper Corallian Beds (Figure 38).

The strata were cyclically deposited, and various attempts have been made at resolving these (e.g. Arkell, 1947; Talbot, 1973), particularly as the abundant fauna appear to give a good guide to topographically controlled substrates ranging from open, shallow seas to tidal-flats, channels and reefs (Wilson, 1968a, 1968b; Fuersich, 1976, 1977).

SOUTH OF THE HAMPSHIRE–DIEPPE HIGH

About 100 m of typical succession, of which lower Corallian Beds account for 60 to 70 m, have been proved in boreholes in the Kimmeridge Bay area and to the west, although in the southern part of the Weymouth Anticline the estimated full thickness is only about 65 m, indicating some shallowing of the basin in that direction. Eastwards, similar attenuation may occur because only 37 m of strata are present in well 98/11-1 (Figure 30), where the upper part of the sequence is faulted against Kimmeridge Clay, so that the lower part may belong structurally to the southern flank of the Hampshire–Dieppe High. To the east, 50 m were proved in Arreton 2, apparently with condensed or absent upper Corallian Beds (Figure 37).

To the south, the sequence thins very gradually as the limestones of the lower part become thinner and more argillaceous, and the upper part boasts well-developed, poorly calcareous mudstones capped by thin argillaceous limestones. The absence of data between the Central English Channel High and France precludes evaluation, but the resemblance between the successions exposed on the French and Dorset coasts is well known (Arkell, 1956; Mégnien, 1980).

This French succession appears to thicken towards the Wight–Bray Fault, and may be compared to that present in the Portland–Wight Basin. However, a well-developed limestone facies of the lower part shows that the argillaceous limestones of the Portland–Wight Basin must pass into a shallower-water facies more typical of the lower Corallian Beds in Dorset, and reflect the topographic control of sedimentary facies by the Armorican Massif (Mégnien, 1980).

HAMPSHIRE–DIEPPE HIGH

The entire length of ground marginal to the Portland–Wight Basin, from west Dorset to the Isle of Wight, is characterised by the whole or partial absence of Corallian Beds beneath Cretaceous overstep (Whittaker, 1985). Where they reappear to the north of the Isle of Wight, they are thin at 25 to 30 m, and only the lower Corallian Beds appear to be present beneath Kimmeridge Clay. Such nonsequence or condensation of the upper part is widespread, and occurs even where the succession thickens northwards to the Wardour–Portsdown Faults (Whittaker et al., 1985). Eastwards along the strike, the thickness is maintained, although the limestones become thinner, more argillaceous and silty, and are succeeded by calcareous mudstones and thin sandy limestones, as at

Portsdown (Tait and Kent, 1958) and Middleton (Figure 37). It is possible that Cretaceous overstep has exhumed earlier Upper Jurassic overstep across the Hampshire–Dieppe High. As the structure is traced beneath the English Channel, it retains its characteristic core of subcropping Upper Jurassic strata, but it becomes broader (Penn, 1985), and the south-western margin is less sharply defined. At Eawy, near the Wight–Bray Fault, the succession is similar to that farther south-west but, at 155 m, is slightly thinner. Farther to the north-east, the succession is much thinner (115 m) at Nibas, beyond which the Corallian Beds are absent beneath Cretaceous strata (Mégnien, 1980).

WEALD BASIN

The succession here is typically tripartite, with lower and upper units of limestones, sandstones, siltstones and mudstones separated by an intervening mudstone. Generally, the succession thickens gradually north-westwards from less than 50 m around Westham to 130 m at Collendean Farm (Whittaker et al., 1985). The succession thins more rapidly eastwards on to the London Platform, showing the basin to be asymmetric. The Corallian Beds of Kent are noteworthy for their resemblance to the Dorset sequence (Lamplugh and Kitchin, 1911; Lamplugh et al., 1923). In the more southerly boreholes they are almost entirely composed of calcareous mudstones with thin limestones and sandstones, but as they thicken northwards, interbedded siltstones and limestones become more prominent near the base, and form a basal unit over 40 m thick in the basin centre.

Since over 50 m of a sequence comparable to that around Dover occurs in The Boulonnais (Pruvost and Pringle, 1924), it may be deduced that Corallian Beds continue across the easternmost English Channel. To the south-west, however, it must thicken as the axis of the Weald Basin is crossed and thereafter it may be presumed to become more argillaceous and to thin gradually on to the Hampshire–Dieppe High prior to its eventual disappearance.

Kimmeridge Clay

The cliff and foreshore exposures at Kimmeridge Bay constitute the classic section of mudstones, shales, oil-shales and thin limestones of the Kimmeridge Clay, although only the upper two-thirds of the 508 m succession (Cox and Gallois, 1981) come to outcrop. Resting on an erosion surface, it is composed of a complex series of sedimentary rhythms which, in the lower part, comprise thin siltstones or silty mudstones. These are overlain by medium or dark grey, shelly, fissile mudstones which become paler, more calcareous, and less fissile upwards. In the upper part, the rhythms consist of brownish black, shelly and phosphatic mudstones (bituminous shales) which become increasingly calcareous. They grade to medium and dark grey mudstones which in turn pass up to calcareous mudstones and argillaceous limestones that have become well known as marker beds. Superimposed on these small-scale, rhythmic changes are larger-scale changes in kerogen and lime content that enable ammonite-based zones to be correlated over wide areas.

The geophysical-log signature (Figure 37) is characterised by a deeply serrated, generally low-velocity, sonic-log profile and a complementary, but a less-deeply serrated profile of high gamma-ray values. The base of each rhythm is marked by high gamma-ray values and low sonic velocity, except where a basal sandstone may give rise to a sonic 'spike', though even here the presence of phosphatic material may give rise to high gamma-ray values. As the rhythm becomes more calcareous upwards, so the gamma-ray values decrease and sonic velocity increases, and where a coccolith-rich limestone is present, a prominent sonic spike is registered.

The macrofauna is dominated by ammonites, pseudonektonic bivalves and, particularly in the oil-shale, median part of the sequence, by an opportunistic, bivalve benthos which flourished in conditions of reduced oxygenation in an otherwise open-marine shallow sea. The ubiquitous ammonites show the Kimmeridge Clay to be coextensive with the Kimmeridgian Stage (*sensu anglico*), though locally the mudstone facies appears to extend into the Portlandian Stage.

SOUTH OF THE HAMPSHIRE–DIEPPE HIGH

In the Weymouth area, as at Kimmeridge Bay, the complete succession is unknown, but the considerable thickness of the basal zones (Cox and Gallois, 1981) suggests that the basin strikes as far westwards. To the east, a well-developed argillaceous limestone is present, probably within the lowest part of the Upper Kimmeridge Clay, and forms a mappable seismic reflector. In Bournemouth Bay, the reflector occurs within a complete succession which is so thin (170 m at well 98/11-1) as to suggest that it is really part of the structure to the north of the basin, the more so because the full succession at Arreton is over 340 m thick (Figure 37). Here too, thin calcareous siltstones occur near the top of the sequence; the succession retains this character across the basin to the south where it thins gradually to just over 250 m in well 98/18-1.

Shallow drilling by BGS at boreholes 75/32 and 75/33 (Figure 30) shows both Upper and Lower Kimmeridge Clay to be present immediately to the north of the Central English Channel High (Dingwall and Lott, 1979), and typical Dorset facies are known to occur almost as far as the Cotentin Peninsula (Mégnien, 1980). On the French coast, the sequence of clays, marls and thin glauconitic sandstones is somewhat different, and thickens north-eastwards to 140 m at Hugleville and to over 130 m towards the Wight–Bray Fault. These changes indicate positive movement of the Armorican Massif, and it may be that Kimmeridgian rocks are thin beneath French waters.

HAMPSHIRE–DIEPPE HIGH

To the north-west of Kimmeridge Bay the succession halves in thickness (Arkell, 1947; Cox and Gallois, 1981), and a nonsequence is present beneath the Portland Beds. Farther east, the sequence is thin and complicated by faulting; in Bournemouth Bay at well 98/11-1 the complete succession is reduced to 170 m. Any further indication of Kimmeridgian thinning is hidden as a result of widespread Cretaceous overstep on the Hampshire–Dieppe High. In mid-Channel, well 99/16-1 drilled 117 m of Lower Kimmeridge Clay preserved beneath unconformable Portland Beds, and as the structure is followed to France, variable thicknesses of Kimmeridgian (*sensu anglico*) strata have been proved. At Nibas (Figure 30), and possibly therefore over a large area beneath the English Channel, no Kimmeridge Clay is present.

WEALD BASIN

To the north of the core of the Hampshire–Dieppe High, the Kimmeridge Clay is again present beneath Cretaceous rocks. It is a full and typical sequence, thickening northwards from 120 m at Marchwood (Figure 30) to 580 m at Bolney (Figure 37; Gallois and Worssam, in press). In the thicker successions, fine-grained sandstones and siltstones occur at the base, whereas in the highest beds, thin siltstones to the south pass northwards into thicker beds of Portland Sand aspect (Whittaker et al., 1985).

To the east in Kent, interbedded glauconitic sandstones and mudstones are overlain by a mudstone-dominated succession. The whole thins from 80 m at Brabourne to 13 m to the west of Dover by loss of the higher beds, showing that its eventual eastward disappearance is by Cretaceous overstep (Lamplugh and Kitchin, 1911). A sandy, 'marginal' facies with pebble beds is well developed in the 120 m of Kimmeridgian strata exposed in The Boulonnais (Pruvost and Pringle, 1924; Arkell, 1933; Mégnien, 1980). It may be presumed, therefore, that in UK waters beneath the easternmost English Channel this 'marginal' facies is lost by Cretaceous erosion, but as the beds are traced south-westward they thicken and become more argillaceous, firstly in their median part and eventually throughout the sequence, prior to their thinning on to the Hampshire–Dieppe High. In French waters, however, the effect of the London Platform is stronger, and the marginal facies is likely to persist.

Portland and Purbeck beds

The Portland Beds are generally well exposed on the Isle of Portland, although their base is concealed, and much of their uppermost parts is lost due to recent erosion. To the east, an overall upward gradation from the Kimmeridge Clay, and a sharp passage to the overlying Purbeck Beds, may be seen in the steep cliffs that characterise the Isle of Purbeck. The summaries of Arkell (1947), Townson (1975) and Melville and Freshney (1982) show that three upward-shallowing cycles, in which mudstones pass up through fine-grained limestones to condensed hardground beds, can be correlated along the entire stretch of coast. Sandstones dominate in the lower part, giving rise to some 60 m of Portland Sand, but some 30 to 40 m of Portland Limestone occur above them.

The base of the Portland Sand comprises argillaceous siltstones interbedded with thin mudstones. Higher in the succession, calcareous siltstones and locally glauconitic, fine-grained sandstones predominate. The sandy beds are capped by a variety of limestones at the top of the first cycle, which are in turn overlain by a thin, dolomitised, calcareous claystone beneath fine-grained, extensively burrowed, sandy, argillaceous dolomite.

The succeeding limestones are the basal part of the Portland Limestone, and form at the top of the median cycle. They comprise burrowed, sponge-spicule-rich limestones interbedded with thin, extensive, nodular cherts overlain by fine-grained, shell-fragmental limestones. These beds are capped by nodular, cherty, hardground limestones. The third of the cycles begins with a repetition of the cherty limestones facies, but this is replaced upwards by an oolitic, shell-sand limestone much prized in building. The top of the formation again comprises shelly, hardground limestones.

The gamma-ray signature of the Portland Beds is typically finely serrated (Figure 37), reflecting the finely interbedded nature of the sequence. It is characteristically funnel-shaped, since the amount of argillaceous material decreases as the succession is climbed. The sonic trace does not exactly mirror the gamma-ray log because distinct, high-velocity sonic spikes occur opposite the limestones and well-cemented sandstones.

The fauna is marine throughout the Portland Beds, and closely related to lithology. The sands are generally thought to have been deposited on an upper shore face, and their succeeding limestones are perhaps the products of deposition in shallow water, or even intertidal mud flats and lagoons.

Over 100 m of Purbeck Beds (Arkell, 1947) on the Isle of Purbeck typically comprise rapid alternations of thin, laminated, argillaceous limestones and laminated mudstones with sporadic lenses of sandstone and diagenetically altered, nodular, gypsiferous or anhydrite beds. A stratigraphically significant oyster lumachelle, the Cinder Bed, separates some 60 m of Lulworth Beds below from about 40 m of lithologically similar Durlston Beds above. Casey (1963; 1973) drew the base of the Cretaceous System at the base of the Cinder Bed.

The Purbeck Beds rest with rapid transition, sharp, or erosional contact on the Portland Beds. At the base, about 9 m of laminated, algal and pelletoidal limestones show clear evidence of replacement by calcite and chalcedony after gypsum. They are succeeded by over 40 m of alternating, thin, laminated, pelletoidal limestones, and variably calcareous, laminated mudstones. The upper part of the Lulworth Beds comprises alternating shales and calcareous clays with subordinate limestones at the top of the succession. The Cinder Bed, at the base of the Durlston Beds, is succeeded by some 40 m of interbedded limestones and shales that are partly sandy. Near the top, greenish clays and limestones with freshwater bivalves herald the onset of the predominantly nonmarine Wealden Beds.

The geophysical-log signature of the Purbeck Beds is characteristically highly serrated, reflecting the limestone/shale alternations (Figure 37). The internal stratigraphical sequence also gives rise to an overall shape which is diagnostic throughout southern England (Whittaker et al., 1985). The increasingly argillaceous nature of the succession as it is climbed results in the lowest gamma-ray values and highest sonic velocity being found near the base. Towards the top, limestones again predominate around the Cinder Bed level, and give rise to a localised decrease in gamma-ray values and increase in sonic velocity, which never reach the extremes of values found in the lowest part of the Lulworth Beds. Since gamma-ray values increase again to the top of the Durlston Beds, the Purbeck Beds as a whole yield asymmetric log profiles.

The Purbeck Beds are abundantly fossiliferous, typically containing large numbers of few species which indicate deposition in reduced-marine, brackish, or even fresh waters, most probably in sheltered lagoons. Fossil soils are common, and locally the remnants of fossil forests occur which, with the presence of formerly evaporitic beds, indicate the sporadic, although widespread development of terrestrial environments of deposition.

SOUTH OF THE HAMPSHIRE–DIEPPE HIGH

Both the Portland and Purbeck beds are considered to be of similar thickness, around 100 m, between the Isle of Purbeck and the Isle of Portland, where the Portland Beds show considerable facies change along the strike. In the east, the limestones are fine grained and both they and the sandstones are argillaceous, whereas to the west the limestones, which may be lateral equivalents of sandstones, can be extremely shelly and oolitic. Both the limestones and the sandstones are partly dolomitic (Townson, 1975; Melville and Freshney, 1982).

Farther east in Bournemouth Bay, no Portland Sand is present, although silty beds in the uppermost 20 m of Kimmeridge Clay may prove to be their lateral correlatives. Some 28 m of argillaceous limestone in well 98/11-2 thin northwards to 12 m in well 98/11-1 beneath over 100 m of Purbeck Beds which are typically developed, although the upper parts are lost by pre-Wealden Beds erosion in the more northerly well. The principal feature of the Purbeck Beds here, and at Arreton, is the presence of well-developed, interbedded anhydrite near the base (Figure 37).

To the south the strata become thinner, and mid-way to the Central English Channel High comprise 10 to 20 m of sandy, glauconitic limestone or calcareous mudstone beneath 60 to 70 m of typical Purbeck Beds in which the anhydrite of the basal beds is locally replaced by calcite. North of Cotentin, at the northern limit of the Armorican Massif, they are presumed to have been removed by pre-Cretaceous erosion (Mégnien, 1980).

HAMPSHIRE–DIEPPE HIGH

The Portland Beds thin westwards from the Isle of Purbeck to Swanage and Ringstead, and the Purbeck Beds decrease in thickness by 50 per cent in the same direction prior to their disappearance beneath Cretaceous strata (Arkell, 1947; Townson, 1975; Melville and Freshney, 1982). It may be that these thickness changes are really oblique to northward attenuation on to the Hampshire–Dieppe High. Elsewhere, the beds are largely absent along the entire length of the core of the structure (Whittaker, 1985; Penn, 1985). Locally, as in well 99/18-1, 54 m of Purbeck Beds rest on 5 m of Portland Limestone, and pass down to thin silty clays resembling those beneath the Portland Beds, which are strongly unconformable on Kimmeridge Clay.

WEALD BASIN

On the gently sloping northern flank of the Hampshire–Dieppe High, the beds thicken northwards into the Weald Basin. Generally, the Portland Beds comprise thin, glauconitic siltstones, argillaceous sandstones and phosphate-nodule beds; these are interbedded with mudstones, and pass up to a thin, apparently condensed limestone. The typical absence of higher beds and the sharp, though not always obviously unconformable contact with the Purbeck Beds, may be taken to indicate widespread nonsequence at the base of the latter.

The Portland and Purbeck beds thicken northwards such that the Purbeck Beds are known to be over 140 m thick near to their outcrop within the Weald (Young and Lake, 1988; Lake et al., 1987). Here, the Portland Beds are developed as mudstones and silty mudstones that are indistinguishable from the subjacent Kimmeridge Clay, though locally, fine-grained argillaceous sandstones may be present at the top. Since the same beds can be shown to pass northwards into typical Portland Sand (Gallois and Worssam, in press; Whittaker et al., 1985), it appears that a belt of clay deposition was located in the central south-eastern part of the basin.

Eastwards, the succession is poorly known; there is eastward thinning of both Purbeck and Portland beds, and the sequence in The Boulonnais is only 13 m thick and formed of concretionary sands and limestones (Mégnien, 1980). Such facies must also persist beneath the easternmost English Channel, but it is likely that as the beds are traced westwards and south-westwards, a more typical Portlandian sequence will be preserved. Before thinning on to the Hampshire–Dieppe High, it is likely that the Portland Beds become increasingly argillaceous, particularly in UK waters, and become indistinguishable from the Kimmeridge Clay. As with subjacent Upper Jurassic strata, first the Purbeck Beds then the Portland Beds are likely to be progressively removed to the south-west beneath succeeding Cretaceous strata as they overstep on to the Hampshire–Dieppe High.

7 Cretaceous

The Cretaceous System takes its name from *creta*, the Latin for chalk, and while the Upper Cretaceous is virtually synonymous with the Chalk, lithologies within the Cretaceous System as a whole are many. There are the marine clays of the Gault, the marine sands of the Lower and Upper Greensand, and the complex fluvial and lagoonal deposits of the Wealden Beds. Even the Chalk itself is lithologically varied, including layers of nodular flint, thin seams of marl, and hardgrounds (Figure 39).

In the 1920s, the French researcher Dangeard showed by sampling that the Chalk crops out widely on the floor of the English Channel (Dangeard, 1929). More recent studies have confirmed the occurrence of Chalk, and have also proved Lower Cretaceous rocks to be present over large areas (Figure 2). The distribution of Cretaceous rocks is related both to the original limits of sedimentary basins and to subsequent structural history, giving a complex sea-bed outcrop pattern. The youngest Cretaceous rocks are preserved in synclines, and the oldest exposed in eroded anticlines; where erosion has been most severe, Jurassic rocks are exposed. Cretaceous rocks are concealed over large areas beneath Tertiary sediments.

The Lower Cretaceous is well exposed in cliffs of sandstone and clay at several localities along the south coast of England, and the Chalk forms spectacular and characteristic cliffs including those at The Needles on the Isle of Wight, and Beachy Head. The Chalk also appears in cliffs between Folkestone and Dover, and extends in a south-easterly direction beneath the Dover Strait to the French coast near Cap Blanc-Nez. North of the Dover Strait, the Cretaceous continues to dip eastwards and northwards into the North Sea, where it becomes progressively more deeply buried beneath Tertiary and Quaternary sediments.

In parts of the English Channel where sea-bed sediment cover is less than 0.5 m thick, or where solid rocks are exposed on the sea floor, BGS has collected 230 shallow cores of Cretaceous age; these are generally less than 0.3 m in length but provide sufficient rock for lithological determination and biostratigraphical analysis. South of the Isle of Wight, five BGS boreholes (Figures 39 and 40) drilled Cretaceous rocks (Dingwall and Lott, 1979). More complete information about formation thicknesses, lithologies and facies is provided by five commercial wells south of the Isle of Wight. Detailed information about the Middle and Lower Chalk is available from boreholes drilled for the Channel Tunnel project (Chapter 10).

The Cretaceous geology of southern England and northern France has long been well known, and stratigraphical correlations have been made between the English Channel and southern England (Figure 39). However, there is as yet insufficient information from the English Channel to enable the Cretaceous to be subdivided at the same level of detail as onshore.

LOWER CRETACEOUS

Ryazanian to Barremian

Late Jurassic earth movements created areas of land over most of north-west Europe. The Wessex–Channel Basin in the northern part of the Anglo-Paris Basin became a subsiding area in which nonmarine sedimentation occurred. Continuous sedimentation took place during the early part of the Cretaceous in the English Channel area; a comparison of Lower Cretaceous rocks proved in onshore boreholes adjacent to the English Channel with the same formations in offshore wells (see Figure 43) shows the thickest development of Wealden Beds to be 700 m in the Portland–Wight Basin (Whittaker, 1985). However, the Wealden Beds are absent around the north-western margins of the basin where the landmasses were subject to erosion. An unconformity has been proved in the Portland–Wight Basin where Aptian or Albian rocks rest on the Jurassic (Donovan and Stride, 1961; Portland Solid Geology sheet), as in the most eastern part of the English Channel, adjacent to which the Folkestone borehole proved Wealden Beds resting on Kimmeridge Clay.

PURBECK BEDS

The Jurassic ended with the deposition of the lower part of the Purbeck Beds, termed the Lulworth Beds. Conditions of deposition were generally nonmarine, but the lakes and mud flats were sometimes invaded by the sea. Varied rock types in the Lulworth Beds include fossil soils, freshwater limestones, marls, evaporites and some sands. The Cretaceous Period opened with a short-lived marine transgression, which in southern England produced the oyster-rich Cinder Bed (Casey, 1973). This is a thin, dark grey, sandy limestone consisting mainly of crushed oysters whose base is taken to mark the Jurassic–Cretaceous boundary. The Cretaceous part of the Purbeck Beds is termed the Durlston Beds; these consist of shelly limestones with layers of shaly mudstone and clay containing bivalves, gastropods and ostracods. Sands and brightly coloured clays become more common in the topmost beds. Some of the earliest Lower Cretaceous beds are exposed on the sea bed in the vicinity of Dungeness (see Figures 42 and 43), although the Cinder Bed has not been identified. BGS core 50/01/863 penetrated 1.2 m of limestone and mudstone of Ryazanian age, probably representing part of the Purbeck and/or Hastings Beds.

WEALDEN BEDS

After the brief transgression associated with the deposition of the limestones and evaporites of the Purbeck Beds, there was a gradual change to nonmarine clastic deposition throughout the Wessex–Channel Basin. A freshwater environment was maintained, despite rapid tectonic subsidence, by the combination of abundant sediment supply and the existence of coastal topographic barriers (Allen, 1981). The English Channel area was largely separated from the North Sea by the London–Brabant Massif, and other landmasses occurred to the west and south-west (Figure 41). Evidence suggests that the Portland–Wight and Weald basins were separated by the Portsdown Swell, which may well have extended into the area of the present English Channel. It is thought that the

Figure 39 Stratigraphical correlation chart and summary of Cretaceous events. After Rawson et al. (1978), Anderton et al. (1979), Casey (1973), Allen (1976), Hancock (1976), Kaufmann (1977) and Haq et al. (1987; 1988).

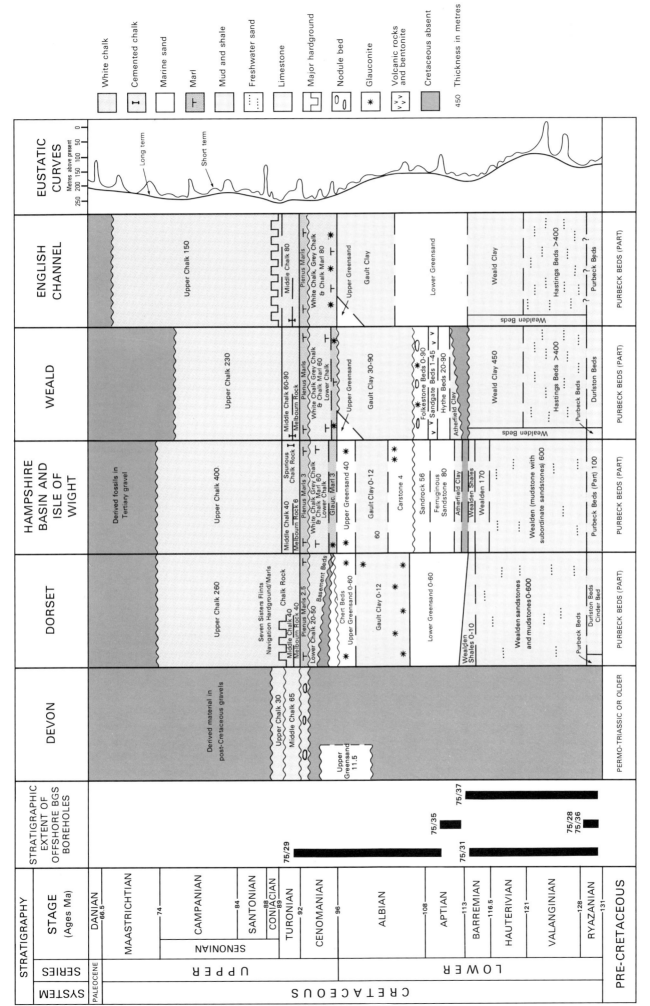

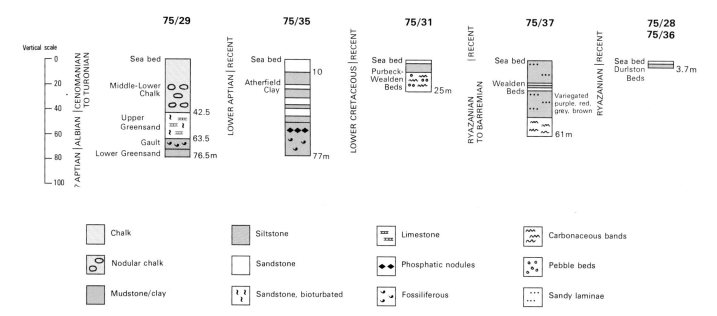

Figure 40 BGS boreholes in the English Channel which cored Cretaceous rocks. Adapted from Dingwall and Lott (1979). See Figure 42 for locations.

Wealden sediments (Allen, 1976, Allen, 1981; Stewart, 1981, 1983; Lake and Shephard-Thorn, 1987) were deposited in predominantly freshwater environments in a large lake or lagoon that occupied much of the present Hampshire Basin and Weald areas, and extended eastwards across the English Channel into the Paris Basin. Clastic sediments were derived from the London–Brabant Massif, the Cornubian and Armorican landmasses, and the Cranborne–Fordingbridge High. However, sediments from Cornubia only reached the western part of the basin, and there is evidence for southerly derivation of certain deposits. Alluvial and lagoonal mud-plains were periodically invaded by braided rivers which laid down sandy sheets; some of the major siltstone–sandstone bodies may have been formed by lateral accretion in migrating channels, whereas the thicker sandy units are attributed to rejuvenation of source areas by block-faulting. Most of the clays were laid down in distal environments, including bays and lagoons, but some were deposited in more proximal, fluvial, overbank environments. Water depths were shallow within the lagoons, for desiccation features and dinosaurian footprints are preserved in the sediments.

The Wealden Beds consist of two major units; a lower unit of mainly sandy sediments termed the Hastings Beds, and an upper, muddier formation called the Weald Clay (Wealden Shales in the Wessex Basin). This bipartite subdivision is clearest in the Weald.

Offshore, there does not appear to be a predominance of sandstones in the lower part of the Wealden Beds as is the case with the Hastings Beds onshore, for during Ryazanian to Barremian times the central part of the English Channel was probably the farthest part of the basin from the landmasses which provided arenaceous sediments (Figure 41). In this central part of the English Channel, the Wealden Beds conformably succeed the Purbeck Beds, but farther north in well 99/12-1 the highest Jurassic rocks are absent, and 17 m of Wealden Beds rest unconformably on Oxford Clay (Figure 42). This is the result of uplift and erosion along the Hampshire–Dieppe High at the end of the Jurassic and the start of the Cretaceous.

Wealden Beds proved south of the Isle of Wight in boreholes 75/31 and 75/37 (Figures 40 and 42) comprise sand-stone and loose sand interbedded with variegated mudstone, and include some carbonaceous fragments (Dingwall and Lott, 1979). Well 99/16-1, south-south-east of the Isle of Wight, proved 480 m of Wealden Beds consisting of an interbedded sequence of sandstone, variegated mudstone, siltstone and shale (Figure 43). Nearer the eastern margin of the Portland–Wight Basin, well 99/18-1 proved 157 m of Wealden Beds consisting of variegated mudstone with abundant carbonaceous material and numerous beds of lignite, sandstone and siltstone. The abundance of sandstone suggests that nearshore conditions prevailed here throughout the period of deposition, possibly due to the effect of the Hampshire–Dieppe High.

Approximately 10 km south-east of Eastbourne, a borehole drilled as part of the Royal Sovereign Light Tower site investigation cored 30 m of mudstone with interlaminations of silt, thin bands of lignite, and a 1 m-thick sandstone (Figure 43). This is probably equivalent to part of the Hastings Beds (Lake et al., 1987). The Hastings Beds were also recovered in core 50/00/477, which consists of 0.3 m of well-cemented sandstone overlying 2.24 m of greenish grey mudstone of Ryazanian to Barremian age.

Shallow-seismic surveys across submarine outcrops of the Wealden Beds produce seismic records with numerous discontinuous and variably dipping reflectors. Minor irregularity of the sea-bed topography is characteristic, probably due to the interbedded sandstones and siltstones. No subdivisions of the Wealden Beds can be mapped offshore.

Gradual erosion of the London–Brabant Massif and other landmasses resulted in the rivers reaching a mature state, and caused a reversion to mudswamp environments with occasional short-lived and local arenaceous input during the Hauterivian (Allen, 1976). This resulted in the deposition of the Weald Clay, which comprises shales and mudstones with subordinate siltstones, sandstones, shelly limestones and clay ironstones. The clays are normally dark grey, but weather to mottled yellow and brown. Cyclic sedimentation occurred, with thin sandstone beds grading upwards into silty mud-stones and thin shales with shelly limestones; these limestones are overlain by the basal sandstones of the next cycle. Towards the top of the Weald Clay there is a return to ma-

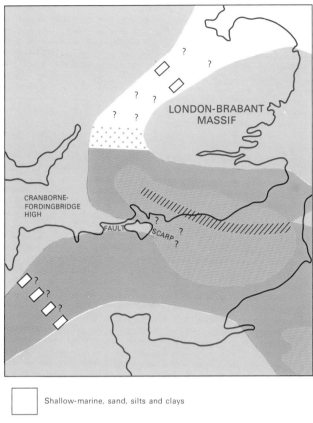

	Shallow-marine, sand, silts and clays
	Coarse continental clastics and fluvial sands, silts and clays
	Lacustrine silty clays and silts
	Area of nondeposition
	Barrier or partial barrier
	Portsdown Swell

Figure 41 Early Cretaceous (Ryazanian–Barremian) palaeogeography. After Anderton et al. (1979), Rayner (1981), Whittaker (1985) and Ziegler (1982).

rine deposition, marking the beginning of the Aptian transgressive phase.

Attempts have been made to correlate the Wealden Beds across the English Channel into The Boulonnais in northern France (e.g. Robaszynski and Amédro, 1986). However, because of rapid lateral facies and thickness variations it is impossible to establish a lithological correlation. In the eastern part of the Weald Basin, near to the coast of the English Channel, the Wealden Beds are between 100 and 200 m in thickness, whereas in The Boulonnais only 30 m of these beds occur (Whittaker, 1985; Mégnien, 1980). However it is possible to consider a chronostratigraphical comparison between English and French Wealden Beds from the Ryazanian to the late Barremian (Rawson et al., 1978); the upper part of the Wealden facies of The Boulonnais, which consists of white, fine-grained, siliceous, unfossiliferous sands and mottled reddish clays, can be correlated with the contemporaneous Weald Clay of the Weald and English Channel (Robaszynski and Amédro, 1986). Weald Clay was cored at site 50/00/340 (Figure 43) some 10 km east-south-east of

Beachy Head, where 0.2 m of Hauterivian to Barremian, variegated to pale grey mudstone was recovered.

Aptian to Albian

In earliest Aptian times, the London–Brabant Massif was transgressed from the North Sea (Figure 44), while the English Channel and adjacent land areas continued to subside intermittently but moderately rapidly throughout the Aptian and Albian, with the accumulation of more than 100 m of strata. It was however late in the Aptian before the English Channel was completely submerged from the south via the Paris Basin, resulting in the deposition of sediments which overstep westwards and northwards on to progressively older formations, depositing the Lower Greensand, Gault and Upper Greensand. Periods of erosion during the Aptian to Albian resulted in minor disconformities within the sequence.

LOWER GREENSAND

The Aptian and early Albian stages are represented by a lithologically variable muddy and sandy sediment known as the Lower Greensand, which was laid down in a variety of tidally influenced, shallow-marine and shoreline environments. It has a rich, dominantly molluscan fauna of neritic, littoral, and estuarine facies, with local abundance of brachiopoda, polyzoa or sponges (Casey, 1963). The Lower Greensand strata are neither usually green nor predominantly sandy; they may have got their name from the Upper Greensand with which they were locally mistaken.

All the wells drilled offshore to the base of the Lower Greensand proved it to rest conformably on Wealden Beds (Figure 43). An unconformity proved by boreholes in Dorset, where Lower Greensand and Gault rest on Kimmeridge Clay, has however been identified south of Weymouth Bay (Donovan and Stride, 1961). Westwards, progressively younger Aptian and Albian beds overstep Jurassic formations that had been eroded during the period of uplift associated with the late-Cimmerian Unconformity.

In the Dorset coastal area and on the Isle of Wight, the Lower Greensand is subdivided into four units: Atherfield Clay, Ferruginous Sandstone, Sandrock and Carstone (Figure 39). The Atherfield Clay consists of greyish silty clay, rich in bivalves and gastropods. The Ferruginous Sandstone is also rich in fossils; it consists of greyish brown clayey sand impregnated with calcite, and includes phosphatic and ferruginous concretions and glauconitic sands. The Sandrock is an unfossiliferous white and yellow sand or sandstone, whereas the Carstone comprises gritty and pebbly sands with phosphatic nodules. The only marked break in sedimentation is at the base of the Carstone, in contrast to the Weald where both palaeontological and lithological evidence point to nondeposition and possible erosion in the shallow seas at several intervals during the Aptian.

In the Weald, the Lower Greensand is again divided into four major lithological formations: Atherfield Clay, Hythe Beds, Sandgate Beds and Folkestone Beds (Figure 39). These divisions can be extended into the eastern English Channel, for the variation in lithology within the Lower Greensand has resulted in a variable sea-bed profile caused by differential erosion of hard and soft beds; the observed seismic characteristics of the units can be related to the established lithostratigraphical subdivisions (Figure 45). Study of seismic records and comparison with onshore sequences has therefore allowed accurate mapping of the Aptian to Albian outcrop, a pattern confirmed by sampling (BGS Dungeness–Boulogne Solid Geology sheet).

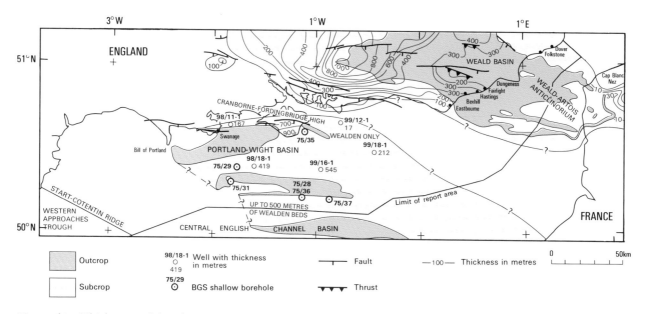

Figure 42 Thickness and distribution of Purbeck and Wealden beds. Adapted from Whittaker (1985), and Mégnien (1980).

The Atherfield Clay in this area consists of shales and mudstones with concretions of clay, ironstone and fine-grained sandstone; it is rich in ammonites, bivalves, corals, echinoids and brachiopods. The Atherfield Clay has been cored east of Dungeness at location 51/01/1115 (Figure 43), where 2.28 m of bioturbated, dark grey, finely laminated clay with pale grey silt laminae were recovered. BGS borehole 75/35 (Figure 40), located near the coast of the Isle of Wight, cored 66.35 m of clay, mudstone, silt and sandstone with calcareous and phosphatic nodules; these lithologies are comparable with those of Atherfield Clay exposed on the Isle of Wight (Dingwall and Lott, 1979).

The Hythe Beds typically consist of alternating layers of hard, bluish grey, sandy limestone (locally known as rag) and grey, loosely cemented, calcareous, argillaceous sandstone with glauconite (locally known as hassock). Fossils are abundant at some levels. At site 51/01/1072 (Figure 43), 2.29 m of sandy, hard limestone with thin lenses of sandy, glauconitic clay are probably equivalent to the Hythe Beds.

The Sandgate Beds are very variable in thickness and lithology; they consist of up to 45 m of argillaceous sands or sandstones and glauconitic silty mudstones, with some pebbly calcareous sandstone and beds of phosphatic pebbles and ferruginous sands. The calcareous and ferruginous beds are fossiliferous, but fossils are rare in the glauconitic beds. Site 51/01/1085 (Figure 43) yielded 2.2 m of intensely bioturbated, dark grey and greenish grey glauconitic sand with numerous burrow fills of almost black clay; this lithology has been tentatively identified as the Sandgate Beds. Fuller's earth (montmorillonite) occurs mostly in the Sandgate Beds and beds of equivalent Aptian age, which suggests volcanism in the Early Cretaceous not far from the English Channel. A volcano discovered beneath the Waddenzee in The Netherlands is a possible source of the pyroclastic material which gave rise to these deposits (Jeans et al., 1977; Cottençon et al., 1975).

The Folkestone Beds consist mainly of poorly consolidated quartzose sands with pebbles, and thin clay with phosphatic nodules. Hard, ferruginous sandstones and beds of calcareous and glauconitic sandstone also occur; these bands result in an irregular sea floor where the beds crop out, providing a dis-

tinctive signature on seismic records (Figure 45). In the upper part of the formation, cross-bedding is well developed, fossils are absent, and there are polished sand grains and sporadic dreikanter pebbles which suggests aeolian deposition. The sands may originally have accumulated in sand dunes from which they were reworked and deposited in nearby shallow water with strong currents. Fossils occur in the phosphatic nodules and sandstone bands; these include ammonites, bivalves, echinoids, gastropods, annelids, driftwood, and fish and reptilian remains. The Folkstone Beds have been cored at site 51/01/1088 (Figure 43) where 1.21 m of coarse-grained, slightly calcareous, glauconitic sandstone interbedded with greenish grey, sandy clay was recovered. BGS borehole 75/29 (Figure 40) cored 6.85 m of Lower Greensand consisting of intensely bioturbated, dark grey to black, glauconitic siltstone and mudstone (Dingwell and Lott, 1979). Well 98/18-1 proved 164 m of Gault clay and Lower Greensand from the sea bed, but this is probably not a maximum figure, for farther north over 200 m have been proved (Figure 46).

Not all offshore samples of Lower Greensand can be related to the onshore subdivisions; 1.27 m of greenish grey, argillaceous sandstone with phosphatic nodules proved at site 50/00/523 is probably part of the Lower Greensand. Well 99/16-1 south-east of the Isle of Wight (Figure 43) proved 92 m of Lower Greensand consisting of coarse-grained glauconitic sandstone that is interbedded with silty, glauconitic mudstone in its lower part.

GAULT AND UPPER GREENSAND

The further major transgression of the Early Cretaceous began in the early Albian, resulting in the deposition of sediments that overlapped the Aptian strata and overstepped on to older rocks exposed in the south-west. In Dorset, both the late Albian Upper Greensand and basal Cenomanian strata rest on rocks of Triassic age. Still farther west in Devon, similar sandstones rest unconformably on beds of Permian age (Durrance and Hamblin, 1969). The same unconformity occurs west of approximately 2°20'W in the English Channel, where the Cretaceous rocks overlie progressively older rocks from Permo-Triassic to Middle Jurassic in age.

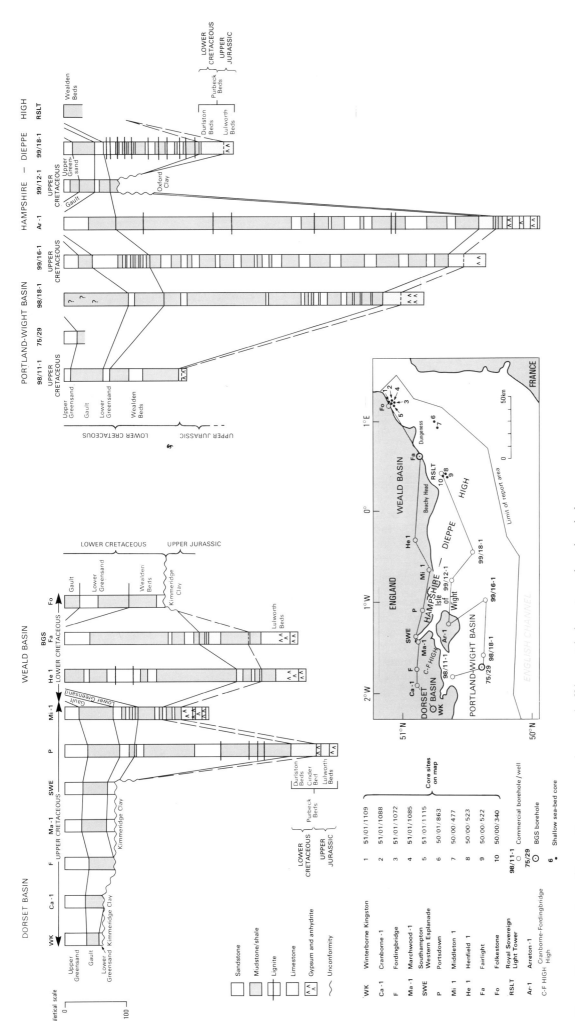

Figure 43 Comparison of Lower Cretaceous rocks proved offshore with those in onshore boreholes adjacent to the English Channel.

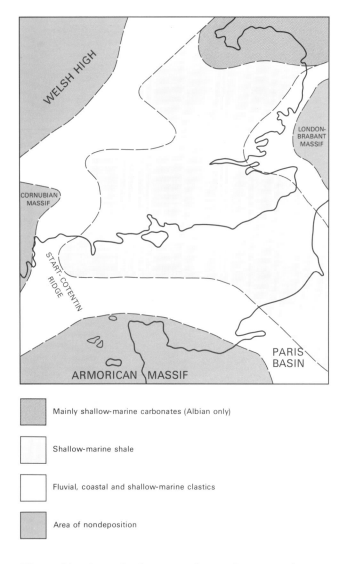

Mainly shallow-marine carbonates (Albian only)

Shallow-marine shale

Fluvial, coastal and shallow-marine clastics

Area of nondeposition

Figure 44 Generalised Aptian–Albian palaeogeography. After Ziegler (1982).

Links between the Wessex–Channel Basin and the Western Approaches Trough were maintained intermittently throughout the Early Cretaceous, although the two basins were separated by the Start–Cotentin Ridge (Lott et al., 1980). The early Albian transgression resulted in deeper-

water marine conditions in the basinal areas, where up to 90 m of Gault clay were deposited some distance from the shore. The Upper Greensand is probably partly a laterally equivalent, shallow-water, nearshore deposit, for it replaces the Gault in the west. However, the Upper Greensand is best regarded as a facies variation of only the highest Gault, and may not always be arenaceous. Both these Albian formations contain distinctive faunas indicative of their environment of deposition; the Gault has a large proportion of thin-shelled benthonic and pelagic forms, whereas the Upper Greensand includes thick-shelled and strongly ribbed molluscs which could withstand the strong currents of nearshore environments.

The Gault in southern England consists of dark, bluish grey to pale grey, soft mudstones and silty mudstones, although the basal part is silty or sandy and some beds are glauconitic or calcareous with layers of phosphatic nodules. The clay becomes more sandy upwards as it passes into the Upper Greensand. It is rich in marine fossils that include ammonites, bivalves, gastropods, fish fragments, echinoids, corals, crustaceans and foraminifera. In northern France and the Paris Basin there is a similar lithological sequence in the Albian; direct correlations have been made between the Gault at Folkestone and that at Wissant on the north coast of France (Owen, 1971).

BGS borehole 75/29, south-west of the Isle of Wight, (Figure 40) cored 7 m of Gault consisting predominantly of dark grey, silty, micaceous, intensely bioturbated, fossiliferous mudstone with some siltstone and silty sandstone (Dingwall and Lott, 1979). The Gault was also proved in several wells, including 99/16-1 which proved 24 m of dark grey, micaceous, glauconitic mudstone with minor interbeds of sandstone in its lower part. It has also been cored in the eastern English Channel; site 51/01/1109 yielded 2.65 m of pale grey, soft calcareous mudstone which has been identified as late Albian in age and is therefore probably upper Gault (Figure 43). Some of the boreholes drilled during exploration preceding the construction of the Channel Tunnel in the eastern part of the English Channel have cored Gault; the formation here consists of grey to blue-grey, calcareous clay which is silty in its upper part (Destombes and Shephard-Thorn, 1971). An approximate thickness of 40 m has been suggested for the Gault in the eastern English Channel, but this thins across the Dover Strait to approximately 11 m at Wissant. Although The Boulonnais and south-eastern England appear to have behaved as a single palaeogeographi-

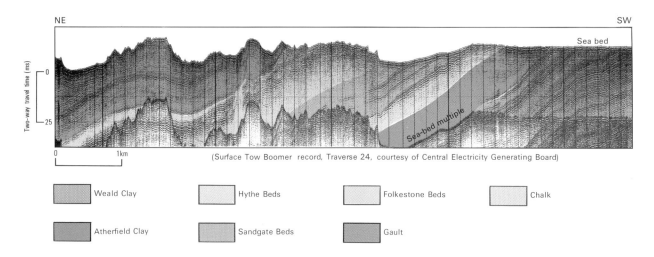

(Surface Tow Boomer record, Traverse 24, courtesy of Central Electricity Generating Board)

Weald Clay

Hythe Beds

Folkestone Beds

Chalk

Atherfield Clay

Sandgate Beds

Gault

Figure 45 Shallow seismic reflection profile across Cretaceous rocks. For line of section see Figure 46.

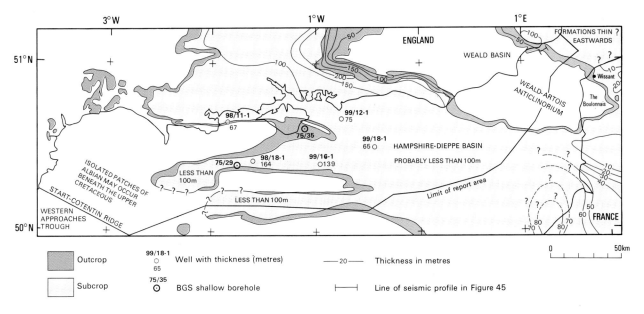

Figure 46 Thickness and distribution of the Aptian and Albian (Lower Greensand, Gault and Upper Greensand). Adapted from Whittaker (1985) and Mégnien and Debrand-Passard (1980).

cal unit, The Boulonnais occupied a more marginal position in the sedimentary basin and was subsiding less, resulting in the transgressive stages occurring slightly later, with the deposition of less sediment.

In Kent and the eastern English Channel, the Upper Greensand is variable in both thickness and lithology, with siltstones, silts, hard siliceous sandstones, and calcareous sandstones that in places grade laterally into siliceous limestones. Some beds are rich in ammonites, lamellibranchs and sponges. Farther west in Hampshire and the central English Channel, the Upper Greensand is less varied in lithology and consists mainly of speckled, pale, greenish to bluish grey sandstones, although mudstone concretions, phosphatic nodules, chert and spheroidal doggers of calcareous sandstone occur throughout the formation.

Offshore borehole 75/29 (Figure 40) cored 26 m of dark green, fine-grained, fossiliferous, glauconitic sandstone with doggers of limestone and phosphatic nodules; this lithology can be correlated with the Foxmould Formation (Upper Greensand) of Dorset (Dingwall and Lott, 1979). The top of the core is very calcareous, and includes round clasts of limestone similar to the Chert Beds of Dorset. However, in seabed cores it is difficult to distinguish between the Upper and Lower Greensand from lithology alone. Core 50/00/522 (Figure 43) may represent part of the Upper Greensand as it was collected near to the base of the Lower Chalk outcrop; it consists of 1.86 m of fine- to very fine-grained, well-sorted, glauconitic and bioturbated sandstone.

Micropalaeontological studies on cores from the Channel Tunnel boreholes have revealed the presence of an unconformity at the base of the Cenomanian (Carter and Destombes, 1972). The Lower Chalk overlying the unconformity includes some detrital components such as glauconitic sand, silt or clay, dependant on whether the underlying facies is Gault or Upper Greensand.

UPPER CRETACEOUS

A eustatic rise in sea level at the start of the Late Cretaceous (Haq et al., 1988) resulted in the Cenomanian Transgression, which, combined with regional tectonic subsidence, led to the spread of the Chalk Sea to cover much of

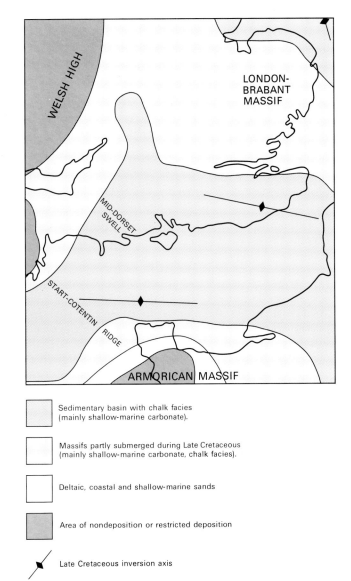

Figure 47 Generalised Late Cretaceous palaeogeography (Cenomanian–Maastrichtian). After Anderton et al. (1979), Hancock (1976) and Ziegler (1982).

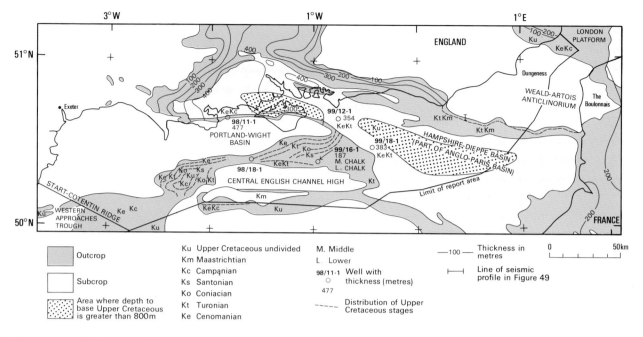

Figure 48 Thickness and distribution of Upper Cretaceous rocks.

Europe. After initial deposition of Glauconitic Marl in the Cenomanian, very little terrigenous material was carried into this area of deposition, resulting in the formation of the Chalk (Figure 47). Maximum Chalk deposition in the report area was in the Hampshire–Dieppe Basin, where it reaches a thickness of over 400 m (Figure 48). Measurements from seismic-reflection profiles in the English Channel show Upper Cretaceous formations resting with an angular discordance of between 5° and 10° on underlying strata (Auffret and Colbeaux, 1977).

Chalk is a micritic limestone consisting of a matrix of debris from planktonic algae that contains coarser calcite components such as calcispheres, foraminifera and fragmentary debris from larger invertebrates. Nearly all the material was deposited as low-magnesian calcite, which is stable at sea-bed temperatures and pressures, so that most chalk did not suffer early lithification. Nevertheless, deep burial, high heat flow, or local tectonic stresses have in places hardened the Chalk and reduced its porosity. The Chalk was deposited in a sea 100 to 600 m deep of normal salinity (Hancock, 1976), and intense bioturbation indicates that the sea bed was generally in a thixotropic state, being permanently firm only at depths of a few tens of centimetres. Nodular beds represent shallow-

er-water deposition, whereas marls indicate an increase in terrigenous material, possibly derived from landmasses elevated as a result of tectonic stresses.

Flint is common at certain levels within the Chalk as irregularly shaped nodules or beds which mostly follow, but sometimes cut across, bedding planes. The nodules commonly infill crustacean burrows. Flint consists of silica in the form of micron-sized, randomly arranged quartz crystals. The silica was probably derived from biogenic sources such as sponge spicules, although a small contribution from distant volcanic sources is possible (Anderton et al., 1979). Flints are rarely found in the Lower Chalk, and are generally most numerous in the upper part of the Chalk succession, although a belt of maximum flint development occurs at the top of the Turonian Chalk. This bed can be traced to northern France and is an approximately contemporaneous sedimentary phenomenon (Mortimore and Wood, 1983).

Continuous deposition throughout the Late Cretaceous meant that rates of sedimentation were quite high; it has been estimated that in basinal areas more than 500 m of sediment were deposited in less than 30 Ma (Whittaker, 1985). By contrast, only 100 to 200 m accumulated over submerged massifs or highs, where subsidence was less. Along the west-

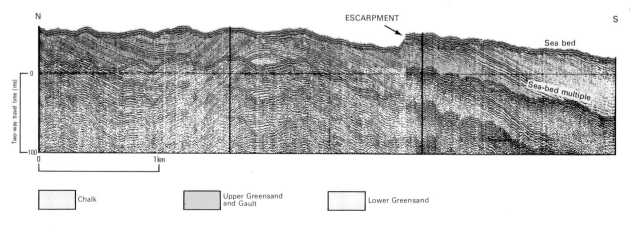

Figure 49 Seismic profile showing the sea-bed escarpment formed by the differential erosion of the Chalk, Upper Greensand and Gault. For line of profile see Figure 48.

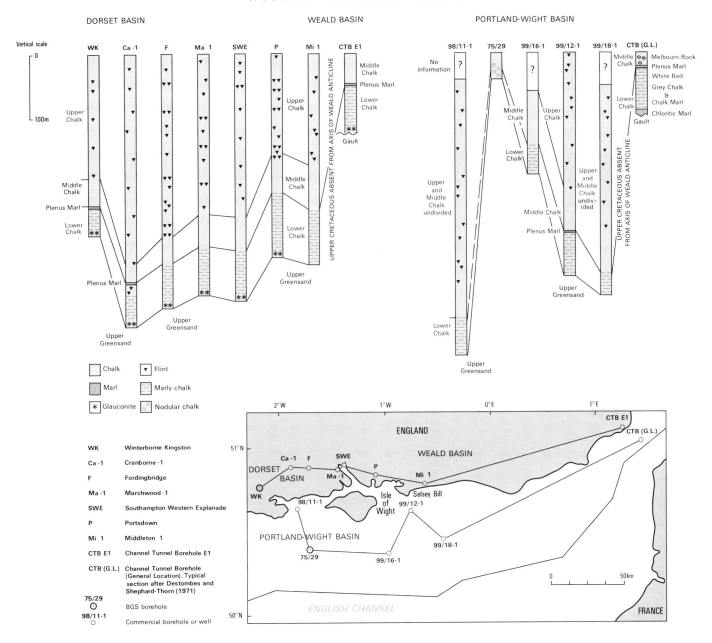

Figure 50   Comparison of Upper Cretaceous rocks proved offshore with those in onshore boreholes adjacent to the English Channel.

ern margin of the Central English Channel Basin, the Start–Cotentin Ridge was probably a high during much of the Cretaceous, as shown by the thinning of Cretaceous strata towards it. In Dorset, late Albian and Cenomanian sedimentation was affected by intermittent movements along a deep structure termed the Mid-Dorset Swell (Figure 47), resulting in extensive reworking, condensation and erosion of deposits over its crest (Drummond, 1970). Studies of hardgrounds within the Chalk (Jarvis and Woodroof, 1981) suggest periods of uplift and faulting in Coniacian and Santonian times, following which some basins began to undergo inversion late in the Cretaceous. The term hardground was first used in the reports of the Challenger Expedition for rocky sea floors, and since then has been used widely for inter- or intraformational surfaces in marine sediments which show evidence of exposure as lithified rocky bottoms (Kennedy and Garrison, 1975).

Synsedimentary structures including carbonate banks, slump beds, nodular chalks and hardgrounds have been described in

Chalk both from the coast of Normandy (Kennedy and Juignet, 1974) and from southern England (Kennedy and Garrison, 1975). Seismic surveys of the English Channel (Larsonneur et al., 1975; Curry and Smith, 1975) have also shown such structures; some may result from instability during late Turonian/early Coniacian times along the line of the Wight–Bray Fault (Smith, 1984), which probably protected this part of the English Channel from the severe faulting seen farther west.

Quine (1988) interpreted concave-up structures on seismic records from the English Channel as channel and scour features, and demonstrated that they increase in number towards the crests of anticlines. The channels are orientated roughly east–west, and range in size from 5 to 20 m in depth and 50 to 500 m in width. They were eroded on the Chalk Sea floor by oceanic and tidal currents generated by shallowing of the sea during regressional phases and tectonic uplift. These unusual sedimentary features in the Chalk may therefore provide evidence of tectonic movements during the Late Cretaceous (Mortimore and Pomerol, 1987).

On the basis of lithology, the Chalk of southern England has been divided (Rawson et al., 1978) into Lower, Middle and Upper Chalk (Figure 39). The Lower Chalk equates with the Cenomanian Stage, and the Middle Chalk to part of the Turonian. The Melbourn Rock lies at the base of the Middle Chalk and the Upper Chalk sequence begins with the Chalk Rock. In southern England the Upper Chalk represents the late Turonian to Campanian stages, although Maastrichtian Chalk occurs in the English Channel. Indeed all Late Cretaceous stages have been shown to be present in the English Channel (Figure 48), although their distribution is affected by erosion and they have only been mapped locally (Dingwall and Lott, 1979). South of the Isle of Wight, Cenomanian to Campanian rocks have been proved north of the Central English Channel High; Maastrichtian Chalk is mainly restricted to the south of this structure, although it has also been recovered from the eastern edge of the Hampshire–Dieppe Basin. To the east of the Weald–Artois Anticlinorium, the Chalk is of Cenomanian to Campanian age.

Unlike the Lower Cretaceous, where rapid lateral facies variations make correlations between England and France difficult, there are similarities between the Chalk of southern England and northern France (Robaszynski and Amédro, 1986; Pomerol et al., 1987; Mortimore and Pomerol, 1987). Lithological marker beds with key fossils can be recognised throughout the basin, and major lithological changes consistently occur at certain levels, although not necessarily equally strongly developed (Mortimore and Pomerol, 1987). For example the Navigation Hardground/Marls and the Seven Sisters Flints can be recognised throughout the Anglo-Paris Basin and coincide with biostratigraphical markers. On both sides of the English Channel, the occurrence of *Micraster normanniae* below the Navigation Hardground defines the base of the Coniacian Stage (Pomerol et al., 1987). However because of the general lack of detailed information, little correlation has been possible within the English Channel.

Lower Chalk

The Lower Chalk is of Cenomanian age and has a relatively high terrigenous content. A sandy, glauconitic bed at the base, called the Glauconitic Marl or Chloritic Marl, is succeeded by the Chalk Marl and Grey Chalk. The top of the Lower Chalk is marked by the thin but very widespread Plenus Marl.

Where the base of the Chalk crops out on the sea bed it can be readily mapped using shallow-seismic data, for it commonly forms an escarpment due to the erosion of the underlying softer Upper Greensand and Gault (Figure 49). In some places, recent marine sediments have buried the escarpment, masking its bathymetric effect, but it can still be identified on seismic sections. BGS borehole 75/29, south-west of the Isle of Wight, recovered 43.4 m of Cenomanian to Turonian Chalk (Figures 40 and 50) resting upon late Albian Upper Greensand. The Chalk is white with grey argillaceous bands, and is stylolitic and slickensided throughout. The Cenomanian section consists of white, chalky nodules in a grey, argillaceous matrix which is glauconitic towards the base of the borehole and probably represents the Glauconitic Marl facies. Samples collected throughout the English Channel have shown Cenomanian basal beds to consist of glauconitic sands or marly chalk rich in glauconite.

Well 99/12-1 off Selsey Bill (Figure 50) proved 70 m of Lower Chalk described as white to pale grey, soft and glauconitic, grading down to marl with a trace of glauconite. It is similar to the Lower Chalk cored in the Channel Tunnel boreholes, where it has been possible to divide the Lower Chalk into four units (Figure 50). At the base is the Chloritic Marl, comprising 1 to 5 m of dark greenish grey, sandy marl with glauconite. It is succeeded by the Chalk Marl made up of 22 to 27 m of dark grey, chalky marl, above which 22 to 26 m of Grey Chalk is formed of pale to medium-grey, less-marly chalk. At the top is the White Bed or White Chalk, described as 18 to 20 m of homogeneous, very pale, yellowish grey, marly chalk (Destombes and Shephard-Thorn, 1971). The Lower Chalk thins slightly from about 80 m at Dover to 68 m at the French coast (Shephard-Thorn et al., 1972; see also Figure 73).

The top of the Lower Chalk is marked by the Plenus Marl (Rawson et al., 1978), a greenish grey marl band which onshore is characterised by the rare presence of the belemnite *Actinocamax plenus*. It ranges in thickness from 0.05 to 8.5 m, and occurs throughout the Wessex–Channel Basin; an approximately equivalent bed has been traced from the South-west Approaches to the northern North Sea (Andrews et al., 1990; Hart and Bigg, 1981). The unit represents a brief interval of clay deposition in restricted basins within the normally clear Chalk Sea.

In offshore wells such as 99/12-1, a distinct marl band within the lower part of the Chalk is taken as the equivalent of this bed. The marl can be identified on downhole gamma-ray logs by its high values, and has been identified in the Channel Tunnel boreholes as a thin (c.2 m) but persistent unit of yellowish green marl and paler, marly chalk forming a distinctive marker at the top of the Cenomanian. The top of the Lower Chalk was cored in borehole 75/29 (Figures 40 and 50) where the boundary is the top of a grey-green clayey band less than 1 m thick, below which the Chalk is strongly bioturbated (Dingwall and Lott, 1979).

Middle Chalk

The Middle Chalk is of early to mid-Turonian age and consists mainly of massively bedded, white chalk up to 90 m thick that generally lacks flints, except in the top few metres. There is always a hard basal bed termed the Melbourn Rock, which is a complex of nodular chalks and incipient hardgrounds.

The Middle Chalk in well 99/12-1 (Figure 50) consists of 67 m of white to pale grey, soft chalk with some flint and marl. In borehole 75/29 it comprises nodular, white chalk which is slickensided and stylolitic throughout, and includes common undulating bands and seams of marl. Sea-bed samples of Middle Chalk have been collected where it crops out in the English Channel, but in the Channel Tunnel boreholes, only the Melbourn Rock has been recognised; it consists of a hard, white, nodular chalk with greenish marl wisps (Destombes and Shephard-Thorn, 1971).

Upper Chalk

The boundary between the Middle and Upper Chalk in Dorset is placed at the base of the Chalk Rock, which in parts of the Hampshire Basin is known as the Spurious Chalk Rock. This is another complex hardground unit that includes nodules and pebbles of chalk and numerous fossils. The Upper Chalk ranges from late Turonian to Maastrichtian in age, and is the thickest of the three Chalk units, with up to 400 m preserved in Hampshire, 404 m in the Isle of Wight, and up to 260 m in Dorset (Melville and Freshney, 1982). It comprises massively bedded, white chalk with occasional nodular beds and hardgrounds, but is generally not distinguished offshore from other Chalk units. Flints occur throughout, concentrated as tabular seams; thin seams of marl are also present (Melville and Freshney, 1982). In well 99/12-1 it is 216 m thick and consists of massively bedded, white chalk with abundant flint.

From Late Cretaceous times onwards, minor episodes of inversion affected the Wessex–Channel Basin before the main inversion episode during the Tertiary. West of the Start–Cotentin Ridge, Chalk sedimentation continued into the Danian, but no evidence of this has yet been found in the report area. Certainly Maastrichtian Chalk was eroded onshore, although it is still found in the English Channel.

8 Tertiary

The existence of Tertiary outcrops in the eastern English Channel was first revealed by the abundant presence of the middle Eocene foraminifer *Nummulites laevigatus* (Bruguière) in dredged samples (Dangeard, 1923; 1929). The first geological map of the area (King, 1949) showed a large Tertiary basin entirely separated from the onshore outcrop. It was later termed the Dieppe Basin (Robert, 1971), for the Tertiary outcrop of the Hampshire Basin was believed at that time to extend only a short distance offshore. A separate east–west-orientated, elongate outcrop of Tertiary sediments was subsequently discovered (King, 1954) and is referred to here as the Central Channel Outlier (Figure 51). A second elongate, east–west-orientated outlier was later found off the coast of Normandy (Robert and Ville, 1971a; 1971b; Bignot, 1974); this has been named the Bassin du Nord-Baie de Seine.

With the use of modern seismic profiling techniques, the Dieppe Basin was found to be the eastward prolongation of the Hampshire Basin, and was accordingly renamed the Hampshire–Dieppe Basin (Curry and Smith, 1975). Thus two major Tertiary outcrops occur in the report area, the northern part of the Hampshire–Dieppe Basin and the Central Channel Outlier. The Bassin du Nord-Baie de Seine lies entirely in French waters (Figure 51).

The Hampshire–Dieppe Basin is a broad, gently dipping structure approximately 280 km in length. Estimates of the thickness of Tertiary in this basin have increased since the work of King (1954) who, by extrapolation from onshore, estimated a total of 213 m. Robert (1971), using shallow seismic reflection profiling, estimated 274 m, whereas Bignot (1974) reported 450 to 500 m and Curry and Smith (1975) agreed that more than 400 m of sediment is preserved. Modern commercial deep-seismic reflection profiling has revealed approximately 500 m of sediment in the deepest part of the offshore basin (Figure 52), but the greatest proven thickness is 652 m in the Sandhills 1 borehole on the Isle of Wight (Edwards and Freshney, 1987b).

The Central Channel Outlier is approximately 72 km long and up to 11 km wide. This synclinal basin is markedly asymmetric, with a very steep northern limb and a southern limb with dips of only approximately 1°. On some maps the basin is shown as fault-bounded to the north (Robert and Ville, 1971b; Smith and Curry, 1975; Larsonneur et al., 1975). The maximum thickness of the Tertiary sequence in this basin is approximately 105 m.

The Bassin du Nord-Baie de Seine is also some 72 km long and up to 12 km wide, and is bounded to the north (Figure 51) by a major fault (Robert and Ville, 1971a; 1971b;

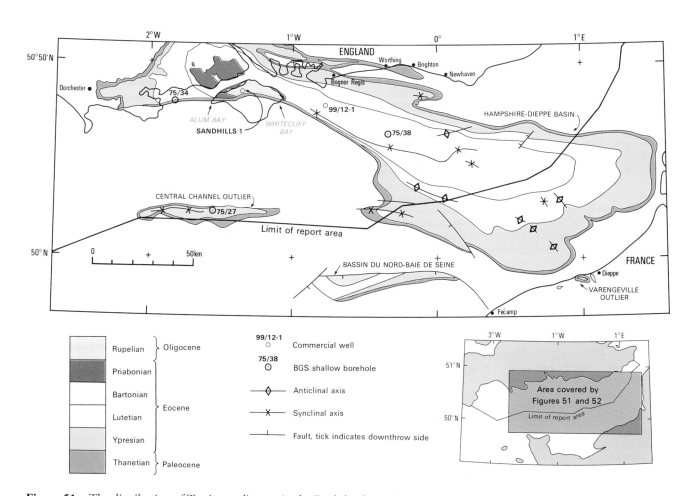

Figure 51 The distribution of Tertiary sediments in the English Channel region.

66

Larsonneur et al., 1975). Curry and Smith (1975) show a Tertiary thickness of around 160 m for this basin.

The base of the Tertiary sequence is marked by a conspicuous seismic reflector over most of the offshore area of outcrop, indicating a strong lithological contrast with the underlying Chalk. No samples of Danian age have been recovered in the report area. A strong, well-defined reflector approximately 20 to 30 m above the base of the sequence is believed to represent the base of the Eocene. This has been confirmed by sampling in French waters (e.g. Auffret et al., 1975), but data are lacking in the report area. The overlying sediments are portrayed on seismic records as a layered sequence of reflectors from which it is difficult to pick formational boundaries. Strong or distinctive reflectors may become less strong, or change in character, across the area, indicating lateral facies changes. Published maps by BGS, BRGM and Auffret and Gruas-Cavagnetto (1975) have thus relied heavily on the position and age assignation of core samples to determine boundaries within the Tertiary sequence, and most show chronostratigraphical stages. Exceptions to this are the lithostratigraphical maps of Curry and Smith (1975) and the BGS Wight Solid Geology sheet.

In the map shown in Figure 51, all available data have been referred to the standard stage stratigraphy of Haq et al. (1987), which is shown in Figure 53. Where these are used in a different sense, or where other stage names are used, they are shown in this text in inverted commas. Suggested correlations with stage nomenclatures of previous authors are given in Figure 54.

REGIONAL EVOLUTION

Until late Thanetian times, the entire English Channel area was probably land. The first marine influences occurred in NP9 times with a marine incursion from the north (Figure 55) that linked the Paris Basin directly with the North Sea Basin. Even then, much of the English Channel area consisted of swampy lowlands with lush vegetation draining into a semienclosed marine basin. It was not until early Ypresian times that this lowland barrier was breached (Figure 56) as a result of rising sea levels in conjunction with the progressive degradation of tectonic relief previously induced by the Laramide phase of foreland compression. This transgression opened a seaway through the English Channel area, linking the colder waters of the North Sea Basin with warmer Atlantic waters. At this time, planktonic foraminifera became abundant within the sediments throughout the region, giving rise to the 'planktonic datum' of Wright (1972). During the late Ypresian, further evidence of a westerly marine connection .comes from the migration of *Nummulites planulatus* (Lamarck) from the Tethyan faunal province through the English Channel area as far east as Belgium (Blondeau, 1972).

A hiatus occurs onshore which separates late Ypresian ('Cuisian') sediment from those of Lutetian age. This hiatus corresponds with a eustatic sea-level lowstand (Haq et al., 1987; Figure 57). During Lutetian times, a narrow marine embayment with a fluctuating coastline existed in the region of the present-day Solent (Figure 58). Conditions within the embayment were slightly hyposaline due to freshwater runoff, with turbid, muddy water less than 100 m deep. The sediment responsible for the turbidity was probably mostly derived from land areas to the west (Plint, 1982). This turbid water meant that seagrass was absent, a fact reflected by the foraminiferal assemblages (Murray and Wright, 1974); farther offshore in the basin, seagrass flourished in clearer water.

In early Bartonian ('Auversian') times, the sea in this 'Solent' inlet appears to have become warmer, clearer, and of normal marine salinity, indicating a reduction in terrestrial runoff. However, muddy, hyposaline waters indicative of increased runoff returned later in the Bartonian. *Nummulites variolarius* (Lamarck), *N. prestwichianus* (Jones) and *N. rectus* Curry migrated into the area from the west during the Bartonian. These are important markers, and *N. rectus* is the last *nummulite* species to have migrated into the area, for post-Bartonian deposition was dominated by nonmarine sediments.

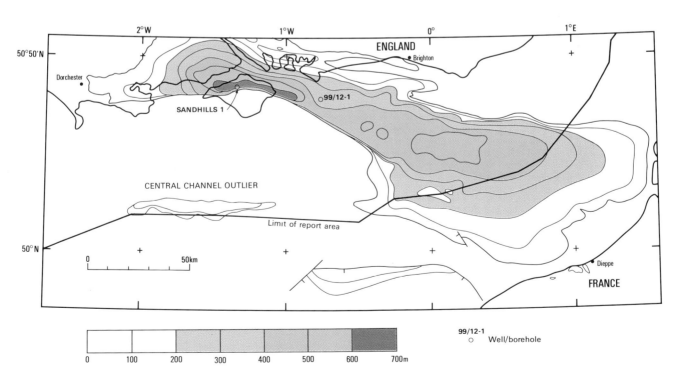

Figure 52 Depth below sea level to the base of the Tertiary in the English Channel region.

Stratigraphic correlation chart of the Palaeogene of the Hampshire and adjacent basins.

AGE (Ma)	Epoch	Sub	STANDARD STAGES	NANNOPLANKTON ZONES	DINOFLAGELLATE ZONATION	HAMPSHIRE BASIN	WESTERN HAMPSHIRE BASIN	EASTERN HAMPSHIRE BASIN	CENTRAL CHANNEL OUTLIER	HAMPSHIRE-DIEPPE BASIN (OFFSHORE)
30	OLIGOCENE	LATE	CHATTIAN	NP25	D15	Hamstead Beds		Bouldnor Formation (Solent Group)		
			CHATTIAN	NP24	D15					
35	OLIGOCENE	EARLY	RUPELIAN	NP23	D14					
			RUPELIAN	NP22	D13	Bembridge Beds		Bembridge Limestone Formation		
			RUPELIAN	NP21	D13	Headon Beds	Headon Formation	Headon Hill Formation		
	EOCENE	LATE	PRIABONIAN	NP20	D13					
			PRIABONIAN	NP19	D12	Upper Barton Beds / Middle Barton Beds (Barton Group)	Becton Sand Formation / Chama Sand Formation (Barton Group)	Becton Sand Formation / Chama Sand Formation (Barton Group)		Barton or Huntingbridge Formation
40			PRIABONIAN	NP18	D12		Barton Clay Formation / Boscombe Sand Formation	Barton Clay Formation		
	EOCENE	MIDDLE	BARTONIAN	NP17	D11	Lower Barton Beds				
			BARTONIAN	NP16	D10	Huntingbridge Formation (Bracklesham Beds)	Branksome Sand Formation (Bournemouth Group)	Selsey Sand Formation (Bracklesham Group)		Selsey Formation
45			LUTETIAN	NP15	D10	Selsey Formation		Marsh Farm Formation		Earnley Formation
			LUTETIAN	NP14	D9	Earnley Formation	Poole Formation	Earnley Sand Formation		
			LUTETIAN	NP13	D8	Wittering Formation		Wittering Formation	Wittering Formation	Wittering Formation
			LUTETIAN	NP12	D8	Wittering Formation / Bagshot Sands				
50	EOCENE	EARLY	YPRESIAN	NP11	D7	London Clay	London Clay Formation	London Clay Formation	London Clay Formation	London Clay Formation
			YPRESIAN	NP10	D6					
			YPRESIAN	NP9	D5	Woolwich and Reading Beds	Reading Formation	Reading Formation	Reading Formation	Woolwich Formation
55	PALEOCENE	LATE	THANETIAN	NP8	D4					
			THANETIAN	NP7	D4					Limestone with Microcodium
			THANETIAN	NP6	D4					
			THANETIAN	NP5	D3					
60	PALEOCENE	EARLY	DANIAN	NP4	D2					
			DANIAN	NP3	D2					
			DANIAN	NP2	D1					
65			DANIAN	NP1	D1					

68

Figure 53 Tertiary stratigraphy in the English Channel region.
Age, standard stages and nannoplankton zones after Haq et al. (1987); dinoflagellate zones after Costa and Manum (1988). Lithostratigraphy for the Hampshire Basin after Aubrey (1983), for the western Hampshire Basin (Bournemouth–Poole district) after Edwards and Freshney (1987a), and for the eastern Hampshire Basin after Edwards and Freshney (1987a) and Insole and Daley (1985). Offshore lithostratigraphies modified after Curry et al. (1978).

During the Priabonian, sediments deposited in southern England were dominantly lacustrine and brackish lagoonal, although a marine inlet seems still to have existed in the eastern Solent area. Gradual uplift along the Artois axis had severed the connection to the North Sea Basin, and it is not clear whether a marine connection remained with the Atlantic Ocean at this time. By the Oligocene, almost all marine connection with the report area appears to have been lost (Figure 59), although a brief marine incursion is recorded in the top of the Tertiary sequence in the Isle of Wight. It is therefore demonstrable that marine conditions existed locally in the region during early Oligocene times.

The early Oligocene climate in southern Britain is interpreted as having been humid, warm and temperate (Daley, 1972). A major eustatic sea-level fall occurred in mid-Oligocene times associated with the initiation of the Antarctic ice cap. Evidence for Neogene transgressions into the area is lacking, but any incursions are likely to have come from the west. It is probable that renewed connection with the North Sea Basin did not occur until Pleistocene times.

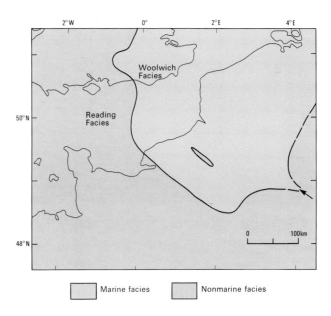

| Marine facies | Nonmarine facies |

Figure 55 Palaeogeography of the English Channel region in late Thanetian times. After Bignot (1974). Arrow indicates direction of river input.

PALEOCENE

In contrast to the area west of the Start–Cotentin Ridge (Evans, 1990), Danian sediments are absent from the report area, and late Paleocene sediments rest upon Turonian to Maastrichtian Chalk. The earliest Tertiary sediments so far recognised in the English Channel are white, crystalline limestones containing *Microcodium elegans* (Gluck) recovered in five cores from the southern margin of the Hampshire–Dieppe Basin between Dieppe and Fécamp (Auffret et al., 1975). *Microcodium* consists of groups of elongate, radiating crystals approximately 1 mm long that occur in subcylindrical or sheet-like clusters. It is believed to represent a codiacean alga, although a bacterial mat or even an inorganic, diagenetic origin cannot be ruled out (Wray, 1977).

These limestones can be correlated with the 'Calcaires du Cap d'Ailly' of northern France, a 3 m-thick unit of gypsiferous, silty limestones containing *Microcodium* and the moulds of freshwater gastropods and rootlets (Bignot, 1974; Destombes et al., 1977). In France, this unit unconformably overlies up to 7 m of fine-grained, poorly sorted sands with an impersistent boulder and pebble bed which infills an irregular solution surface in the Chalk. These sands yield a limited fauna of bivalves and gastropods indicative of brackish conditions. The solution of the Chalk probably predated the deposition of the 'Calcaires du Cap d'Ailly', allowing the basal deposits to subside and to be preserved in hollows. These basal deposits have been correlated with the *Arctica scutellaria* Zone and therefore with the Woolwich Bottom Bed and Woolwich Marine Beds of southern England; they are thus of late Thanetian age. They have not been recorded offshore, probably due to their thin and variable thickness and resultant narrow width of outcrop.

The remainder of the late Thanetian sequence in the English Channel area is better known, and dozens of short cores have been recovered from these beds. As in southern England, the sequence includes both marine ('Woolwich Beds') and nonmarine ('Reading Beds') facies (Figures 53 and 55). Marine facies dominate in the east, but with progressively less marine influence to the west. These sediments have generally been referred to as 'Sparnacien' in French publica-

STANDARD STAGES	FRENCH STAGES	
Rupelian	Stampien (g₂b)	Stampien *(Sensu lato)* (g₁-g₂)
	Sannoisien (g₁-g₂a)	
Priabonian	Ludien (e₇)	Bartonien (e₆-e₇)
Bartonian	Marinésien (e₆b)	
Lutetian	Auversien (e₆a)	Lutetien (e₅)
	supérieur (e₅a)	
	moyen (e₅b)	
	inférieur (e₅a)	
Ypresian	Cuisien (e₄)	Yprésien (e₃-e₄)
	Sparnacien (e₃)	
Thanetian	Thanétien (e₂)	

Figure 54 Comparison of commonly used French stages, and their normal stage notations, with the standard stratigraphy of Haq et al. (1987).

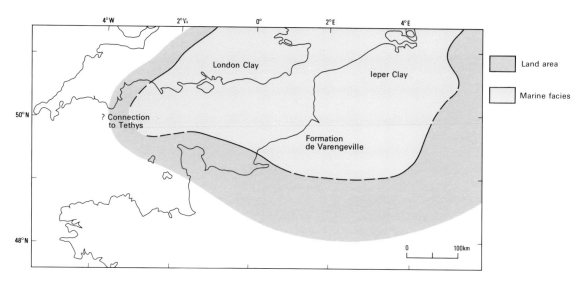

Figure 56 Palaeogeography of the English Channel region in early Ypresian times. After Bignot (1974) and King (1981).

tions, although this term has been applied in different senses by different authors and therefore causes confusion (Bignot, 1980). However, most French authors have regarded the 'Sparnacien' (or occasionally 'Ilerdian') as a substage forming the lower part of the 'Yprésien' Stage, and therefore of early Eocene age (e.g. Bignot, 1974). This usage is followed on BRGM maps of the English Channel region. The stratotype section yields dinoflagellate cysts indicative of the Hyperacanthum Zone (Bignot, 1980), although the section also includes younger sediments which elsewhere have been termed 'Cuisien' (Figure 54). In the UK, the Woolwich Beds also contain Hyperacanthum Zone dinoflagellate assemblages,

and have traditionally been assigned to the 'Sparnacien', but are here considered to be of late Paleocene age. It follows that the 'Yprésien' of French usage differs both from that traditionally used in the UK and from the standard stratigraphy depicted in Figure 53.

The pollen from three cores from the southern margin of the Hampshire–Dieppe Basin were studied by Auffret and Gruas-Cavagnetto (1975). These late Thanetian deposits consist of 20 m of clays and lignites containing charophytes, and marls with oysters and ostracods. The facies was described as lagoonal–continental, similar to sediments of equivalent age on the coast of northern France which include shell beds with a restricted fauna similar to the Woolwich Shell Beds of southern England.

In both northern France and the southern part of the Hampshire–Dieppe Basin, the Paleocene thus shows initial late Thanetian deposition in brackish coastal lagoons, followed by a brief regression that allowed the formation of nonmarine lakes and the deposition of the 'Calcaires du Cap d'Ailly', with a subsequent return to brackish, coastal lagoons. On the French coast, the top of the Paleocene sequence consists of sands showing large-scale cross-bedding thought to indicate the development of small deltas prograding into coastal lagoons, or washover sands produced during storm surges (Destombes et al., 1977).

On the northern side of the Hampshire–Dieppe Basin, a number of short cores into Paleocene sediments south of Brighton recovered muddy, fine-grained sands and muds containing shell fragments. The shelly muds have yielded dinoflagellate cysts indicating the Hyperacanthum Zone. The Woolwich Beds onshore at Newhaven are around 18 m thick; the lower part is formed of the approximately 7.6 m-thick Woolwich Bottom Bed, composed of sands with cross-bedding and *Ophiomorpha* burrows, and including a basal pebble bed of flints in a sandy clay matrix (Bone, 1986). These are overlain by approximately 12 m of layered clays and sandy clays with shell horizons termed the Woolwich Shell Beds. Similar deposits of estuarine or lagoonal facies are found as far west as Worthing (Bone, 1986; Young and Lake, 1988).

However, farther west at Felpham near Bognor Regis (Figure 51), the Paleocene comprises up to 30 m of Reading Formation. These are mottled clays with penecontemporaneous channel deposits of clays and lignite (Bone, 1986). The base of the channel fill contains a lag of clay clasts in a sandy clay matrix, and a dark brown lignitic clay 1.6 m thick that

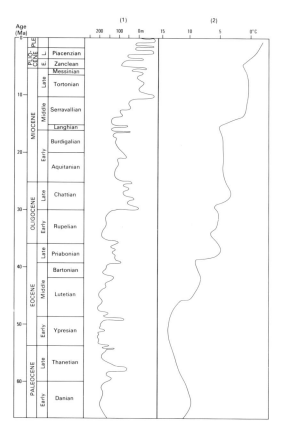

Figure 57 Eustatic sea level (1) and ocean-bottom water temperature (2) during the Tertiary. After Haq et al. (1987) and Savin (1977).

includes a rich flora of fruits, seeds, leaves and other plant remains. Tree stumps are found in growth position on the foreshore, together with logs up to 6 m long. A crocodile skull and teeth, and a turtle femur have also been found. Collinson (in Bone, 1986) interpreted the environment as a forest with lianas in a warm, and at least seasonally, humid climate. The lignite bed was deposited in a marsh or swamp comparable to the present-day Florida Everglades.

Farther west at Alum Bay on the Isle of Wight, Buurman (1980) estimated the thickness of the Reading Beds as 40 m. Here they consist of mottled clays with little structure except burrows and rootlets; a repeated sequence of sedimentation followed by emergence and soil formation was recognised. Deposition was believed to have been under fluvial or fluvio-marine conditions, and increasing smectite content towards the top of the formation was thought to reflect increasing marine influence.

Offshore, red clays originally thought to be of Triassic age were noted by King (1949) in the Central Channel Outlier, and Curry (1962) obtained cores of mottled and variegated clays from its southern flank. The latter were probably deposited under similar conditions to those at Alum Bay. Reading Beds have not been sampled from the northern limb of the syncline where the beds are near vertical and the Paleocene outcrop is extremely narrow. Reading Beds were penetrated by well 99/12-1 in the Hampshire–Dieppe Basin (Figure 51), which proved 34.8 m of grey to reddish grey, silty clay.

EOCENE

Ypresian

Early Eocene deposition was initiated by a major marine transgression which entered the area from the North Sea region. In southern England, this transgression was responsible for deposition of the London Clay Formation, and in northern France for the Formation de Varengeville in the Varengeville Outlier (Figure 51).

Along the southern flank of the Hampshire–Dieppe Basin, a number of cores have sampled clays and silts within a unit which appears homogeneous on seismic records (Bignot, 1972). Auffret and Gruas-Cavagnetto (1975) refer to this unit as 'Lower Ypresian, London Clay facies' and describe

from it a subtropical assemblage of tree pollen. Offshore cores on the northern flank of the Hampshire–Dieppe Basin contain sediments comparable with the London Clay Formation of southern England (Venables, 1962; King, 1981). These sediments are commonly decalcified, but yield well-preserved dinoflagellate cysts which allow age assessment.

In the Central Channel Outlier, sediments equivalent in age to the London Clay (King, 1954; Curry, 1962) reveal a close similarity of facies to that of the onshore part of the Hampshire Basin. Much of the sediment is sandy and decalcified, although one sample contains a fauna of bivalves, ostracods and foraminifera. BGS borehole 75/27 (Figure 51) penetrated 20 m of Ypresian sediments equivalent to part of the London Clay Formation. At 15.4 m below sea bed, a layer of black, well-rounded flint pebbles marks an unconformity within the unit. Beneath this, the sediments are dominantly muddy sands, whereas above they are sandy silts. Siderite concretions are found at several horizons, and $CaCO_3$ contents vary from 1 to 6 per cent. Curry (1962) estimated the thickness of the London Clay Formation in the Central Channel Outlier to be about 61 m; this can be compared with 120 m in the Sandhills 1 borehole (Edwards and Freshney, 1987a). A thickness of 161 m for the London Clay Formation has been recorded in well 99/12-1 to the east of the Isle of Wight, but this is possibly an overestimate.

According to Murray and Wright (1974), the London Clay Formation of the onshore part of the Hampshire–Dieppe Basin contains a low diversity foraminiferal fauna due to hyposaline conditions caused by a continual influx of river water. From foraminiferal evidence, they estimated a water depth of around 50 m, and certainly less than 100 m. Water temperatures are believed to have been similar to those of the present-day Western Approaches; this seems to contradict evidence from land-derived plant fossils which include the palm *Nipa* and the mangrove *Avicennia* that are thought to represent tropical or subtropical conditions (Reid and Chandler, 1933; Montford, 1970). Reid and Chandler (1933) compared the flora to that from the rainforests of south-east Asia. However the London Clay flora also includes coniferous wood with well-developed growth rings indicating seasonality, as well as temperate genera such as *Alnus*, *Betula*, and *Corylus* that are interpreted as being derived from contemporaneous, cooler, upland areas. Nevertheless, it seems

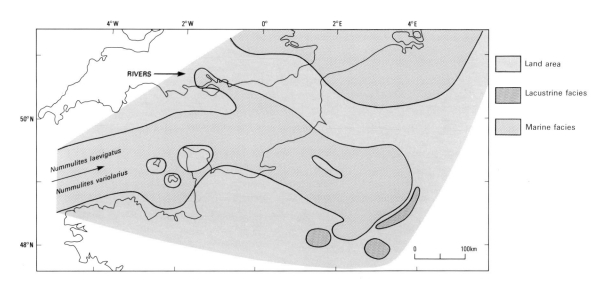

Figure 58 Palaeogeography of the English Channel region in Lutetian times. After Pomerol (1982) and Plint (1982).

unlikely that any uplands of significant altitude existed in the region at that time (discussion in Daley, 1972).

The early Eocene is believed to have been a time of global warm temperatures (Figure 57); at such times, latitudinal temperature gradients were less well marked than today, and the climate more equable. Environmental stability and absence of frost are important factors in rainforest growth, but rainfall may be the primary limiting factor in rainforest distribution; rainforests presently receive over 200 cm of rain per year. Increased ocean temperatures may have led to greater precipitation, so that during London Clay times, rainforest conditions may have existed in cooler regions than those in which they exist at present (Daley, 1972). Conditions are believed to have been very moist in the swampy lowland areas; modern species of the genus *Nipa* grow in muddy estuaries and coastal saline or brackish swamps, and *Avicennia* is a mangrove which colonises mudflats (Montford, 1970). The more temperate plants probably lived in inland, perhaps more elevated, areas with less moist conditions (Daley, 1972).

The overlying Ypresian sediments are those referred to as 'Cuisien' in the literature (Figure 54). Auffret et al. (1975) noted conspicuous seismic reflectors which divide the Ypresian sequence in the southern Hampshire–Dieppe Basin into two parts of approximately equal thickness. The lower they termed 'Yprésien inférieur' as already described, and the upper as 'Cuisien'. They obtained samples only from the base of the upper sequence; it consists of sands and calcareous sandstones. These samples were characterised as 'Cuisien' by the presence of *Nummulites planulatus* which had migrated from the Tethyan faunal province to the west, through the English Channel, into the southern North Sea Basin as far as Belgium (Blondeau, 1972). The dinoflagellate-cyst assemblage has allowed correlation with the Coleothrypta Zone (Auffret and Gruas-Cavagnetto, 1975).

Curry and Smith (1975) obtained samples from the eastern part of the Hampshire–Dieppe Basin. These consist of glauconitic calcareous sandstones and glauconitic sandy clays, and contain abundant *Ditrupa* as well as *N. planulatus*. One sample in particular contains a fauna of molluscs and foraminifera which indicates a correlation with part of the Wittering Formation (Bed IV of Fisher, 1862) of the Bracklesham Group of southern England (Figure 53).

'Cuisian' samples obtained by Curry (1962) from within the Central Channel Outlier consist of silty clays containing molluscs, ostracods and foraminifera; some samples include bryozoans, calcareous algae and brachiopods. *N. planulatus* has not been found in this outcrop but *N. lucasianus* Defrance was recognised by Larsonneur et al. (1975). These sediments were also correlated with the Wittering Formation by Curry et al. (1978), and are the youngest Tertiary sediments preserved in the Central Channel Outlier.

The thickness of the Wittering Formation offshore is poorly known, but it is approximately 63 m thick at Bracklesham Bay (Curry et al., 1977) and 83 m in Sandhills 1 (Edwards and Freshney, 1987b). At Bracklesham Bay, the formation consists of silty sands and clayey silts which can be divided into two transgressive sequences, each with a basal pebble bed (Plint, 1988). Heavy-mineral assemblages show a dramatic change within the formation, with an influx of tourmaline-rich sands reflecting uplift of the Cornubian Massif to the west (Morton, 1982). At the top of the formation is a complex series of channelled, lignitic silts and fine-grained sands with pebble beds indicating regressive conditions. This facies has been recognised offshore and correlated with the Argile de Laon of the Paris Basin (Auffret and Gruas-Cavagnetto, 1975). The climate at this time continued

to be warm, with the land-bearing trees typical of rainforests and mangroves.

There appears to be a hiatus at the top of the Ypresian that corresponds to a brief eustatic sea-level lowstand (Figure 57) before renewed transgression in early Lutetian times. Aubry (1985) believed this hiatus to occur within the Wittering Formation (Figure 53), but the nannoplankton from the Wittering Formation do not indicate the presence of zone NP14, so it seems most likely that the whole formation can be placed within the Ypresian.

Lutetian

A group of strong seismic reflectors noted by Curry and Smith (1975) within Lutetian sediments is believed to correlate with hard calcareous beds in the middle part of the sequence. Lutetian sediments have been extensively sampled offshore, and short cores in the southern part of the Hampshire–Dieppe Basin have recovered glauconitic sandy clays and sandy limestones with abundant *N. laevigatus*. The abundance of this *nummulite* in sea-bed sediments in this area was first recorded by Dangeard (1923). Other fauna include bryozoans, echinoderms, molluscs and tubes of the polychaete *Ditrupa strangulata* Deshayes. In some samples, *N. variolarius* occurs together with *N. laevigatus*, indicating mid-Lutetian age. Lutetian samples have also been recovered offshore from the Bassin du Nord-Baie de Seine (Larsonneur et al., 1975) and around the Cotentin Peninsula. The youngest part of the Lutetian includes the 'Auversian' of many authors. On published French maps (Auffret et al. 1975; Auffret and Gruas-Cavagnetto, 1975) this is sometimes distinguished from the 'Lutetian' and 'Bartonian' although some authors may include it within the 'Bartonian'. Auffret (1973) obtained a number of samples characterised by the presence of *N. variolarius* and the absence of *N. laevigatus*; these he assigned to the 'Auversien' and correlated with beds XIII to XVII of Fisher (1862). These latter beds correspond with the upper part of the Selsey Sand Formation of southern England, and consist of sandy marls commonly rich in glauconite. The sediments contain an abundant marine microplankton and a pollen assemblage dominated by conifers; the flora indicates the persistence of a warm climate.

Bartonian

Although the Bartonian outcrop covers a large area of the English Channel (Figure 51), it was not sampled until 1972 (Auffret, 1973), and even to the present time few cores have been obtained. This may be partly due to the cover of Quaternary sediments which occupy the central part of the English Channel. Bartonian sediments recovered in short cores include sandy clays with *N. rectus*, indicating correlation with the lower Barton Beds of early Bartonian age. BGS borehole 75/38 (Figure 51) penetrated approximately 56 m of sandy silts and silty sands equivalent to the Barton Clay Formation (Figure 53) of Edwards and Freshney (1987b).

The Barton Clay Formation includes sediments of Lutetian age, and the 'Bartonian' of the literature may include 'Auversian' deposits herein considered as Lutetian; such deposits were considered by Bignot (1974) to be 200 m thick in the eastern English Channel, which compares with 185.3 m for the Barton Group (including some Lutetian).

Priabonian

Priabonian sediments have not been recorded offshore, although the Headon Hill and Bembridge Limestone forma-

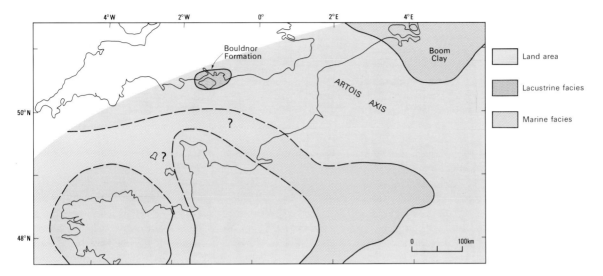

Figure 59 Palaeogeography of the English Channel region in Rupelian times. After Pomerol (1982).

tions of the Isle of Wight are of Priabonian age, and it is likely that their outcrop extends a short distance east of the Isle of Wight into the English Channel (Boillot and Lefort, 1974). The Headon Hill Formation of southern England and the Isle of Wight comprises a variety of lithologies including muds, silts, sands, marls, limestones and lignites, with characteristically rapid lateral lithological changes (Insole and Daley, 1985). The lower contact is sharp where the Headon Hill Formation overlies the fine-grained sands of the Becton Sand Formation. The thickness varies from 75 to 100 m on the Isle of Wight.

Most of the Headon Hill Formation is highly fossiliferous, although the assemblages are generally of low diversity. Study of the ostracods (Keen, 1977) revealed freshwater, brackish and marine facies; the freshwater ostracods lived in shallow, alkaline lakes up to 15 m deep. The palaeogeography at the time is believed to have been similar to that of Lutetian times (Figure 58), with a narrow marine inlet occupying the general area of the present-day eastern Solent, with fringing coastal, brackish lagoons (Keen, 1977). The foraminifera indicate water temperatures of 16 to 18°C (Murray and Wright, 1974).

The Bembridge Limestone Formation varies from 1 to 19 m in thickness, and is known only from the Isle of Wight where it consists of beds of marly limestones and marls with subordinate muds (Insole and Daley, 1985). Thin lignites are present at the western end of the island. The fauna consists mostly of freshwater gastropods, although terrestrial gastropods are also found. The muddy layers generally correlate with more brackish conditions, for they contain brackish-water ostracod faunas (Keen, 1977). Daley and Edwards (1971) believed that thickness variations within this formation were due to penecontemporaneous tectonic uplift along west-north-westerly trending fold axes.

OLIGOCENE

The Oligocene is represented on the Isle of Wight by the Bouldnor Formation (Hamstead Beds of Curry et al. 1978, Bembridge Marls and Hamstead Beds of other authors). It consists of grey, blue-green or green muds with a conspicuous basal erosion surface (Insole and Daley, 1985), and is 96 m thick at the western end of the island. The fauna is dominantly freshwater or brackish, except at the base and the top of the formation where marine faunas are found. Plant

fossils, particularly fruits and seeds, are common at some levels.

The lowermost member of the Bouldnor Formation, the Bembridge Marls Member, has a 0.6 m-thick basal muddy shelly sand termed the Bembridge Oyster Bed, which represents a brief transgressive episode (Daley, 1973). Above the basal sand, the sequence consists of muds deposited in extensive, shallow, freshwater lakes in a low-lying floodplain. Some lignitic clays are present, and the freshwater gastropod *Viviparus* is abundant. Water depths were probably less than 4 to 5 m, and the lakes may have occasionally become in-filled and the sediments subaerially exposed (Daley, 1973). Daley (1973) noted the occurrence of fresh flint pebbles at the base of the sequence which he believed to indicate exposure of the Chalk at this time, possibly within the uplifted monocline to the south.

Oligocene sediments are recorded offshore only from the Bassin du Nord-Baie de Seine, where two samples of fresh-water limestone containing *Planorbis* have been recorded (Curry and Smith, 1975). These were assigned to the Oligocene on indirect evidence, including the fact that they were taken 80 to 100 m higher in the sequence than a sample of 'Lutetien' age. The outcrop of the Oligocene on the Isle of Wight may extend a short distance into the western Solent, but sample data are lacking. A suggestion by Robert (1971) that Oligocene beds might be present in the Hampshire–Dieppe Basin was based on the preserved thickness of the sequence rather than sample information.

NEOGENE

The Miocene was the time of major inversion of the Wessex Basin in response to the Helvetic orogenic events, and Miocene deposits are unknown both offshore and in southern England. Early Miocene fluviatile deposits found along the lower parts of the Seine Valley do not extend out to sea; Pomerol (1982) believed that the river flowed westwards towards a coastline which at that time lay to the west of the Cotentin Peninsula (Evans, 1990).

Pliocene deposits are unknown offshore in the eastern English Channel, although a Pliocene fossiliferous deposit near Fécamp (Figure 51) was used by Larsonneur (1972) as evidence for the eastern extent of the Pliocene sea. The Lenham Beds are ferruginous sands preserved in pipes in the Chalk surface of south-eastern England; they have traditionally been used as evidence for the southern extent of the Pliocene North Sea Basin, which was separated from the Channel Basin by uplift of the Artois axis. However, recent molluscan evidènce (Janssen in Balson, 1990) suggests an Atlantic rather than North Sea affinity for the fauna of the Lenham Beds; this may be an indication of extensive transgression from the west in Pliocene times.

9 Quaternary, including sea-bed sediments

In the English Channel area, the boundary between the youngest Tertiary sediments of Oligocene age and those of the Quaternary represents a long hiatus. The Quaternary deposits are limited to palaeovalley infill of Pleistocene and early Holocene age, as well as Holocene sea-bed sediments. The palaeovalleys are believed to be wholly Pleistocene, and appear to represent a complex river system much modified by marine processes. Most authors agree that there has been no glaciation within the area, although farther west in the Celtic Sea (Evans, 1990) it appears that at least one ice sheet extended south to at least 50°40'N, probably during the Dimlington Stadial of the late Devensian (Figure 60).

During the Pleistocene, sea level rose and fell according to the amount of water locked up in ice caps. This world-wide or eustatic variation of sea level was such that the entire English Channel became dry land during glacial maxima, and was inundated during periods of ice retreat. The late Devensian glaciation lasted from approximately 26 to 13 ka, when sea level in the Celtic Sea fell to some 135 m below present sea level (Bouysse et al., 1976), and during earlier stadials sea level may have fallen as much as 205 m (Evans, 1990). At such times, the area was subject to subaerial erosion in a periglacial climate, and river systems developed to drain southern England and northern France.

Figure 60 attempts to summarise the Quaternary history of the English Channel, southern England, northern France and the Channel Islands. Correlation and dating are however tenuous since few fossils are found, and relative sea levels can be affected simultaneously by several factors, including the eustatic movements, glacial loading and offloading as ice sheets waxed and waned in the English Midlands, and tectonic movements in the final stages of the Alpine orogeny.

At the close of the Tertiary, sea levels were high; marine Pliocene sediments are known 183 m above OD at Lenham in Kent, and 120 to 130 m above sea level at St Eustache east of Le Havre, although an unknown amount of uplift has occurred. Deeper-water Pliocene sediments occur at a lower level at St Erth, Cornwall (Jenkins et al., 1986). Early Pleistocene marine sediments are known at 183 m above OD at Netley Heath in Surrey, and estuarine sediments at 100 m above sea level at La Londe in Normandy. Contemporaneous early Pleistocene deltaic sediments in the southern North Sea are now found well below sea bed due to later subsidence. During this interval, marine sediments would have been deposited over much of the English Channel area, but have since been removed. However the Dover Strait was not open, and a ridge of land ran from Surrey through Kent to The Boulonnais, thus separating the English Channel from the North Sea Crag basins of eastern England (West, 1972). Sea level dropped later during the early Pleistocene, for marine stillstands are recognised in southern England, ranging between 183 m and 112.5 m above OD. This regression was probably caused by a combination of tectonic uplift and a eustatic drop in sea level as the climate cooled.

Onshore studies (Bowen et al., 1986) suggest at least one glaciation within the British Isles before the Anglian, and evidence from the southern North Sea (Cameron et al., 1992) suggests that this was not during the early Pleistocene. Thus it is likely to have occurred during the Cromerian Complex Stage, when the English Channel may have dried out completely as a result of eustatic drop in sea level. If this was so, then the river system within the English Channel was initiated at that time.

Sea levels are believed to have risen in late Cromerian Complex times, and marine deposits of this age are known close to present sea level in Brittany (Plogoff) and East Anglia (West, 1972). However, raised beach deposits at Goodwood and Slindon (Shephard-Thorn et al., 1982; Melville and Freshney, 1982) at 25/40 m above OD, with a temperate marine fauna and Palaeolithic implements, are now considered to be of Cromerian Complex age. These deposits contain metamorphic and igneous pebbles of westerly provenance (Reid, 1902; Fowler, 1932), but none large enough to require an origin more exotic than longshore drift. At Bracklesham Bay, marine sediments indicating a mean tidal level 0.7 to 1.0 m below its present position may be either late Cromerian Complex or late Hoxnian (West et al., 1984).

During the Anglian, a major glaciation extended as far south as the Thames Valley in eastern England, and possibly as far as the Scilly Isles in the west (Bowen and Sykes, 1988). Sea levels dropped, and the English Channel dried out, allowing the river system to be either initiated or resurrected; it is considered most probable that the Dover Strait formed at this time by overflow from a proglacial lake in the southern North Sea.

During the Hoxnian interglacial, sea level rose again to form raised beaches with marine sediments at 18 m above OD on Jersey and 13 m above sea level at Herzeele in northeastern France (Lautridou et al., 1986). The English Channel is believed to have dried out again during the Wolstonian glacial interval, when the rivers Rhine and Meuse flowed out through it.

Sea levels rose in the Ipswichian interglacial to form raised beaches at up to 15 m above OD; West and Sparks (1960) record a marine transgression at 1.8 m below OD at Selsey, with estuarine deposits overlain at 7 m above OD by beach gravel. From Brighton and Bognor Regis to Selsey Bill and Portsmouth, erratic boulders up to 3 m across of granite, basalt, diorite, quartz porphyry, biotite gneiss and mica schist are found associated with marine clay underlying Ipswichian raised beach deposits (Godwin-Austen, 1857; Reid, 1892; Hodgson, 1964; Young and Lake, 1988). These are derived principally from Brittany, the Channel Islands and Cotentin (Kellaway et al., 1975). Kellaway et al. (1975) suggested transport by an ice sheet, but this would require a major glaciation of northern France and the English Channel, for which there is no other evidence. The most likely explanation is transport by floating ice (Reid, 1892; Kidson and Bowen, 1976), which would require only a restricted valley glaciation of northern France. However, this would be unlikely during the Ipswichian, when the climate would have been too warm, or during the Devensian, Wolstonian or even Anglian, when sea levels were too low. To account for ice floating to Sussex, when sea level was higher than the present, would appear to require the glaciation to be of Cromerian Complex age or earlier, that is, much older than the overlying Ipswichian raised beach.

The last glaciation, during the late Devensian, caused the English Channel to dry out again, and the present form of the palaeovalleys was developed as the rivers Rhine and

MARINE OXYGEN ISOTOPE STAGES	AGE (Ka)	CHRONOSTRATIGRAPHY		CLIMATIC CONDITIONS	SOUTHERN ENGLAND	ENGLISH CHANNEL	NORTHERN FRANCE CHANNEL ISLANDS
		SERIES	UK STAGE (NW European Stage)				
1	10 / 13	HOLOCENE	FLANDRIAN	TEMPERATE	Valley mouths drowned, peats and submerged forests preserved below sea level Solent River disrupted, formation of West Solent, Christchurch Bay, Poole Harbour	Mobile sediments (sandbanks) initiated Lag sediments cover sea bed as transgression completed	Submerged peats in estuaries and off coasts
2-4	120	PLEISTOCENE — LATE	DEVENSIAN (WEICHSELIAN)	PERIGLACIAL	Dimlington Stadial Head and Coombe Rock formed Fisherton brickearth (mammalian fauna)	Palaeovalleys infilled with estuarine then marine sediments as transgression begins Channel dried out, fluvial drainage, major rivers of northern Europe flow through Dover Strait, palaeovalley system developed to present form	Periglacial head and loess formation in France and Channel Islands
5	130	PLEISTOCENE — LATE	IPSWICHIAN (EEMIAN)	TEMPERATE	First river terrace Raised beaches of Selsey(5m), Brighton (7.5m) Portland raised beach (15m)	Marine conditions, English Channel and North Sea joined by Dover Strait	Annoville-Hauteville and Grandcamp formations: marine interglacial raised beach deposits at up to +1.5m Lys Formation with peat Jersey: raised beach at +8m
6-8	300	PLEISTOCENE — MIDDLE	WOLSTONIAN (SAALIAN)	PERIGLACIAL	Discontinuous local permafrost Contortions & ice wedges in earlier gravels	Channel dried out, fluvial drainage, major rivers of northern Europe flow through Lobourg Channel	Formation de St. Pierre-lès-Elbeuf: loess overlies middle terrace of Seine Formation de Nantois: head, sands, loess
9-11	440	PLEISTOCENE — MIDDLE	HOXNIAN (HOLSTEINIAN)	TEMPERATE	Solent river system disrupted by transgression	Marine conditions, English Channel and North Sea joined by Dover Strait	Formation d'Herzeele: marine interglacial raised beach at up to +13m Jersey ? 18m raised beach
12-14	560	PLEISTOCENE — MIDDLE	ANGLIAN (ELSTERIAN)	PERIGLACIAL	Inland terraces at 70m,56.5m 'Solent River' formed as integrated system	? Dover Strait formed as overflow channel Lobourg Channel and Northern Palaeovalley cut English Channel dried out, fluvial drainage	Formation du Valois. heads and gravelly sands (periglacial)
15	770	PLEISTOCENE — MIDDLE	'CROMERIAN COMPLEX' (CROMERIAN)	COLD/ TEMPERATE	Goodwood & Slindon raised beaches (25-40m), marine bluff at 44m	Marine conditions, Dover Strait not in existence ? Channel dried out during glacial periods ? River system developed on floor of English Channel	Formation de Mesnil Esnard, loess affected by ice wedges Jersey: ?30m raised beach Formation de Plogoff: marine
16-40		PLEISTOCENE — EARLY	BEESTONIAN TO PRE-LUDHAMIAN (MENAPIAN TO PRAETIGLIAN)	BECOMING COLD	5 marine stillstands at between 183m and 112.5m High level plateau gravels Clay-with-flints continue to be developed Early Pleistocene marine deposits at Netley Heath, Surrey, at 183m	Shallowing marine conditions	St. Prest Formation: sandy loess altered by red leached palaeosol Formation de Roumois:lacustrine and fluvial Ice wedges and cryoturbation Formation de Fourmetot: lacustrine and fluvial Pierrepont Formation and Boscq d'Aubigny: marine, preserved in basin downwarped by tectonics in Cotentin La Londe clays: estuarine: 100m above present
	2550	PLIOCENE		TEMPERATE	Lenham Beds, in Kent, O D +183m ?Clay-with-flints started to develop	Marine conditions over most of English Channel Dover Strait not in existence	Saint-Eustache Sands: marine. 120/130m above present Maximum transgression

770 (between Middle and Early Pleistocene boundary)

Figure 60 Quaternary history of the English Channel region after Gallois (1965), Edmonds et al. (1975), Keen (1978), Melville and Freshney (1982) and Lautridou et al. (1986). Absolute ages and marine oxygen-isotope stages taken from Shotton (1986), Sibrava (1986) and Bowen et al. (1986). Odd- and even-numbered stages refer respectively to warm and cold maxima.

Meuse flowed through the report area (Zagwijn, 1974; Oele and Schüttenhelm, 1979), and rivers draining southern England cut overdeepened valleys which extended well inland of the present coastline. Most of the sediments infilling the palaeovalleys date from the late Devensian and early Flandrian, when rising sea levels first laid down estuarine deposits, and then marine sediments as the transgression proceeded.

At the start of the Holocene, sea level stood at about 65 m below OD (Jelgersma, 1979); later stages in the transgression can be elucidated from coastal deposits and peat formed in drowned valleys in south-east England (Shephard-Thorn, 1975). The oldest are preserved at 23/28 m below OD and were formed from 10 to 8 ka; those aged 6 to 3 ka are preserved at 9 below to 3 m above OD; and sediments aged 3 to 1.5 ka are also found at about 3 m above OD. Similar results were obtained from the estuary of the River Seine (Huault et al., 1975) and from Fawley on The Solent (Godwin and Switzur, 1966). The maximum incision recorded at Southampton Water is 24.4 m below OD (Curry et al., 1968). There was a slowing down of the rate of transgression at about 6 ka, and a possible stillstand between c.4.5 and 3 ka (Devoy, 1982). The rise in sea level was not however continuous, and there were temporary reversals (West 1972); there is some evidence that during the last 6 ka, sea level has varied between ±4 m on several occasions (Guilcher, 1969). However, Heyworth and Kidson (1982) found no evidence of sea levels above OD; they compared sea-level curves for the Bristol Channel, English Channel and Cardigan Bay, and concluded that the changes are eustatic, with no isostatic effects apparent.

PALAEOVALLEYS

Examination of the bathymetry map (Figure 4) shows three major valleys cut into the floor of the English Channel: the Lobourg Channel in the Dover Strait, St Catherine's Deep south of the Isle of Wight, and the Northern Palaeovalley (A J Smith, 1985) which falls south-westward into the Hurd Deep (Evans, 1990). However, shallow-seismic surveys also reveal infilled palaeovalleys (Figures 61 and 62); such valleys were reported following investigations for the Channel Tunnel in the Dover Strait (Destombes and Shephard-Thorn, 1971; Destombes et al., 1975) where they are eroded down to about 170 m below OD. The largest of these was named the Fosse Dangeard (Figure 62). Dingwall (1975) recorded narrow, steep-sided infilled channels north of Cherbourg, and Dyer (1975) proved another within the East Solent.

Surveys by university teams have led to the production of maps of the eastern English Channel showing bedrock contours, thickness of palaeovalley infill sediment, and thickness of the overlying Holocene mobile sediments (Auffret and Alduc, 1977; Auffret et al., 1980; Larsonneur et al., 1982a). Further surveys by BGS led to more detailed maps (Dungeness-Boulogne and Wight Quaternary Geology and Sea-bed Sediment, sheets; Hamblin and Harrison, 1990).

Generalised syntheses are reproduced in Figures 61, 62 and 63. Figures 61 and 62 are not continued west of 2°10′W, for apart from the nearshore zone off south Devon (Figure 64), no palaeovalleys are known in the western part of the report area, and the rockhead contours would be indistinguishable from isobaths (Figure 4).

The processes involved in the excavation of the palaeovalleys have been the subject of many theories. Dingwall (1975) proposed a fluvial origin for those north of the Cotentin Peninsula, possibly initiated as early as the Miocene and rejuvenated during successive Pleistocene marine regressions. Auffret et al. (1980) similarly considered the palaeovalley system to be of fluvial origin, pointing out the links between the majority of the palaeovalleys and present-day rivers. They explain overdeepened sections by the interplay between strong currents in shallow water and the outcrop of easily eroded strata.

A J Smith (1985; 1989) invoked a catastrophic origin for the palaeovalley system as a whole, with an ice-dammed lake in the southern North Sea overflowing a Chalk barrier across the Dover Strait. The flood waters spread out to cut the palaeovalley system, then recombined with renewed vigour to excavate the Hurd Deep.

Destombes et al. (1975) proposed a subglacial tunnel-valley origin for palaeovalleys in the Dover Strait, with glacial scouring cutting the Northern Palaeovalley during the Wolstonian. They thus followed Kellaway et al. (1975) in proposing a Wolstonian glaciation in the eastern English Channel, for Kellaway et al. (1975) considered the Clay-with-flints of southern England to be a decalcified till associated with this glaciation. However, the Clay-with-flints is now generally accepted as a largely in-situ weathering product (Catt, 1986), and no authenticated erratics are recorded from it (E R Shephard-Thorn, oral communication, 1990). Landforms attributed by Kellaway et al. (1975) to glacial scour have alternatively been attributed to marine erosion (Kidson and Bowen, 1976).

Wingfield (1989; 1990) invoked a Devensian ice sheet in the western English Channel to explain the Hurd Deep and St Catherine's Deep by outbursts from englacial lakes. However, it is difficult to accept that a glaciation could have occurred in the area so recently without leaving more evidence (Hamblin et al., 1990; 1991). Wingfield (1990) considers the Fosse Dangeard to have formed during the Elsterian by a similar outburst from an ice sheet covering Kent, although no evidence was put forward for the latter, and erratics appear completely absent from that area south of Sandwich (Catt, 1986).

Theories involving glaciation of the English Channel have not gained wide acceptance (Oele and Schüttenhelm, 1979), and BGS surveys of the southern North Sea and English Channel have yielded no evidence of ice extending south of the traditionally accepted limits in the southern North Sea (Bowen et al., 1986). It would appear most likely that the palaeovalley network comprises a complex fluvial system, locally modified by marine processes.

Infilled palaeovalleys north of the Northern Palaeovalley

From the Dover Strait westward almost to Selsey Bill, a large number of small channels have been identified (Figure 62) which, from their dendritic nature, are clearly of fluvial origin. Offshore extensions of the courses of the rivers Adur and Ouse can be detected, and seismic profiles across the offshore continuation of the Adur show two terrace surfaces and a deep, narrow, central channel. Other palaeovalleys generally have uneven cross-sections, and it is not clear whether the

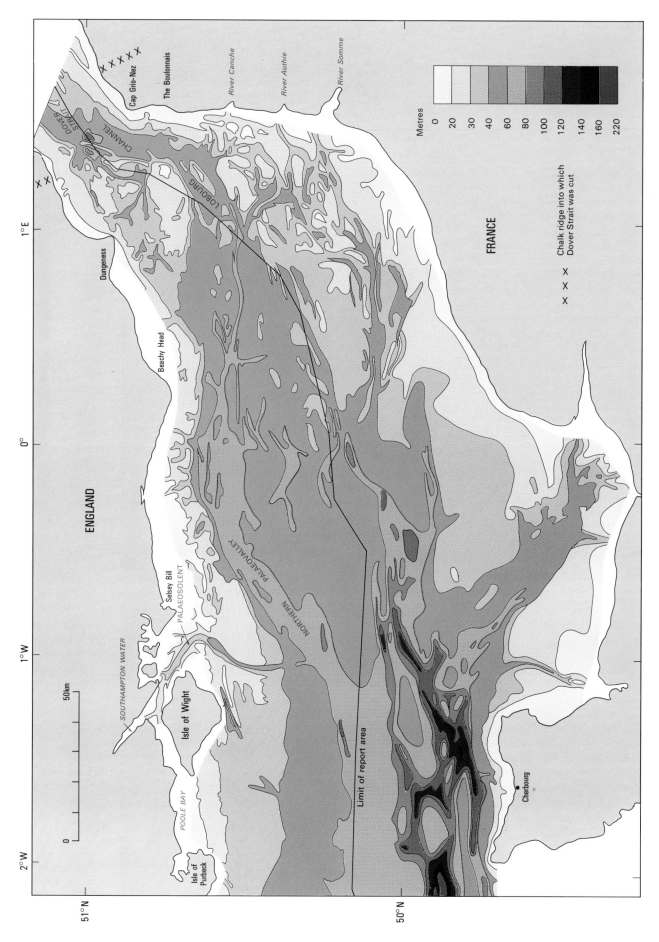

Figure 61 Rockhead contours (depth to base of Quaternary below sea level) in the English Channel region.

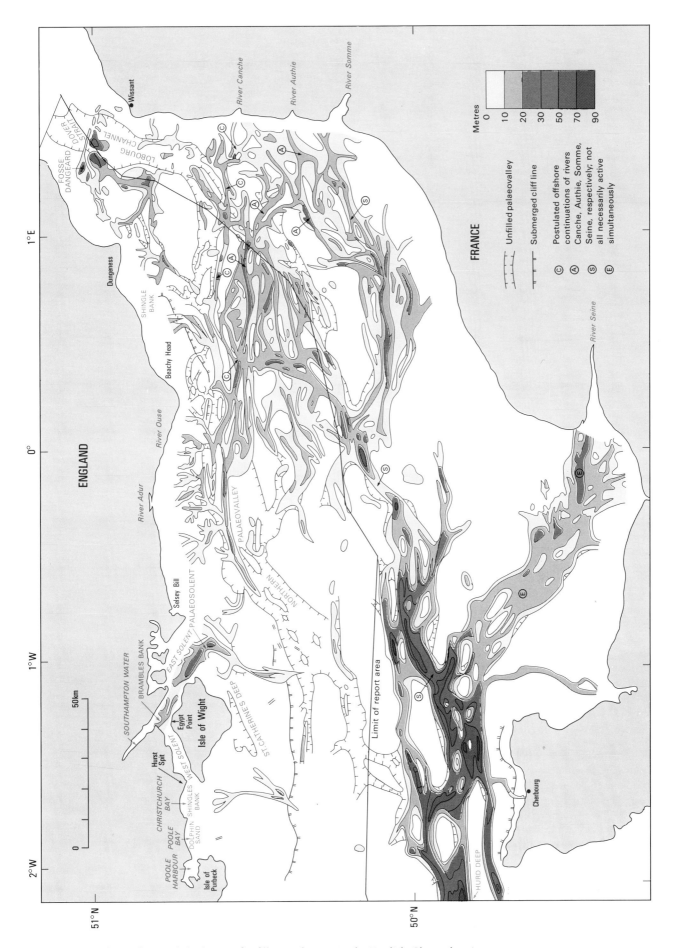

Figure 62 Palaeovalleys and thickness of infilling sediment in the English Channel region.

79

two terraces and central channel of the offshore Adur represent erosion during three separate periods.

Vibrocores sited in these channels west of Beachy Head proved soft, grey clays, silts and sands that are locally finely laminated; they include scattered pebbles, shells, organic bands and specks, and a peat band. It is suggested that these represent an estuarine sequence formed at a time of rising sea levels in the late Devensian and early Holocene, at the end of the last glaciation. The softness of the sediments would appear to preclude their dating from an earlier transgression, since they would have become hardened on drying out. However, the base of the deposit was not penetrated, and earlier generations of sediment may be preserved at depth.

West of Selsey Bill, the Palaeosolent (Figures 61 and 62) is the offshore continuation of the rivers that feed Southampton Water. Within the East Solent is a partly infilled, north-westerly orientated palaeovalley incised to at least 46 m below OD, with a complex infill that includes gravel layers which cause difficulty in the interpretation of seismic records (Dyer, 1972; 1975). Terraces on the sides of the valleys appear to correlate with similar features in Southampton Water. More recent BGS seismic surveys have demonstrated that the Palaeosolent continues south-south-westwards to join the Northern Palaeovalley; two vibrocores from the Palaeosolent recovered olive-grey and yellowish brown, well-sorted, pebbly, quartz sand.

West of the Isle of Wight, another system of infilled palaeovalleys (Figure 62) also appears to be a dendritic fluvial system (Hamblin and Harrison, 1990); one of the branches may have drained from the West Solent, although Dyer (1975) found no buried channel there. Vibrocores in this palaeovalley system proved soft, finely bedded sediments similar to those east of Selsey Bill, including another peat bed. It is likely that the sediments had a similar estuarine origin at the end of the last glaciation.

St Catherine's Deep (Figure 62) is a bathymetric feature that extends some 60 m below the surrounding sea bed, with almost no sediment infill. Its most likely mode of origin is tidal scour during successive marine advances, for it lies in an area of strong tidal currents which would be expected to have been stronger when sea level was lower. Nevertheless, it may represent overdeepening of a pre-existing river valley, for its south-western end is aligned with a branch of an infilled fluvial palaeovalley. It is reasonable to expect that a river would have developed along the line of the deep, since it follows an outcrop of soft Lower Cretaceous strata immediately north of the Chalk.

An almost north–south-orientated buried channel off the coast of east Devon (Clarke, 1970) is believed to connect with overdeepened channels in the estuaries of the Exe and the Teign (Durrance, 1969; 1971). Pollen analyses of intertidal muds deposited along the margins of this channel, and now lying at 16.7 to 42.7 m below sea level, indicate a Flandrian age, and a peat sample gave a radiometric age of 8589 + 830 - 755 years BP. The sediments are interpreted as indicating salt-marsh, mud-flat, coastal-lagoon and nonmarine, perhaps lacustrine environments. All the sediments recorded by Clarke (1970) are included here as sea-bed sediment on Figure 63, since he does not distinguish palaeovalley deposits from sea-bed sediments.

Farther south in Start Bay (Figure 63), Kelland and Hails (1972) recorded eight infilled valleys which they considered to be extensions of present-day valley systems. These were 100 to 450 m wide, up to 30 m deep in the case of the River Dart, and filled with clay, sand and gravel.

The Northern Palaeovalley, Lobourg Channel and Fosse Dangeard

On the bathymetry map (Figure 4), the Northern Palaeovalley and Lobourg Channel appear to be separate, but the rockhead contour map (Figure 61) shows them to be a continuous feature. This system differs from the other palaeovalleys by its great size, its very limited infill except for mobile sandbanks, and its broad, flat-bottomed shape.

From west of Dungeness to the Palaeosolent, the Northern Palaeovalley is joined from the north by a number of tributaries, so it would appear to constitute an early element in the fluvial drainage of the area, possibly dating back to the first drying out of the English Channel during the Cromerian or Anglian. An infilled palaeovalley cut into the bottom of the Northern Palaeovalley, and into which the continuations of the rivers Adur and Ouse fall (Figure 62), can be traced upstream to the French coast in the east, and may be the offshore continuation of the rivers Canche and Authie. However the Lobourg Channel, lying within the Dover Strait, is not easily explained as an original element of the onshore drainage since the Dover Strait, which cuts through the Chalk ridge on the north side of the Weald Anticline (Figure 61), was probably initiated by the overflow of an ice-dammed lake in the North Sea after the English Channel river system was initiated (Stamp, 1927; A J Smith, 1985; 1989). Presumably the overflow waters cut a largely new channel until they reached the existing valleys of the Canche and Authie, and then followed them to excavate the greatly enlarged Northern Palaeovalley.

Within the Dover Strait, the Fosse Dangeard (Figure 62) and two almost circular adjacent infilled 'holes' are cut to depths of up to 100 m below the sea floor. These are explained by A J Smith (1985) as plunge pools, formed as an ice-dammed lake overflowed the Chalk escarpment and cut its new channel. Certainly their position relative to the Chalk ridge (Figure 61) is in accord with this theory, and it is difficult to explain their shape and arrangement by tidal scour. The theory that they formed as tunnel valleys beneath an ice sheet extending from the North Sea (Destombes et al., 1975) accords neither with their shape nor with the orientation of the Fosse Dangeard, and there is no evidence of ice this far south. The suggestion that the Fosse Dangeard was formed by an eastward-flowing glacial lake outburst (Wingfield, 1989) would require an ice sheet in eastern Kent, which would be incompatible with the evidence of Quaternary deposits there (Shephard-Thorn, 1988). Thus it seems most likely that the 'holes' are indeed plunge pools. A further overflow channel infilled with gravels, sands and clays has been identified onshore near Wissant on the French side of the Dover Strait (Roep et al., 1975).

It seems most likely that excavation of the Dover Strait was initiated during the Anglian (Gibbard, 1988). Jenkins et al. (1986) concluded from foraminiferal studies of the St Erth Beds of Cornwall that no link was present between the English Channel and the North Sea during the Pliocene, and there is indirect biostratigraphical evidence that a barrier existed between the English Channel and the North Sea for much of the Pleistocene (Gibbard, 1988). During the early Pleistocene, the rivers of Belgium and Holland drained northward to form a huge delta in the North Sea (Zagwijn, 1979), with no suggestion of drainage southward through the Dover Strait. However, during the Anglian glaciation, a proglacial lake formed in the southern North Sea when British and Scandinavian ice sheets coalesced to block northward drainage, so that the lake overflowed southwards to cut the Dover Strait (Gibbard, 1988). The actual excavation is likely to have been quite rapid (Gibbard, 1988), but not catastrophic as suggested by Smith (1985), since the Chalk would be relatively resistant to erosion.

As the Dover Strait was cut and the col lowered, it is likely that rivers in adjacent areas of the southern North Sea, such as the Scheldt system of The Netherlands (Gibbard, 1988), took up courses through this outlet. This led to the development of a major channel by the start of the Hoxnian interglacial, when sea levels rose and the strait apparently became flooded, with marine strata deposited on the French/ Belgian coastal plain east of Wissant (Sommé, 1979; Paepe and Baeteman, 1979; Zagwijn, 1979). Archaeological evidence (Wymer, 1988) suggests that England was not isolated from the Continent during the Hoxnian, and it is possible that a land bridge extended from East Anglia to The Netherlands.

During the Wolstonian stage, glaciolacustrine sediments were again formed in the southern North Sea (Oele and Schüttenhelm, 1979), when ice advance in Holland forced rivers to flow westward (Gibbard, 1988). During this period of low sea level it is likely that the rivers Rhine, Meuse and Thames all flowed through the Dover Strait (Gibbard, 1988). The Lobourg Channel was cut as their fluvial channel within the strait.

During the Ipswichian interglacial stage, the Dover Strait was inundated once more (Oele and Schüttenhelm, 1979), and when sea levels dropped during the Devensian, the River Rhine again flowed down the Lobourg Channel, further contributing to the considerable width and depth of the feature along its entire length (Zagwijn, 1974; Jelgersma et al., 1979; Oele and Schüttenhelm, 1979). During the Holocene marine transgression the strait became submerged between 9 and 8.7 ka (Jelgersma,1979), but for a time a land barrier survived between Lincolnshire and The Netherlands, north of the outlet of the Rhine. Full marine connection between the English Channel and the North Sea was not achieved until about 8.3 ka. Peat samples collected in the Dover Strait (Callow et al., 1966) have yielded dates of 10 530±120 and 9920±120 BP at depths of 36 and 37 m below OD respectively, and peat from a borehole near Cap Gris-Nez yielded ages of 12 600±250 and 8250±300 BP (Morzadec-Kerfourn and Delibrias, 1972).

No terraces have been found in the Lobourg Channel and Northern Palaeovalley, but the limited development of infill within the main channel, including a course of the River Canche, may represent Devensian excavation. Sediments would presumably have formed during each period of emergence, but most must have been destroyed as the subsequent marine transgression advanced; the distinction between the largely empty Lobourg Channel/Northern Palaeovalley and the infilled condition of all the other fluvial features in the English Channel is considered to be one of size, the larger feature being swept clear of sediment during transgression while the sediments of the smaller channels were protected by their impounding banks.

Few boreholes have proved the infill of either the Northern Palaeovalley, Fosse Dangeard or Lobourg Channel. Of three BGS vibrocores within the Northern Palaeovalley west of Beachy Head, one proved possible estuarine sediments resembling those in the northern tributaries, and the others recovered greyish brown, quartzose sands with clay bands; these are of indeterminate origin. In the Fosse Dangeard, a borehole (Destombes et al., 1975) proved 48.8 m of laminated, alternating, pale brown silty clay and pale quartz sand beneath 10 m of marine sand with flint, greensand and limestone pebbles. This sequence rests directly upon the Gault. The lower sediments would appear to resemble those proved in vibrocores west of Beachy Head, and yielded foraminifera and pollen indicating estuarine, cold-water conditions, possibly of the Brörup interstadial (early Devensian), although this age has been disputed (Turner, in discussion of Destombes et al., 1975; Zagwijn, 1979).

Palaeovalleys south of the Northern Palaeovalley and Lobourg Channel

To the south of the Northern Palaeovalley, several palaeovalleys comprise an anastomosing network that is almost entirely infilled. Mostly they extend to less than 20 m below the sea bed, but they are relatively wide compared to the valleys in the north. Channels are locally overdeepened, with their bases 20 m or more below the sea floor; these overdeepened areas commonly coincide with the confluences of channels. The overdeepening becomes greater towards the west where the channels eventually combine with the Northern Palaeovalley to join the Hurd Deep (Evans, 1990).

The form of the palaeovalley network (Figure 62) indicates a braided-river system, and the deeper channels within it represent the offshore continuations of rivers known onshore. The courses of the rivers Seine and Somme can be clearly seen, joining east of Cherbourg. Two possible courses of the River Authie can be detected, one flowing west-north-west to join the Canche, and the second running west-south-west to merge with the Somme; possibly both have been occupied at different times. There is no direct evidence of the age of the network, and possibly it has been occupied during several regressions.

The change from individual channels to a braided system is indicative of a relatively rapid increase in water flow, the quantity of water becoming too great to be constrained within existing channels and overflowing to form the anastomosing pattern. This is unlikely to relate to the overflow of the Dover Strait, as suggested by A J Smith (1985), since the braided streams can be traced back to the French coast and connect with pre-existing rivers. More likely it reflects greatly increased runoff from northern France as periglacial conditions waned at the end of the glacial period. It is notable that braided streams did not develop on the north side of the English Channel; this may be because the catchment area of the streams in the north was too small to overload the streams, or because being farther north the catchment area did not thaw significantly before sea level had risen and drowned the river valleys.

Some overdeepened areas within the fluvial system may be formed by fluvial excavation, as in the River Thames (Berry, 1979), where overdeepened areas up to 30 m deep at the confluence of streams are accredited to the scouring of frozen ground at times of high runoff during climatic warming. However, the extreme overdeepening at the western end of the Seine/Somme complex and in the Hurd Deep (Evans, 1990) requires an alternative process; tidal scour during marine transgression may be the most likely (Hamilton and Smith, 1972; Hamblin et al., 1990; 1991). The deepest incision (from the erosional base to the level of the surrounding sea bed) observed in the English Channel is 200 m in the Hurd Deep; this is not considered excessive for a tidal scour hollow (Mogi, 1979; Belderson et al., 1982).

SEA-BED SEDIMENTS

Figure 63 classifies the grain size of the sea-bed sediment in the area; it is largely based on samples taken with a Shipek grab, which scoops the top 15 cm or so of sediment. South of the median line, the map is partly based on French data

(Larsonneur et al., 1979).

The sediments as a whole demonstrate two dominant size ranges of lithoclasts (Larsonneur et al., 1982b), the coarser of which (10–60 mm) comprises lithic fragments, dominantly of flint. The finer fraction (0.15–0.5 mm) is largely mature quartz showing evidence of aeolian and aquatic weathering, with immature quartz abundant only in French nearshore zones subjected to recent littoral erosion. Garnet, epidote, tourmaline, hornblende and zircon dominate the heavy-mineral associations. Muddy sediments are rare, with the clay assemblage dominated by illite and kaolinite; montmorillonite is present in the east.

The sea-bed sediment can be divided into two categories. A coarse lag deposit that is not mobile in the present tidal-current regime occurs over almost the entire area; it was formed by the winnowing away of fine-grained material to leave a relatively coarse residual sediment. The lag is locally overlain by a suite of finer-grained sediments, including major sandbanks which are mobile under the present current regime.

Figure 64 shows the thickness of sea-bed sediment. Comparing Figures 63 and 64, it can be seen that most of the area is underlain by thin lag deposit comprising gravels and sandy gravels which locally, and particularly in the east and west, is overlain by a greater, but variable thickness of mobile sediment comprising sand, muddy sand and gravelly sand. There is almost no relationship between the thickness of palaeovalley infill sediments (Figure 62) and that of sea-bed sediment as defined here, except in some areas between 0° and 2°W where there is local thickening of the sea-bed sediment over infilled channels. Where sea-bed sediment of significant thickness overlies palaeovalley infill sediment, the junction can usually be identified as a seismic reflector.

The lag deposit

The lag covers the entire area apart from small zones of rock outcrop (Figure 63). Its maximum grain size reflects local tidal velocities at the time of formation, but its sand:gravel ratio has been modified by current winnowing since formation. Gravels and sandy gravels present over most of the area result from winnowing by high-velocity currents, whereas gravelly sands occur where winnowing has been less intense because current velocities were lower. The deposits of gravel are almost all thinner than 0.5 m (Figure 64), but are locally thicker where they rest upon palaeovalley infill sediment, or where they are associated with a submerged cliffline (Figure 62), as at Shingle Bank off Hastings and in an east–west strip south of the Isle of Wight. Hamblin and Harrison (1990) demonstrated that in the vicinity of the Isle of Wight, the gravel fraction of the deposit coarsens away from the coast from fine-pebble gravel to coarse-pebble and cobble gravel.

Locally, loose blocks of boulder size are found which have probably not moved from their original position in the bedrock. A block of glauconitic sandstone 83 cm long was recovered from the Lower Greensand outcrop south of the Isle of Wight (Hamblin and Harrison, 1990), and site investigation work at Royal Sovereign Shoals (Higginbottom, 1973) revealed boulders of sideritic, chamosite-oolite ironstone from the Wealden outcrop.

Dickson and Lee (1973) demonstrated that the lag deposits are not presently mobile; in July 1971 they dredged a pit 3.5 m deep through sandy gravel at Shingle Bank, and this was not infilled at all over the winter before it was re-examined in May 1972. The lack of mobility of the megaclasts has been further confirmed throughout the area by the presence of encrusting serpulids, bryozoa and barnacles on only one side of the clasts, demonstrating that they do not change orientation. The deposit was formed as a transgressive beach and shallow-water deposit at the end of the last glaciation. Thus it is largely of early Holocene age, but late Devensian where found in water depths greater than about 50 m.

Where the lag deposit comprises gravels and sandy gravels, the sand fraction is generally coarse grained (0.5–1.0 mm), with patches of very coarse sand (1–2 mm) both in the Dover Strait and south of the Isle of Wight (Figure 65). This testifies to the winnowed nature of the deposit. The sand fraction of the gravels and sandy gravels is however classified as poorly or moderately sorted (Figure 66), when a highly winnowed deposit might be expected to become well sorted. Possibly the degree of sorting has been reduced by the addition of shell debris broken down by the strong current action and reduced to sand-fraction size; certainly the sand fractions of the gravels and sandy gravels have high carbonate contents (Figure 67). Where the lag deposit comprises less-intensively winnowed gravelly sands, the sand fraction is well sorted and medium grained (0.5–0.25 mm), with a low carbonate content. The mud content of the lag deposit is almost everywhere very low; where it is significant, the sediment has incorporated mud from underlying strata.

The megaclasts are everywhere dominated by flints; these include fresh, little-worn flints derived directly from the Chalk and retaining their white patinas and black hearts, as well as brown, worn flints derived via Tertiary gravels. Both varieties may be derived by sea-bed or cliff erosion during transgression, by further cliff erosion during the Holocene adding to the deposit nearshore, or by fluvial transport during Pleistocene regressions. Hamblin and Harrison (1990) found brown or brownish grey, rounded flints overlying the Tertiary outcrop south-east of the Isle of Wight, and white-patinated, black-hearted, angular to subangular flints on the Chalk outcrop south of the Isle of Wight and off Beachy Head. The Chalk-derived flints are generally more common on the Chalk outcrop than elsewhere, so it is likely that they are largely derived from sea-bed and cliff erosion during transgression.

Apart from flints, other locally derived rock types are important components of the gravel fraction. Hamblin and Harrison (1990) found that chalk clasts constitute up to 80 per cent of the gravel fraction of sediment overlying the Chalk outcrop south of the Isle of Wight and off Beachy Head. Gravels overlying the Lower Cretaceous outcrops south-west and south-east of the Isle of Wight contain locally derived sandstone, mudstone, ironstone, shelly limestone and grey chert, although flint is dominant. There is little evidence of rocks other than flint being introduced to the area by fluvial transport.

An interesting minor constituent of the deposit is a suite of igneous and metamorphic rocks of westerly provenance, including aplitic granites that resemble those of Porthleven, Cornwall (Strong, 1987). Hamblin and Harrison (1990) record these rocks making up less than 5 per cent of the gravel fraction of the lag deposit. A study of heavy minerals of sand grade (Morton, 1989) has shown tourmaline common as far east as the Isle of Wight. Erratics at Chesil Beach (Arkell, 1947) are dominated by quartzite, porphyry and granite from Devon, and Dangeard (1929) recovered igneous and metamorphic rocks from the whole length of the English Channel, although they are much less abundant east of 2°W. Martin (1841, p. 161) recorded that off Ramsgate the fishermen were 'impeded by masses of granite, serpentine, sandstone, slate ...'. These larger clasts have most likely been introduced into the area by floating ice, as is the case of the erratic boulders which underlie the Ipswichian raised beach.

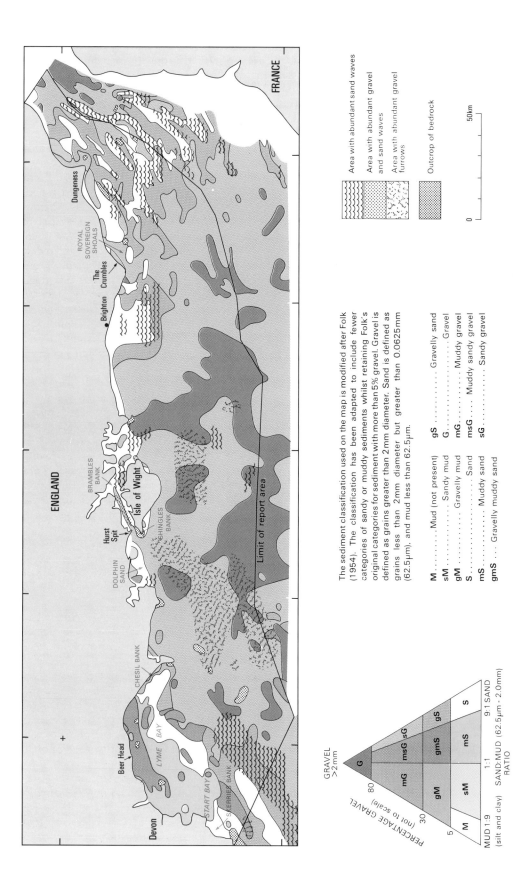

The sediment classification used on the map is modified after Folk (1954). The classification has been adapted to include fewer categories of sandy or muddy sediments whilst retaining Folk's original categories for sediment with more than 5% gravel. Gravel is defined as grains greater than 2mm diameter. Sand is defined as grains less than 2mm diameter but greater than 0.0625mm (62.5μm), and mud less than 62.5μm.

M........Mud (not present)   gS .... Gravelly sand
sM .... Sandy mud   G............... Gravel
gM .... Gravelly mud   mG........... Muddy gravel
S .... Sand   msG .... Muddy sandy gravel
mS .... Muddy sand   sG .... Sandy gravel
gmS ... Gravelly muddy sand

Area with abundant sand waves
Area with abundant gravel and sand waves
Area with abundant gravel furrows
Outcrop of bedrock

0   50km

Figure 63 Sea-bed sediments of the English Channel. Sediment classification modified from Folk (1954).

83

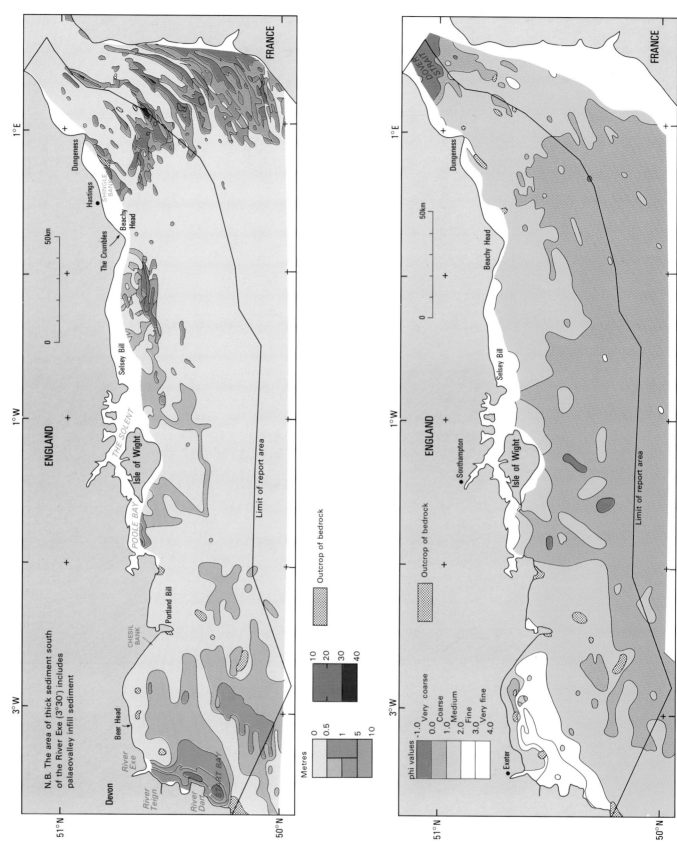

Figure 64 Thickness of sea-bed sediments.

Figure 65 Mean grain size of the sand fraction in sea-bed sediments.

84

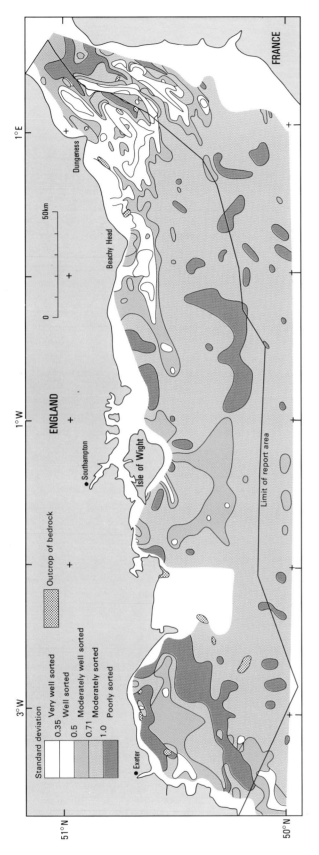

Figure 66 Sorting of the sand fraction in sea-bed sediments.

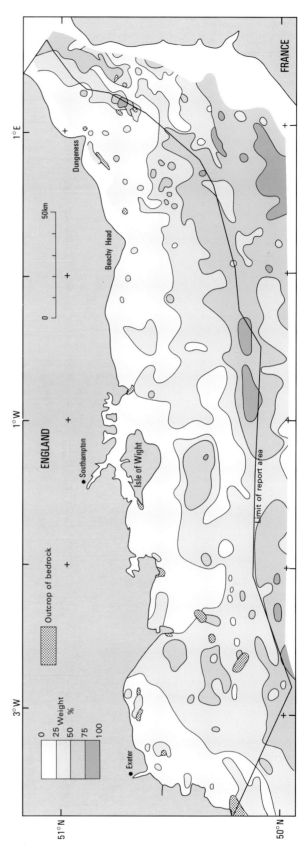

Figure 67 Carbonate content of the sand fraction in sea-bed sediments.

Mobile sea-bed sediments

Mobile sediments locally overlie the lag deposit, and are thickest off the coast of Devon, immediately south-west of the Dover Strait, and in the coastal zone from Beachy Head to Poole Bay, including The Solent (Figure 64). They have been formed since the early Holocene transgression and are in equilibrium with the present-day current regime. They are very largely mature sands, dominated by well-rounded quartz grains with a little feldspar, mica and heavy minerals. The varied sources of sand include sea-bed and cliff erosion during transgression, later cliff erosion, sea-bed winnowing up to the present day, and fluvial transport, particularly during Pleistocene periglacial conditions. Contemporary fluvial input is limited, partly because terrestrial erosion is reduced during periods of temperate climate, but mainly because all the largest rivers have drowned estuaries where they deposit all but the finest sediment. The largest river entering the area is the Seine, which transports 500 000 to 1 000 000 tonnes of sediment per year, but deposits most of it in its estuary (Avione et al., 1981). Sufficient silt and clay is present in suspension in the English Channel to make the waters cloudy and hamper bottom photography (Curry, 1989), but this remains in suspension to be transported out of the area.

The thickest mobile sediment bodies are the tidal sand ridges in the Dover Strait (Figure 4); these are major sand bodies formed by tidal currents. They are up to 18 km in length and generally range between 5 and 20 m in thickness, although maxima of almost 50 m are known. The ridges are characterised by well-sorted or very well-sorted, medium-grained sand of low carbonate content (<25 per cent); the grain sizes plot at the finer end of the medium-sand range. Fine-grained sands are restricted to the nearshore zone either side of Dungeness, where the fineness reflects that of the underlying Lower Cretaceous strata from which the sand is derived. East of the Isle of Wight there are several sand bodies up to 5 m thick, and off Brighton a tidal sand ridge up to 30 m thick was found in 50 m of water. The latter is composed of black, sulphide-rich, medium- to coarse-grained, shelly, very well-sorted sand that is oxidised to a pale or medium brown at the surface.

Recent sedimentation in The Solent and Southampton Water has been studied by Dyer (1970a; 1971; 1972). In the West Solent, the sea bed is covered with waves of sand and sandy gravel (Figure 63) in which the sands have a low shell content. Dune asymmetry and sediment distribution indicate eastward transport, with the sea bed being eroded at the western end. Brambles Bank at the junction of the East and West Solent is composed of medium-grained sand, whereas sands and muds dominate in Southampton Water and the East Solent, where the shell content is higher. Coastal erosion of the Isle of Wight and Selsey Bill is the main source of sediment which, as a whole, present a bimodal population of flint gravel and medium-grained quartz sand.

Christchurch and Poole bays have been cut by rapid wave erosion since the Flandrian transgression breached the Chalk ridge between the Isle of Wight and the Isle of Purbeck (Dyer, 1972). The sands released from soft Tertiary strata and gravels derived from Quaternary plateau gravels form Hurst Spit, Shingles Bank and Dolphin Sand (Figure 63); the latter is about 9 km long, 3 km wide, and 9 m high (Stride et al., 1972). The sediments in the bays are sands, sandy gravels and gravels, with some silt in samples from the southern part of Christchurch Bay (Dyer, 1970b), and sandy mud, muddy sand and muddy sandy gravel nearshore (Figure 63). The sands are fine to medium grained, moderately to well sorted, with carbonate contents up to around 5 per cent.

The mainly fine-grained, grey-black, shelly sand of Lyme Bay thickens towards the centre of the bay (Dingwall, 1969). Off south-east Devon, Clarke (1970) recorded an extensive deposit of muddy sand (Figure 63) resting unconformably upon intertidal gravel, and itself becoming gravelly in the north. He considered this sand to have formed diachronously as a series of sublittoral sand bodies during the Flandrian as the sea transgressed at about 7.6 m per year. It is moderately to well sorted, very fine to fine grained and coarsens downward. Much of the quartz has a red haematite coating, indicating derivation from the Permo-Triassic; the lithic grains include granite, slate, mica schist and volcanic rocks. The carbonate content is low, but increases downward to a coarse-grained, shelly, basal deposit.

In Start Bay, Kelland and Hails (1972) and Hails (1975) distinguished barrier, bay, and bank deposits. The barrier deposit is a beach shingle that extends to 200 m beyond the low water mark, and the bay deposits that underlie the rest of the bay comprise medium- to fine-grained sand varying from 1 to 28 m in thickness. The bank deposits are coarse-grained shelly sands which overlie the bay deposits around Skerries Bank (Robinson, 1961), which is believed to have been in its present position since the later stages of the Holocene transgression.

Large shingle beaches are found at Dungeness, The Crumbles and Chesil Bank (Figure 64). Dungeness comprises about 500 shingle ridges over a width of 10 km, each ridge being thrown up when storm conditions coincided with high tide (Eddison et al., 1983). This repeated process implies massive longshore drift of shingle from the south-west. In the Eastbourne area (Jennings and Smyth, 1987), shoreward movement of sediment, rather than longshore drift, has been dominant, resulting in the formation of The Crumbles as a barrier beach that coarsens upward from silty clay to sand then gravel, reflecting Holocene accretion. Chesil Bank (Melville and Freshney, 1982) is a 29 km-long shingle bank, up to 259 m wide and 12 m high, largely composed of flint pebbles; the size of the pebbles increases eastward onshore, but in the reverse direction offshore. Arkell (1947) thought the bank originated as a bay bar, joining Portland Bill to a lost headland south of Beer Head, which had been pushed northward by advancing seas of the Flandrian transgression.

SEDIMENT TRANSPORT AND BEDFORMS

Sediment transport directions and bedforms reflect the oceanography of the English Channel (Huntley, 1980; Pingree, 1980), particularly the tidal regime, and to a lesser extent the climate of the area. Figure 68 shows the amplitude and direction of travel of the semidiurnal lunar tide (M_2), which is the most important tidal-wave constituent in the area. The tidal wave progresses up the English Channel with cotidal lines (lines of simultaneous high water) almost normal to the medial line of the channel, taking about 6.5 hours to progress from Land's End to Dover. Tidal amplitude at neap tides is half that of spring tides.

The speed of the surface tidal stream at spring tide (Figure 69) varies from less than 1 m/s in sheltered areas to more than 2 m/s within the Dover Strait and off the Cotentin Peninsula, with an extreme of 4.6 m/s in the Alderney Race off Cotentin. The strength of the tidal stream decreases with depth owing to bottom friction, so that in 100 m of water the strength 1 m from the sea floor is about half that at the surface. Sediment transport and bedform development are controlled by bottom stress (Pingree, 1980), which is a func-

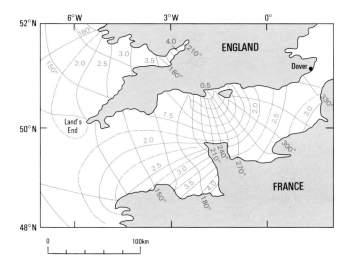

Figure 68 Amplitude (in metres) and direction of travel (in degrees) of the semidiurnal lunar tide (M_2). After Pingree (1980).

tion of tidal velocity, water depth and bottom roughness (Figure 70).

The English Channel is situated at the downwind end of one of the windier seas of the world, resulting in severe wave conditions and high average values of wave energy. The 50-year extreme wind speed drops from 68 knots along the Start–Cotentin Line to 62 knots in the Dover Strait (Draper, 1980), and the 50-year extreme wave height similarly drops from 20 m between Cotentin and Portland to less than 13 m in the Dover Strait. The significant wave height in winter at Sevenstones Light Vessel (Land's End) exceeds 2.4 m for 50 per cent of the time, compared to 0.9 m at Varne (Dover Strait). Hamilton et al. (1980) show that the waves created by a wind speed of 53 knots will lead to the entrainment of medium-grained sand at a depth of 200 m; such wind speeds are known throughout the English Channel during storms, and larger particles would be entrained in shallower water. However, the lack of a clear correlation between water depth (Figure 4) and sand grain size within the sea-bed sediment (Figure 65) suggests that wave entrainment is not as important a factor in sediment transport as tidal currents, although it may be more significant in the nearshore zone, for which data are lacking.

Present-day net sand-transport directions, as derived from bedforms, are shown in Figure 71a. A bed-load parting,

where the net effect of the ebb and flood of tidal currents is to remove material up to medium-grained sand size, runs from the Isle of Wight to the Cotentin Peninsula (Johnson et al., 1982). In the east of the report area there is a bed-load convergence (Kenyon and Stride, 1970) into which tidal currents transport material from both sides, leading to the accumulation of tidal sand ridges. It can be seen that the zones of bed-load parting and convergence coincide with the areas of maximum and minimum bottom stress respectively (Figure 70 and 71a).

The most striking bedforms in the area are the tidal sand ridges south-west of the Dover Strait (Figure 4). The nearshore banks such as Bassurelle de la Somme have a thin, stratified structure inclined from east to west, and have apparently developed as offshore bars by accretion from the west. Lapierre (1975), however, demonstrated that the tidal sand ridges farther out to sea, including Vergoyer and Bassure de Baas, have an eastward prograding structure which transverse profiles show to be asymmetric, with steeper eastern faces (Augris et al., 1987); their long axes are orientated at a small oblique angle anticlockwise to the peak tidal flow direction (Stride, 1982).

A characteristic of active tidal sand ridges, including those in this zone, is that they carry sand waves on their surface (Belderson et al., 1982). Sand waves are normally aligned perpendicular to peak tidal flow, but when associated with tidal sand ridges their orientation may be more complex (Belderson et al., 1982). The sand waves are asymmetric, with their steeper north or north-east downstream faces inclined at the angle of rest of the sediment, about 6°; upstream faces are only very slightly inclined (Augris et al., 1987). Wavelengths are within the range 100 to 480 m, with a maximum amplitude of 15 m. Megaripples with maximum wavelengths of 30 m and amplitudes up to 1 m also occur on both the sand waves and the ridges; these are similarly asymmetric and orientated normal to the current. On Bassure de Baas, the megaripples have a wavelength of less than 5 m at the bottom of the bank, increasing to 15 m toward the top (Augris et al., 1987).

South-west of the tidal sand ridges, little mobile sediment is present, although sparse bedform development reflects the steady rise in tidal current velocity towards the zone of bed-

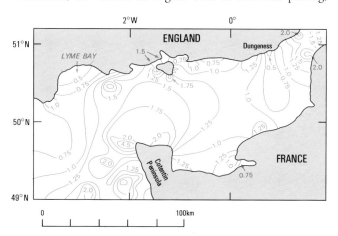

Figure 69 Contours of maximum speed of tidal streams in metres/second at mean spring tide. Adapted from Sager and Sammler (1975).

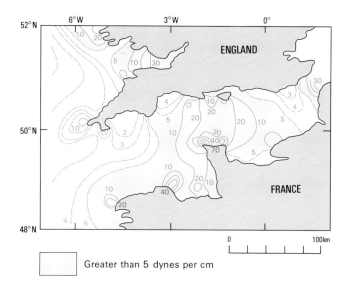

Figure 70 Mean value of the magnitude of bottom stress averaged over a tidal cycle, in dynes per cm. After Pingree (1980).

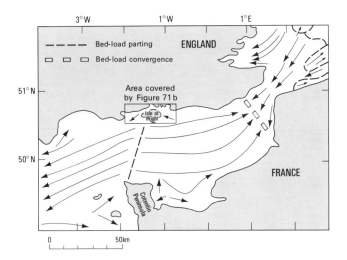

Figure 71a Net sand-transport directions in the English Channel region. After Kenyon and Stride (1970) and Johnson et al. (1982).

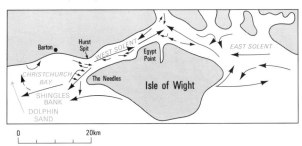

Figure 71b Net sand-transport directions in The Solent and Christchurch Bay. After Dyer (1972; 1980).

load parting. In order of increasing velocity (Kenyon, 1970; Belderson et al., 1982), these bedforms are sand waves (both in trains and as arcuate dunes), sand patches, sand ribbons, and gravel furrows.

Isolated arcuate dunes are found scattered over the exposed lag deposit, and trains of sand waves up to 7 m high were found on the tidal sand ridge south of Brighton (Figure 63). Sand patches are of variable shape and may be orientated parallel or normal to the current direction, dependent on peak tidal flow. Sand ribbons (Stride, 1963; Kenyon, 1970) are thin patches of sand less than 1 m thick, elongated parallel to the current where tidal current velocities exceed 1 m/s;

they are essentially straight, with a length:width ratio >40:1, and a width of 5 to 200 m.

Gravel furrows are found over large areas around the bed-load parting zone (Figures 63 and 71a), where conditions include tidal current velocities greater than 1.5 m/s, a shortage of sand, and a relatively smooth sea bed (Stride et al., 1972; Belderson et al., 1988). They are longitudinal erosional features parallel to the current direction, up to 9 km or more in length, and almost straight or slightly sinuous in plan. They are up to 30 m wide and 1 m deep, with steep sides, and are separated by ridges of gravel or sandy gravel some 25 m wide that have flat or rounded tops. Their relief is greatest where currents are strongest, and they converge and unite down-stream, passing into sand ribbons which themselves widen and eventually give way to arcuate dunes or fields of sinuous-crested sand waves, according to the availability of sand.

Sediment transport within The Solent is complex (Figure 71b). In the West Solent (Dyer 1971), there are both sand and gravel waves. The sand waves are up to 2 km long, typically 0.25 to 2 m in height with 5 to 18 m wavelengths but exceptionally 7 m and 120 m respectively (Dyer 1972, 1980); their asymmetry indicates movement in different directions on opposite sides of the channel. Gravel waves 1 to 2 m high with wavelengths of 10 to 20 m were reported by divers near Egypt Point (Dyer, 1971; 1980). In the East Solent, there are both small, irregular, hummocky, individual sand waves and also narrow trains of sand waves. Within Southampton Water (Dyer, 1970c; Flood, 1981), linear furrows aligned parallel to the tidal flow occur in fine-grained, cohesive, estuarine sediments; these are 0.5 to 15 m wide, up to 1 m deep and up to 4 km long, bifurcating upstream. They appear to be stable features, for they reform after dredging.

Sediment in Christchurch Bay (Dyer, 1970b) appears to be circulating in a clockwise direction (Figure 71b), with sediment originating from cliff erosion at Barton and passing into deeper water via Hurst Spit. Sand is deposited in an arcuate zone south-west of the The Needles, and moves west-ward along Dolphin Sand as a narrow, continous train of sand waves with an amplitude of about 2 m, to recirculate on to the beaches of Poole and Christchurch bays.

The pear-shaped Skerries Bank (Robinson, 1961) off Start Point (Figure 63) is a banner bank formed in the shadow of Start Point (Belderson et al. 1982). Sand-wave asymmetry demonstrates that the ebb tide is dominant on the western half of the bank within Start Bay, and the flood tide on the eastern half off Start Point. The bank has therefore grown as a result of the separation of these paths.

10   Economic geology

Aggregates (sand and gravel) are the only minerals which have been exploited from the English Channel. The search for hydrocarbons has to date been largely unsuccessful, and the coal deposits continuing the defunct Kent Coalfield offshore beneath the Dover Strait have not been investigated. However, the sea-bed data collected during the course of geological surveys have been utilised in the planning and design of telecommunications and electricity cables which have been laid across the area. Routes for gas pipelines have been investigated also, but the major construction project within the area is the Channel Tunnel.

HYDROCARBONS

Hydrocarbons in their various forms have been exploited by man in southern England since at least the Iron Age, when the oil shales of Kimmeridge Bay were burnt as fuel (Gallois, 1978). Since the 1950s, many onshore wells have been drilled in search of oil and gas, and a large number of hydrocarbon shows have been recorded. However, only a few have proved to be economic, due either to complicated structures or to variable porosities and permeabilites in the reservoirs. In 1959, the Kimmeridge 1 well (Figure 72) found oil in a fractured marine limestone of the Cornbrash (Middle Jurassic). The field began producing in 1961, since when it has yielded up to 300 barrels of oil per day (BOPD). In 1964, the Wareham 1 well produced oil from the Inferior Oolite (Middle Jurassic) and the top three metres of the Bridport Sands (Lower Jurassic). The field began production in 1970, but was later abandoned.

The Wytch Farm Oilfield was discovered by BP in 1973. The original producing horizon was the Bridport Sands, but a deeper well on the same structure found substantially more oil in the Sherwood Sandstone Group (Colter and Havard, 1981). The field is an east–west-trending tilted fault-block controlled by a fault to the south, with mainly dip closure on the other flanks. Oil production from Wytch Farm began in March 1979, and approximately 2500 BOPD were produced from the Bridport Sands during 1987. Development of the Sherwood Sandstone reservoir would increase production to 6000 BOPD.

Farther to the north-east during 1980, Carless Exploration discovered oil in an east–west-trending, dipping, faulted horst-block at Humbly Grove (Figure 72). The Humbly Grove-1 well discovered oil in the Great Oolite Limestone and Humbly Grove-2 discovered gas in a deeper Penarth Group reservoir. Development of the field started in 1985, with probable reserves in the Great Oolite of some 13 million barrels of oil, and 3000 million cubic feet of gas (Hancock and Mithen, 1987).

The Wytch Farm Oilfield lies a short distance to the north of the important Portland–Wight Faults. The oil is thought to have its source in Jurassic sequences south of this zone, which in contrast to the rocks north of the Portland–Wight Faults, are known from the Arreton-2 well on the Isle of Wight to have high source potential and to be mature. A phase of pre-Cretaceous faulting gave rise to down-to-the-south movement on the Portland–Wight Faults, resulting in deeper burial of marine source rocks in the south, and erosion

of potential Kimmeridge Clay source rocks to the north. Tertiary compression later gave rise to the northward-facing Portland–Wight monoclines along the line of the pre-existing faults; generation, migration and entrapment of oil is assumed to have occurred between the two events.

The first exploration well offshore in the English Channel was Lulworth Banks-1, drilled in 1963 by BP under an onshore licence (Figure 72). It terminated in the Bridport Sands and proved to be dry. Not until the 5th Round of Offshore Licensing in 1977 did the Department of Energy award exploration licences in the English Channel. Since then, fourteen licences have been awarded in the 7th, 9th, 11th and 12th rounds. Many of the wells drilled have proved to be dry, and many of the blocks have been wholly or partially relinquished (Figure 72).

Early in 1982, the French Government licensed six areas in the English Channel and its Western Approaches. To date only one well has been drilled in the area relevant to this report; well Nautile-1 (Figure 72) was drilled by Elf Aquitane to a depth of 1500 m, bottoming in ?Cretaceous/Jurassic.

The oil and gas discoveries made in the English Channel have all been on the Wytch Farm trend. In 1983, British Gas, looking for an offshore extension to Wytch Farm, drilled four wells in Block 98/11 (Figure 72). Well 98/11-2, just south of the Wytch Farm trend, tested gas from the Sherwood Sandstone Group at the rate of 9.6 million cubic feet per day; the other three wells encountered only minor oil or gas shows. To the east of the Wytch Farm Oilfield, BP drilled well 98/7-2 in 1987 to the north of the Portland–Wight Faults; this yielded oil from the Sherwood Sandstone Group, and was classified as a discovery. In late 1988, BP drilled three offshore appraisal wells (98/6-7, 98/6-8 and 98/6-9) between Wytch Farm and well 98/7-2. The results of these three wells strongly indicate that the productive Sherwood Sandstone Group reservoir extends eastwards towards the Isle of Wight. Tilted fault-blocks and faulted anticlines tend to be the dominant trap style.

The Bridport Sands and the Sherwood Sandstone Group therefore appear to be the two main prospective reservoirs in the area. Minor reservoirs with favourable porosity and permeability characteristics may exist in the Jurassic, particularly in the Cornbrash, Corallian and Portland beds. The Bridport Sands near to Wytch Farm are composed almost entirely of sandstone; they reach a thickness of 112 m in 98/11-2, but pass laterally into arenaceous and calcareous siltstones and shales, and are only 43 m thick in well 98/22-2 in mid-Channel. This makes it unlikely that the Bridport Sands will prove to be a good reservoir any great distance away from the known oil and gas discoveries. The Sherwood Sandstone Group (Figure 27) forms the deeper productive horizon both at Wytch Farm and in wells 98/6-8 and 98/7-2; it thins southwards from 146 m in 98/11-1 to 65 m in 98/22-2 in mid-Channel, and also thins rapidly eastwards where it is 47 m thick in 99/18-1, 17 m in 99/16-1 and is missing from well 99/12-1. The reservoir quality also deteriorates rapidly away from the area of the discoveries, for the formation passes laterally into silty, clayey and conglomeratic beds.

The lower and upper Lias clays, the Oxford Clay and the Kimmeridge Clay possess the greatest potential for sourcing hydrocarbons in the English Channel, the Lias clays being the

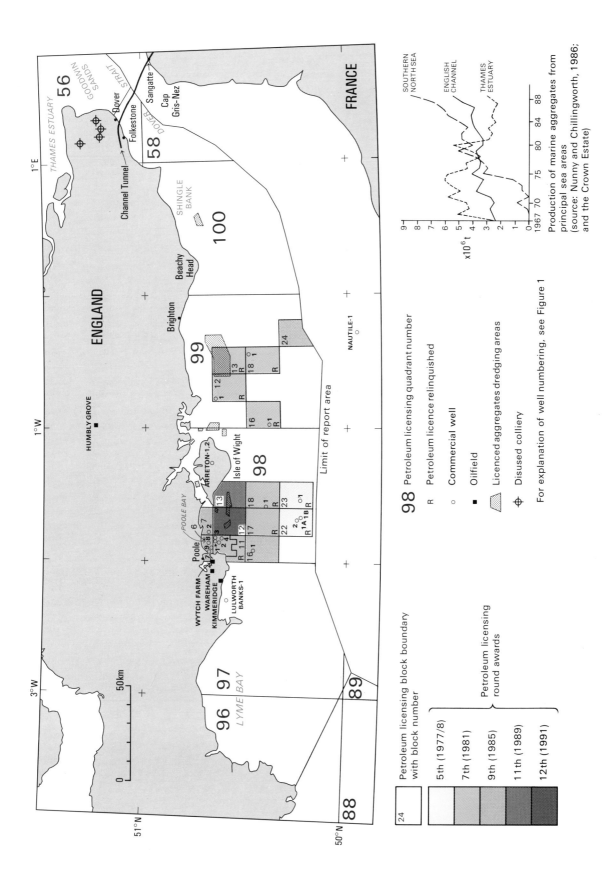

Figure 72 Location of aggregate dredging and petroleum licences, oil wells, collieries and the Channel Tunnel.

most likely primary sources. The maturity of the clays is highly variable; they are only locally mature, with maximum maturity attained in the axial parts of the Central English Channel Basin, an area largely unaffected by late-Cimmerian uplift and erosion. Major hydrocarbon generation and migration probably occurred in mid- to Late Cretaceous times, when the Lias of the Central English Channel Basin was buried some 1000 m deeper than the Sherwood Sandstone Group of the Wytch Farm trend. This enabled accumulation in the post late-Cimmerian structures, and allowed traps in the Sherwood Sandstone Group and higher reservoirs to be filled.

Seals to the major reservoirs are provided by the Mercia Mudstone Group for the Sherwood Sandstone Group, and by the Fuller's Earth for the Bridport Sands. Jurassic clays would provide seals for other possible Jurassic reservoirs.

AGGREGATES

Marine dredged aggregates are an important industry on the south coast of England. Throughout England and Wales, an annual offshore production of over 20 million tonnes satisfies about 16 per cent of sand and gravel requirements, but in London and south-east England, 11 million tonnes provides 35 per cent of the regions' needs. This quantity is derived from the English Channel, the Thames Estuary and the southern North Sea (Figure 72); the English Channel is likely to assume greater importance as the Thames Estuary becomes worked out. Part of the English Channel production is used in south-west England.

Currently licensed dredging areas (Figure 72) are situated on gravel deposits whose existence has been known for some time. Licences are not generally issued for areas of water shallower than about 20 m because of coastal erosion problems, and dredging in excess of 50 m of water is not currently economic. In recognition of the importance of the offshore aggregates industry, the Crown Estate and the Department of the Environment commissioned BGS to carry out resource studies including a survey of part of the English Channel

from Poole to Beachy Head (Hamblin and Harrison, 1989; 1990).

The deposit of most economic value is the gravel or sandy gravel of the Quaternary lag deposit (Figure 63). However, this is practical to work only where thicker than about 0.5 m (Figure 64), largely where the deposit overlies palaeovalley infill, particularly the Palaeosolent, or where it is banked up against a submerged cliffline, as at Shingle Bank (Figure 72). The nature of the pebbles within the deposit is significant, and has been found to be closely related to the underlying solid geology (Hamblin and Harrison, 1990). South of the Isle of Wight, the lag deposit overlying the Lower Cretaceous outcrops (Figure 2) contains, on average, 25 per cent of sandstone, although values range between 5 and 80 per cent; these may include tabular clasts up to boulder size. The intervening offshore outcrop of Chalk is overlain by a lag deposit incorporating 60 to 80 per cent of chalk clasts. Both the Lower Cretaceous sandstone and the chalk pebbles are rather soft for use as aggregate. However, the Tertiary outcrop extending south-eastward from the Isle of Wight is overlain by a much more acceptable aggregate incorporating over 80 per cent flint, generally of pebble size with only a small proportion of the pebbles larger than 32 mm.

Tidal sand ridges occur to the south-west of the Dover Strait, and also off Brighton. These are over 40 m thick (Figure 64) and composed of very well-sorted, medium-grained sand with a low carbonate content (Figures 63 and 65 to 67). All are near to the shore and could be useful for landfill; the Goodwin Sands, just to the north-east of the report area, are currently being utilised as landfill for the Folkestone Terminal of the Channel Tunnel (Jones, 1989) (Figure 72).

COAL

Beneath the Dover Strait, productive Coal Measures extending offshore from the Kent Coalfield are known to underlie the Lower Cretaceous at depths of 250 to 500 m below sea level, but no attempt has been made to investigate this potential resource. The structure of the Coal Measures takes the

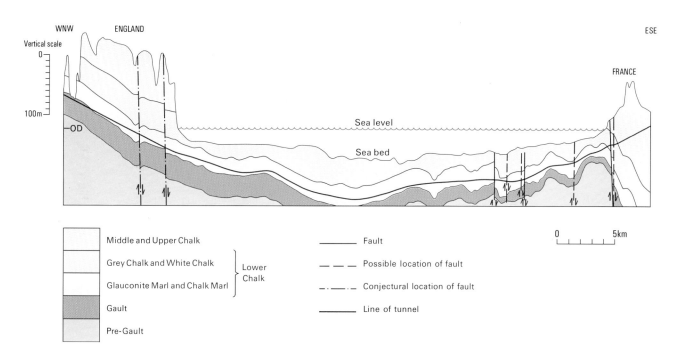

Figure 73 Cross-section along the route of the Channel Tunnel. For route see Figure 72.

form of a double synclinal trough orientated north-west to south-east and plunging to the south-east (Shephard-Thorn, 1988).

Fourteen more or less persistent seams of bituminous and semianthracitic coal are known onshore (Figure 13), although all production has now ceased in the coalfield. The coals are of fairly high rank and calorific value, with low sulphur and ash contents, but they are friable and mostly reached the pit-head as small coal. They meet the specifications for coking coal for steel making, but have most recently been used largely for electricity generation and paper making.

CHANNEL TUNNEL

Early proposals for a tunnel beneath the English Channel by Thomé de Gamond (1857) and Austin (1872) proposed the direct route from Folkestone to Cap Gris-Nez, although it was appreciated even then that this would involve passing through very varied strata ranging from the Inferior Oolite to the Lower Chalk. Topley (1872) pointed out the advantages of keeping the tunnel within the Lower Chalk, and a more northerly route was adopted. Trial headings were begun from both coasts in about 1880, but terminated in that year by decision of the British Parliament. Interest was revived after the Second World War, and an Anglo-French Channel Tunnel Study Group carried out detailed investigations for a bored tunnel in the Lower Chalk, and an alternative 'immersed tube' resting on the sea bed (Beckmann, 1960; Bruckshaw et al., 1961, Bickel, 1966; Grange and Muir Wood, 1970). The bored tunnel was chosen, and further surveys resulted in modifications to the proposed route in order to avoid weathered rock indicated by in-situ permeability tests of boreholes. After pilot tunnels were abandoned in 1974 for political and economic reasons, the project was revived by an Anglo-French agreement in 1986, and in late 1990, a historic meeting occurred between tunnellers working from the French and English sides.

Siting of the present tunnel (Figure 72) has had to take account of rail gradients, drainage, ventilation and cross-overs between the two running tunnels, while avoiding areas of weathered rock and drift-filled palaeovalleys, particularly the Fosse Dangeard. The tunnel keeps as far as possible within the basal portion of the Lower Chalk. The Lower Chalk is made up of the Glauconitic Marl which is 1 to 5 m thick, and the overlying Chalk Marl that is up to 30 m thick (Figure 73). These have a clay content of 30 to 40 per cent, which make them relatively impermeable to groundwater, easily excavated, and strong enough to stand with minimal support. It is relatively simple to keep within these strata on the English side where dips are shallow, but more difficult on the French side where dips are steeper and the strata thinner. Water-bearing fissures in the Chalk are the principal hazard during boring, and angled boreholes are driven ahead of the excavation to locate any such fissures and allow for them to be grouted where necessary.

References

References to BGS maps are not given here, but an index map showing their distribution is presented inside the back cover.

ADAMS, C J D. 1976. Geochronology of the Channel Islands and adjacent French mainland. *Journal of the Geological Society of London*, Vol. 132, 233–250.

AGER, D V, and WALLACE, P. 1966. The environmental history of the Boulonnais, France. *Proceedings of the Geologists' Association,* Vol. 77, 385–417.

ALLEN, P. 1976. Wealden of the Weald: a new model. *Proceedings of the Geologists' Association*, Vol. 86, 389–437.

—— 1981. Pursuit of Wealden models. *Journal of the Geological Society of London*, Vol. 138, 375–405.

ALLSOP, J M, and six others. 1982. Palaeogeological maps of the floors beneath two major unconformities in the Oxford–Newbury–Reading areas. *Report of the Institute of Geological Sciences*, No. 82/1, 48–51.

ANDERTON, R, BRIDGES, P H, LEEDER, M R, and SELLWOOD, B W. 1979. *A dynamic stratigraphy of the British Isles.* (London: George Allen and Unwin.)

ANDREWS, I J, and six others. 1990. *United Kingdom offshore regional report: the geology of the Moray Firth.* (London: HMSO for British Geological Survey.)

ARKELL, W J. 1933. *The Jurassic system in Great Britain.* (Oxford: Clarendon Press.)

— 1947. The geology of the country around Weymouth, Swanage, Corfe and Lulworth. *Memoir of the Geological Survey of Great Britain*, Sheets 341, 342, 343 with small portions of sheets 327, 328, 329.

— 1956. *Jurassic geology of the World.* (Edinburgh: Oliver and Boyd.)

ARTHURTON, R S. 1980. Rhythmic sedimentary sequences in the Triassic Keuper Marl (Mercia Mudstone Group) of Cheshire, northwest England. *Geological Journal*, Vol. 15, 43–58.

AUBREY, M P. 1983. Biostratigraphie du Paléogène épicontinental de L'Europe du nord-ouest. Étude fondée sur les nannofossiles calcaires. *Documents des Laboratoires de Géologie de la Faculté des Sciences de Lyon*, No. 89. [In French.]

— 1985. Northwestern European Palaeogene magnetostratigraphy, biostratigraphy and palaeogeography: calcareous nannofossil evidence. *Geology*, Vol. 202.

AUFFRET, J-P. 1973. Découverte du Bartonien en Manche orientale. *Compte Rendu Hebdomadaire des Séances de l'Académie des Sciences, Série D*, Vol. 276, 1965–1968. [In French.]

— and ALDUC, D. 1977. Ensembles sedimentaires et formes d'erosion du Quaternaire sous-marin de la Manche orientale. *Bulletin de l'Association Française pour l'Étude Quaternaire*, Vol. 14:53, 71–75. [In French.]

— — LARSONNEUR, C, and SMITH, A J. 1980. Cartographie du réseau des paléovallées et de l'épaisseur des formations superficielles meubles de la Manche orientale. *Annales de l'Institut Océanographique*, Vol. 56, 21–35. [In French.]

— BIGNOT, G, and BLONDEAU, A. 1975. Géologie du bassin Tertiaire de la Manche orientale au large du Pays de Caux. *Philosophical Transactions of the Royal Society of London,* Vol. 279A, 169–176. [In French.]

— and COLBEAUX, J-P. 1977. Étude structurale du Boulonnais et de son prolongement sous-marin en Manche orientale. *Bulletin de la Société Géologique de France*, Series 7, Vol. 19, 1047–1055. [In French.]

— and GRUAS-CAVAGNETTO, C. 1975. Les formations Paléogènes sous-marines de la Manche orientale. Données palynologiques. *Bulletin de la Société Géologique de France*, Series 7, Vol. 17, 641–655. [In French.]

— and LARSONNEUR, C. 1975. Le modele sédimentaire Manche-orientale. *9th International Congress of Sedimentology, Nice*, Subject 5, 33–39. [In French.]

AUGRIS, C, CLABAUT, P, DEWEZ, S, AUFFRET, J-P, and BECK, C. 1987. Carte des sediments superficiels au large de Boulogne-sur-Mer. (Boulogne: Ifremer.)

AUSTIN, W. 1872. *Projet de Tunnel Sous-Marin devant relier la France et tout le Continent a l'Angleterre.* (Paris: Morris Père et Fils.) [In French.]

AUTRAN, A, CASTAING, C, DEBEGLIA, N, GUILLEN, A and WEBER, C. 1986. Nouvelles contraintes geophysiques et geodynamiques pour l'interpretation de l'anomalie magnetique du bassin de Paris: hypothese d'un rift Paleozoique referme au Carbonifere. *Bulletin de la Société Géologique de France,* Series 8, Vol. 2, 125–141. [In French.]

AVEDIK, F. 1975. The seismic structure of the Western Approaches and the South Armorican continental shelf and its geological interpretation. 29–43 in *Petroleum geology and the continental shelf of North-West Europe.* WOODLAND, A W (editor). (London: Applied Science Publishers.)

AVIONE, J, ALLEN, G, NICHOLS, M, SALOMON, J C, and LARSONNEUR, C. 1981. Seaward suspended sediment dispersion from the Seine estuary, France. *Marine Geology*, Vol. 40, 119–137.

BACON, M. 1975. A gravity survey of the English Channel between Lyme Regis and St Brieuc Bay. *Philosophical Transactions of the Royal Society of London*, Vol. 279A, 69–78.

BALSON, P S. 1990. The 'Trimley Sands': a former marine Neogene deposit from Eastern England. *Tertiary Research*, Vol. 11, 145–158.

BAMFORD, D, and PRODEHL, C. 1977. Explosion seismology and the continental crust–mantle boundary. *Journal of the Geological Society of London*, Vol. 134, 139–151.

— and eight others. 1976. A lithospheric seismic profile in Britain—1. Preliminary results. *Geophysical Journal of the Royal Astronomical Society,* Vol. 44, 145–160.

BARR, D. 1987. Lithospheric stretching, detached normal faulting and footwall uplift. 75–94 *in* Continental extensional tectonics. COWARD, M P, DEWEY, J F, and HANCOCK, P C (editors). *Special Publication of the Geological Society of London*, No. 28.

BECKMANN, W C. 1960. Geophysical surveying for a Channel Tunnel. *New Scientist*, Vol. 7, 710–712.

BELDERSON, R H, JOHNSON, M A, and KENYON, N H. 1982. Bedforms. 27–57 in *Offshore tidal sands: processes and deposits.* STRIDE, A H (editor). (London: Chapman and Hall.)

— WILSON, J B, and HOLME, N A. 1988. Direct observation of longitudinal furrows in gravel and their transition with sand ribbons of strongly tidal seas. 79–90 in *Tide-influenced sedimentary environments and facies.* DE BOER, P L, VAN GELDER, A, and NIO, S D (editors). (Dordrecht: Reidel.)

BERRY, F G. 1979. Late Quaternary scour-hollows and related features in central London. *Quarterly Journal of Engineering Geology*, Vol. 12, 9–29.

BERTHOIS, L, BRENOT, R, AUFFRET, J-P, and DU BUIT, M-H. 1969. La sédimentation dans la Region de La Bassurelle (Manche orientale); étude hydraulique, bathymétrique, dynamique et granulométrique. *Travaux du Centre de Rechèrches et d'Études Océanographiques*, Vol. 8, 13–29.

BICKEL, J O. 1966. The English Channel Tunnel — geology and construction. *Engineering Geology*, Vol. 3, 65–79.

BIGNOT, E. 1972. Étude biostratigraphique des prélèvements Eocènes. *Mémoires du Bureau de Recherche Géologiques et Minières*, No. 79, 153–156. [In French.]

– 1974. Esquisse stratigraphique et paleogeographique du Tertiaire de la Haute-Normandie. *Bulletin de la Société Géologique de Normandie*, Vol. 61. [In French.]

– 1980. Sparnacien. 198–203 in Les étages Français et leurs stratotypes. CAVELIER, C, and ROGER, J (editors). *Mémoires du Bureau de Recherches Géologiques et Minières*, No. 109. [In French.]

BIRPS and ECORS. 1986. Deep seismic reflection profiling between England, France and Ireland. *Journal of the Geological Society*, Vol. 143, 45–52.

BISHOP, A C, ROACH A D, and ADAMS C J D. 1975. Precambrian rocks within the Hercynides. 102–107 in A correlation of the Precambrian rocks in the British Isles. HARRIS A L, and five others (editors). *Special Report of the Geological Society of London*, No. 6.

BLONDEAU, A. 1972. *Les nummulites*. (Paris: Vuibert.) [In French.]

BOILLOT, G, and LEFORT, J-P. 1974. Carte géologique de la Manche. 1:1 000 000 (Orléans: Bureau de Recherches Géologiques et Minières.)

BOIS, C, and six others. 1987. Crustal laminations in deep seismic profiles in France and neighbouring areas. 279–285 in Deep seismic reflection profiling of the continental lithosphere. MATTHEWS, D, and SMITH, C (editors). *Geophysical Journal of the Royal Astronomical Society*, Vol. 89.

— and six others. 1988. Contribution of deep seismic profiling to the knowledge of the lower crust in France and neighbouring areas. *Tectonophysics*, Vol. 145, 253–275.

— PINET, B, and ROURE, F. 1989. Dating lower crustal features in France and adjacent areas from deep seismic profiles. 17–31 in Properties and processes of Earth's lower crust. MEREU, R F, MUELLER, S, and FOUNTAIN, D M (editors). *Geophysical Monograph, American Geophysical Union*, No. 51/ International Union of Geodesy and Geophysics, Vol. 6.

BONE, D A. 1986. The stratigraphy of the Reading Beds (Palaeocene), at Felpham, West Sussex. *Tertiary Research*, Vol. 8, 17–32.

BOUYSSE, P, HORN, R, LAPIERRE, F, and LE LANN, F. 1976. Étude des grands bancs de sable du sud-est de la mer Celtique. *Marine Geology*, Vol. 20, 251–275. [In French.]

BOWEN, D Q, ROSE, J, and MCCABE, A M. 1986. Correlation of Quaternary glaciations in England, Ireland, Scotland and Wales. *Quaternary Science Reviews*, Vol. 5, 299–340.

— and SYKES, G A. 1988. Correlation of marine events and glaciations on the northeast Atlantic margin. *Philosophical Transactions of the Royal Society of London*, Vol. 318B, 619–635.

BREWER, J A. 1984. Clues to the deep structure of the European Variscides from crustal seismic profiling in North America. 253–263 in Variscan tectonics of the North Atlantic region. HUTTON, D H W, and SANDERSON, D J (editors). *Special Publication of the Geological Society of London*, No. 14.

BRISTOW, C R, and BAZLEY, R A. 1972. Geology of the country around Royal Tunbridge Wells. *Memoir of the Geological Survey of Great Britain*.

— FRESHNEY, E C, and PENN, I E. 1991. Geology of the country around Bournemouth. *Memoir of the British Geological Survey*, Sheet 329 (England and Wales).

— and SCRIVENER, R C. 1984. The stratigraphy and structure of the Lower New Red Sandstone of the Exeter district. *Proceedings of the Ussher Society*, Vol. 6, 68–74.

BROOKS, M, DOODY, J J, and AL-RAWI, F R J. 1984. Major crustal reflectors beneath SW England. *Journal of the Geological Society of London*, Vol. 141, 97–103.

BROWNE, B C, and COOPER, R I B. 1950. The British submarine gravity surveys of 1938 and 1946. *Philosophical Transactions of the Royal Society of London*, Vol. 242A, 243–310.

— — 1952. Gravity measurements in the English Channel. *Proceedings of the Royal Society of London*, Vol. 139B, 426.

BRUCKSHAW, J M, GOGUEL, J, HARDING, H J B, and MALCOR, R. 1961. The work of the Channel Tunnel Study Group 1958–1960. *Proceedings of the Institution of Civil Engineers*, Vol. 18, 149–178.

BUCKMAN, S S. 1893. The Bajocian of the Sherborne district: its relation to subjacent and superjacent strata. *Quarterly Journal of the Geological Society of London*, Vol. 49, 479–522.

— 1910. Certain Jurassic (Lias–Oolite) strata of South Dorset. *Quarterly Journal of the Geological Society of London*, Vol. 66, 52–89.

— 1922. Jurassic chronology: II—Preliminary studies. Certain Jurassic strata near Eypesmouth (Dorset): the Junction Bed of Watton Cliff and associated rocks. *Quarterly Journal of the Geological Society of London*. Vol. 78, 378–436.

BUTLER, D E. 1981. Marine faunas from concealed Devonian rocks of southern England and their reflection of the Frasnian transgression. *Geological Magazine*, Vol. 118, 679–697.

BUURMAN, P. 1980. Palaeosols in the Reading Beds (Paleocene) of Alum Bay, Isle of Wight, UK. *Sedimentology*, Vol. 27, 593–606.

CALLOW, W J, BAKER, M J, and HASSALL, G I. 1966. National Physical Laboratory radiocarbon measurements IV. *Radiocarbon*, Vol. 8, 340–347.

CAMERON, T D J, and six others. 1992. *United Kingdom offshore regional report: the geology of the southern North Sea*. (London: HMSO for British Geological Survey.)

CARTER, D J, and DESTOMBES, J P. 1972. Stratigraphie du Cénomanian du détroit du Pas-de-Calais. *Mémoires du Bureau de Recherches Géologiques et Minières*, No. 79, 117–121. [In French.]

CASEY, R. 1963. The dawn of the Cretaceous period in Britain. *Bulletin of the South-Eastern Union of Scientific Societies*, No. 117.

CASEY, R, 1973. The ammonite succession at the Jurassic:Cretaceous boundary in eastern England. 193–266 in The boreal Lower Cretaceous. CASEY, R. and RAWSON, P F (editors). *Geological Journal Special Issue*, No. 5.

CATT, J A. 1986. The nature, origin and geomorphological significance of clay-with-flints. 151–159 in *The scientific study of flint and chert: proceedings of the Fourth International Flint Symposium held at Brighton Polytechnic, 10–15 April 1983*. SIEVEKING, G DE G, and HART, M B (editors). (Cambridge: Cambridge University Press.)

CAZES, M, and TORREILLES, G (editors). 1988. *Étude de la croûte terrestre par sismique profonde. 1. Profil nord de la France*. (Paris: Editions Technip.) [In French.]

— and nine others. 1986. Large Variscan overthrusts beneath the Paris Basin. *Nature, London*, Vol. 323, 144–147.

CHADWICK, R A. 1986. Extension tectonics in the Wessex Basin, southern England. *Journal of the Geological Society of London*, Vol. 143, 465–488.

— KENOLTY, N, and WHITTAKER, A. 1983. Crustal structure beneath southern England from deep seismic reflection profiles. *Journal of the Geological Society of London*, Vol. 140, 893–911.

— LIVERMORE, R A, and PENN, I E. 1990. Continental extension in southern Britain and surrounding areas and its relationship to the opening of the North Atlantic Ocean. 411–424 in Extensional tectonics and stratigraphy of the North Atlantic margins. TANKARD, A J, and BALKWILL, H R (editors). *Memoir of the American Association of Petroleum Geologists*, No. 46.

— PHARAOH, T C, and SMITH, N J P. 1989. Lower crustal heterogeneity beneath Britain from deep seismic reflection data. *Journal of the Geological Society of London*, Vol. 146, 617–630.

CHEADLE, M J, McGEARY, S, WARNER, M R, and MATTHEWS, D H. 1987. Extensional structures on the western UK continental shelf: a review of evidence from deep seismic profiling. 445–465 in Continental extensional tectonics. COWARD, M, DEWEY, J F, and HANCOCK, P L (editors). *Special Publication of the Geological Society of London*, No. 28.

CLARKE, R H. 1970. Quaternary sediments off south-east Devon. *Quarterly Journal of the Geological Society of London*, Vol. 125, 277–318.

COLTER, V S, and HAVARD, D J. 1981. The Wytch Farm Oil Field, Dorset. 493–503 in *Petroleum geology of the Continental Shelf of North-West Europe*. ILLING, L V, and HOBSON, G D (editors). (London: Heyden and Son.)

COOPER, L H N. 1948. A submerged cliff near Plymouth. *Nature, London,* Vol. 161, 280.

COOPER, M A, and WILLIAMS, G D (editors). 1989. Inversion tectonics. *Special Publication of the Geological Society of London,* No. 44.

COPE, J C W. 1987. The Pre-Devonian geology of south-west England. *Proceedings of the Ussher Society*, Vol. 7, 468–473.

— GETTY, T A, HOWARTH, M K, MORTON, N and TORRENS, H S. 1980a. A correlation of Jurassic rocks in the British Isles. Part One: introduction and Lower Jurassic. *Special Report of the Geological Society of London*, No. 14.

— and five others. 1980b. A correlation of Jurassic rocks in the British Isles. Part 2: Middle and Upper Jurassic. *Special Report of the Geological Society of London*, No. 15.

CORNWELL, J D, EDWARDS, R A, ROYLES, C P, and SELF, S J. 1990. Magnetic evidence for the nature and extent of the Exeter lavas. *Proceedings of the Ussher Society*, Vol. 7, 242–245.

COSTA, L I, and MANUM, S B. 1988. The description of the inter-regional zonation of the Palaeogene (D1–D15) and Miocene (D16–D20). 321–330 in The Northwest European Tertiary Basin. VINKEN, R (compiler). *Geologisches Jahrbuch,* Vol. A100.

COTTENÇON, A, PARENT, B, and FLACELIÈRE, G. 1975. Lower Cretaceous gas-fields in Holland. 403–412 in *Petroleum and the continental shelf of North-West Europe*. WOODLAND, A W (editor). (London: Applied Science Publishers.)

COWARD, M P, and McCLAY, K R. 1983. Thrust tectonics of South Devon. *Journal of the Geological Society of London*, Vol. 140, 215–228.

COX, B M, and GALLOIS, G W. 1981. The stratigraphy of the Kimmeridge Clay of the Dorset type area and its correlation with some other Kimmeridgian sequences. *Report of the Institute of Geological Sciences*, No. 80/4. 44 pp.

CURRY, D. 1962. A Lower Tertiary outlier in the Central English Channel, with notes on the beds surrounding it. *Quarterly Journal of the Geological Society of London*, Vol. 118, 177–205.

— 1989. The rock floor of the English Channel and its significance for the interpretation of marine unconformities. *Proceedings of the Geologists' Association*, Vol. 100, 339–352.

— and six others. 1978. A correlation of Tertiary rocks in the British Isles. *Special Report of the Geological Society of London*, No. 12.

— HODSON, F, and WEST, I M. 1968. The Eocene succession in the Fawley Transmission Tunnel. *Proceedings of the Geologists' Association*, Vol. 79, 179–206.

— KING, A D, KING, C, and STINTON, F C. 1977. The Bracklesham Beds (Eocene) of Bracklesham Bay and Selsey, Sussex. *Proceedings of the Geologists' Association*, Vol. 88, 243–254.

— and SMITH, A J. 1975. New discoveries concerning the geology of the central and eastern parts of the English Channel. *Philosophical Transactions of the Royal Society of London*, Vol. 279A, 155–167.

DALEY, B. 1972 Some problems concerning the early Tertiary climate of southern Britain. *Palaeogeography, Palaeoclimatology, Palaeoecology*, Vol. 11, 77–190.

— 1973. The palaeoenvironment of the Bembridge Marls (Oligocene) of the Isle of Wight, Hampshire. *Proceedings of the Geologists' Association*, Vol. 84, 83–93.

— and EDWARDS, N. 1971. Palaeogene warping in the Isle of Wight. *Geological Magazine*, Vol. 108, 399–405.

DANGEARD, L. 1922. Contribution à l'étude géologique du fond de la Manche d'après les dragages récents du *'Pourquoi Pas?',* Lias et Eocène. *Comptes Rendus de l'Académie des Sciences, séance du 4-12-22*, 1158–1161. [In French.]

— 1923. Découverte de Nummulites en Manche orientale. *Compte Rendu Sommaire et Bulletin de la Société Géologique de France*, Series 4, Vol. 23, 191–193. [In French.]

— 1929. Observations de géologie sous-marine et d'océanographie relatives à la Manche. *Annales de l'Institut Océanographique*, Vol. 6, 1–295. [In French.]

DARTON, D M, DINGWALL, R G, and McCANN, D M. 1979. Geological and geophysical investigations in Lyme Bay. *Report of the Institute of Geological Sciences*, No. 79/10.

DAWSON, J B, CARSWELL, D A, HALL, J, and WEDEPOHL, K H (editors). 1986. The nature of the lower continental crust. *Special Publication of the Geological Society of London*, No. 24.

DAY, G A. 1986. The Hercynian evolution of the south west British continental margin. 233–241 in Reflection seismology: the continental crust. *American Geophysical Union, Geodynamics Series*, Vol. 14.

— and WILLIAMS, C A. 1970. Gravity compilation in the NE Atlantic and interpretation of gravity in the Celtic Sea. *Earth and Planetary Science Letters*, Vol. 8, 205–213.

DESTOMBES, J P, and SHEPHARD-THORN, E R. 1971. Geological results of the Channel Tunnel site investigation 1964–65. *Report of the Institute of Geological Sciences*, No. 11.

DESTOMBES, P, GAMBLE, H J, JUIGNET, P, and OWEN, H G. 1977. Cretaceous and lower Tertiary of Seine-Maritime, France: a guide to key localities. *Proceedings of the Geologists' Association*, Vol. 88, 15–38.

— SHEPHARD-THORN, E R, and REDDING, J H. 1975. A buried valley system in the Strait of Dover. *Philosophical Transactions of the Royal Society of London*, Vol. 279A, 243–256.

DEVOY, R J. 1982. Analysis of the geological evidence for Holocene sea-level movements in southeast England. *Proceedings of the Geologists' Association*, Vol. 93, 65–90.

DICKSON, R, and LEE, A. 1973. Gravel extraction: effects on seabed topography. *Offshore Services,* Vol. 6, 32–39 and 56–61.

DINELEY, D L. 1966. The Dartmouth Beds of Bigbury Bay, South Devon. *Quarterly Journal of the Geological Society of London*, Vol. 122, 187–217.

DINGWALL, R G. 1969. The geology of the central English Channel. *Nature, London*, Vol. 224, 358–359.

— 1971. The structural and stratigraphical geology of a portion of the eastern English Channel. *Report of the Institute of Geological Sciences*, No. 71/8.

— 1975. Sub-bottom infilled channels in an area of the eastern English Channel. *Philosophical Transactions of the Royal Society of London*, Vol. 279A, 233–241.

— and LOTT, G K. 1979. IGS boreholes drilled from *mv Whitethorn* in the English Channel 1973–75. *Report of the Institute of Geological Sciences*, No. 79/8.

DONATO, J A. 1988. Possible Variscan thrusting beneath the Somerton Anticline, Somerset. *Journal of the Geological Society of London*, Vol. 145, 431–438.

DONOVAN, D T. 1967. Henry Marc Brunel, the first submarine geological survey and the invention of the gravity corer. *Marine Geology*, Vol. 5, 5–14.

— and STRIDE, A H. 1961. An acoustic survey of the sea floor south of Dorset and its geological interpretation. *Philosophical Transactions of the Royal Society of London*, Vol. 244B, 299–330.

— — 1975. Three drowned coastlines of probable Late Tertiary age around Devon and Cornwall. *Marine Geology*, Vol. 19, M35–M40.

DORÉ, F. 1972. La transgression majeur du Paléozoïque inférieur dans le Nord-Est du massif Armoricain. *Bulletin de la Société Géologique de la France*, Vol. 714, 79–93. [In French.]

DRANFIELD, P, BEGG, S H, and CARTER, R R. 1987. Wytch Farm Oilfield: reservoir characteristics of the Triassic Sherwood Sandstone for input to reservoir simulation studies. 149–160 in *Petroleum geology of North West Europe*. BROOKS, J, and GLENNIE, K (editors). (London: Graham and Trotman.)

DRAPER, L. 1980. Wave climatology of the UK continental shelf. 353–368 in *The North-West European shelf seas: the sea bed in motion—II. Physical and chemical oceanography, and physical resources*. BANNER, F T, COLLINS, M B, and MASSIE, K S (editors). (Amsterdam: Elsevier.)

DRUMMOND, P V O. 1970. The Mid-Dorset Swell. Evidence of Albian–Cenomanian movements in Wessex. *Proceedings of the Geologists' Association*, Vol. 81, 679–714.

DUFF, K L. 1975. Palaeoecology of a bituminous shale—the Lower Oxford Clay of Central England. *Palaeontology*, Vol. 18, 443–482.

DURRANCE, E M. 1969. The buried channels of the Exe. *Geological Magazine*, Vol. 106, 174–189.

— 1971. The buried channel of the Teign Estuary. *Proceedings of the Ussher Society*, Vol. 2, 299–306.

— and GEORGE, M. 1976. Metatyuyamunite from the uraniferous–vanadiferous nodules in the Permian marls and sandstones of Budleigh Salterton, Devon. *Proceedings of the Ussher Society*, Vol. 3, 435–440.

— and HAMBLIN, R J O. 1969. The Cretaceous structure of Great Haldon, Devon. *Bulletin of the Geological Survey of Great Britain*, No. 30, 71–88.

— and LAMING D J C (editors). 1982. *The geology of Devon*. (Exeter: University of Exeter.)

DYER, K R. 1970a. Grain size parameters for sandy gravel. *Journal of Sedimentary Petrology*, Vol. 40, 616–620.

— 1970b. Sediment distribution in Christchurch Bay. *Journal of the Marine Biological Association of the United Kingdom*, Vol. 50, 673–682.

— 1970c. Linear erosional furrows in Southampton Water. *Nature, London*, Vol. 225, 56–58.

— 1971. The distribution and movement of sediment in the Solent, southern England. *Marine Geology*, Vol. 11, 175–187.

— 1972. Recent sedimentation in the Solent area. *Mémoires du Bureau de Recherches Géologiques et Minières*, Vol. 79, 271–280.

— 1975. The buried channels of the 'Solent River', southern England. *Proceedings of the Geologists' Association*, Vol. 86, 239–245.

— 1980. Sedimentation and sediment transport (in the Solent). *Natural Environment Research Council Publications*, Series C, Vol. 22, 20–24.

EDISON, J, CARR, A P, and JOLLIFFE, I P. 1983. Endangered coastlines of geomorphological importance. *Geographical Journal*, Vol. 149, 39–75.

EDMONDS, E A, McKEOWN, M C, and WILLIAMS M. 1975. *British regional geology: South-West England* (4th edition). (London: HMSO for British Geological Survey.)

EDWARDS, R A, DAY, G A, and LEVERIDGE, B E. 1989. Thrusts under Mount's Bay and Plymouth Bay. *Proceedings of the Ussher Society*, Vol. 7, 131–135.

— and FRESHNEY E C. 1987a. Geology of the country around Southampton. *Memoir of the British Geological Survey*, Sheet 315 (England and Wales).

— — 1987b. Lithostratigraphical classification of the Hampshire Basin Palaeogene deposits (Reading Formation to Headon Formation). *Tertiary Research*, Vol. 8, 43–73.

— and SMITH, S A. 1989. Budleigh Salterton Pebble Beds and Otter Sandstone boundary in East Devon. *British Geological Survey Technical Report*, WA/89/97.

EVANS, C D R. 1990. *United Kingdom offshore regional report: the geology of the western English Channel and its Western Approaches*. (London: HMSO for the British Geological Survey.)

FALCON, N L, and KENT, P E. 1960. Geological results of petroleum exploration in Britain 1945–1957. *Memoir of the Geological Society of London*, No. 2, 1–56.

FANNIN, N G T. 1989. Offshore investigations 1966–87. *British Geological Survey Technical Report*, WB/89/02.

FISHER, M J. 1972. The Triassic palynofloral succession in England. *Geoscience and Man*, Vol. 4, 101–109.

FISHER, O. 1862. On the Bracklesham Beds of the Isle of Wight Basin. *Quarterly Journal of the Geological Society of London*, Vol. 18, 65–94.

FLOOD, R D. 1981. Distribution, morphology and origin of sedimentary furrows in cohesive sediments, Southampton Water. *Sedimentology*, Vol. 28, 511–529.

FOLK, R L. 1954. The distinction between grain size and mineral composition in sedimentary-rock nomenclature. *Journal of Geology*, Vol. 62, 344–359.

FOWLER, J. 1932. The 'One Hundred foot' raised beach between Arundel and Chichester, Sussex. *Quarterly Journal of the Geological Society of London*, Vol. 88, 84–99.

FUERSICH, F T. 1976. Fauna-substrate relationships in the Corallian Beds of England and Normandy. *Lethaia*, Vol. 9, 343–356.

— 1977. Corallian (Upper Jurassic) marine benthic associations from England and Normandy. *Palaeontology*, Vol. 20, 337–385.

GALLOIS, R W. 1965. *British regional geology: the Wealden district* (4th edition). (London: HMSO for Institute of Geological Sciences.)

— 1978. What price oil shales? *New Scientist*, Vol. 77, 490–493.

— and WORSSAM, B C. In press. Geology of the country around Horsham. *Memoir of the British Geological Survey*.

GATRALL, M, JENKYNS, H C, and PARSONS, C. 1972. Limonitic concretions from the European Jurassic with particular reference to the 'snuff boxes' of Southern England. *Sedimentology*, Vol. 18, 79–103.

GERARD, A. 1975. La tectonique du socle sous la Manche occidentale d'apres les données du magnetisme aeroporte. *Philosophical Transactions of the Royal Society of London*, Vol. 279A, 55–68. [In French.]

— and WEBER, C. 1971. L'anomalie magnetique du bassin de Paris interpretée comme element structural majeur dans l'histoire géologique de la France. *Compte Rendu Hebdomadaire des Seances de l'Acadamie des Sciences, Paris*, Series D, Vol. 272, 921–923. [In French.]

GIBBARD, P L. 1988. The history of the great northwest European rivers during the past three million years. *Philosophical Transactions of the Royal Society of London*, Vol. 318B, 559–602.

GODWIN, H, and SWITZUR, V R. 1966. Cambridge University Natural Radiocarbon Measurements VIII. *Radiocarbon*, Vol. 8. 390–400.

GODWIN-AUSTEN, R. 1857. On the newer Tertiary deposits of the Sussex coast. *Quarterly Journal of the Geological Society of London*, Vol. 13, 40–72.

GRANGE, A, and MUIR WOOD, A M. 1970. The site investigations for a Channel Tunnel 1964–1965. *Proceedings of the Institution of Civil Engineers*, Vol. 45, 103–123.

GREEN, G W, and DONOVAN, D T. 1969. The Great Oolite of the Bath area. *Bulletin of the Geological Survey of Great Britain*, Vol. 30, 1–63.

GUILCHER, A. 1969. Pleistocene and Holocene sea level changes. *Earth Sciences Reviews*, Vol. 5, 69–97.

HAILS, J R. 1975. Offshore morphology and sediment distribution, Start Bay, Devon. *Philosophical Transactions of the Royal Society of London*, Vol. 279A, 221–228.

HALL, J. 1986. Nature of the lower continental crust: evidence from BIRPS work on the Caledonides. 223–231 *in* Reflection seismology: the continental crust. BARAZANGI, M, and BROWN, L (editors). *Geodynamics Series, American Geophysical Union*, Vol. 14.

HALLAM, A. 1964. Origin of the limestone–shale rhythm in the Blue Lias of England: a composite theory. *Journal of Geology*, Vol. 72, 157–169.

— 1975. *Jurassic environments.* (Cambridge: Cambridge University Press.)

— 1981. A revised sea-level curve for the early Jurassic. *Journal of the Geological Society*, Vol. 138, 735–743.

HALLEZ, P. 1899. Sur les fonds du détroit du Pas-de-Calais. *Annales de la Société Géologique du Nord*, Vol. 28, 4–23. [In French.]

HAMBLIN, R J O. 1969. The geology of the Haldon Hills. Unpublished PhD thesis, University of Exeter.

— and HARRISON, D J. 1989. Marine Aggregate Survey Phase 2: South Coast. *British Geological Survey Marine Report*, No. 88/31.

— — 1990. The marine sand and gravel resources off the Isle of Wight and Beachy Head. *British Geological Survey Technical Report*, WB/89/41C.

— JEFFREY, D H, and WINGFIELD, R T R. 1990. Glacial incisions indicating Middle and Upper Pleistocene ice limits off Britain: two comments and a reply. *Terra Nova*, Vol. 2, 382–389.

— — — 1991. Discussion: the origin of major incisions within the Pleistocene deposits of the North Sea. *Marine Geology*, Vol. 96, 123–129.

HAMILTON, D, and SMITH, A J. 1972. The origin and sedimentary history of the Hurd Deep, English Channel, with additional notes on other deeps in the western English Channel. *Mémoires du Bureau de Recherches Géologiques et Minières,* Vol. 79, 59–78.

— SOMERVILLE, J H, and STANFORD, P N. 1980. Bottom currents and shelf sediments, southwest of Britain. *Sedimentary Geology*, Vol. 26, 115–138.

HANCOCK, F R P, and MITHEN, D P. 1987. The geology of the Humbly Grove Oilfield, Hampshire, UK. 161–170 in *Petroleum geology of North West Europe.* BROOKS, J, and GLENNIE, K W (editors). (London: Graham and Trotman.)

HANCOCK, J M. 1976. The petrology of the Chalk. *Proceedings of the Geologists' Association*, Vol. 86, 499–535.

HAQ, B U, HARDENBOL, J, and VAIL, P R. 1987. Chronology of fluctuating sea levels since the Triassic. *Science, New York*, Vol. 235, 1156–1167.

— — — 1988. Mesozoic and Cenozoic chronostratigraphy and cycles of sea-level change. 71–108 *in* Sea-level changes—an integrated approach. WILGUS, C K, and five others (editors). *Special Publication of the Society of Economic Paleontologists and Mineralogists*, No. 42.

HARRISON, R K. 1975. Concretionary concentrations of the rarer elements in Permo-Triassic red beds of south-west England. *Bulletin of the Geological Survey of Great Britain*, No. 52, 1–26.

HART, M B. and BIGG, P J. 1981. Anoxic events in the Late Cretaceous chalk seas of North-West Europe. 177–185 in *Microfossils from Recent and fossil shelf seas.* NEALE, J W, and BRASIER M D (editors). (Chichester: Ellis Horwood Ltd.)

HENSON, M R. 1970. The Triassic rocks of south Devon. *Proceedings of the Ussher Society*, Vol. 2, 172–177.

— 1971. The Permo-Triassic rocks of south Devon. Unpublished PhD thesis, University of Exeter.

— 1972. The form of the Permo-Triassic basin in south-east Devon. *Proceedings of the Ussher Society*, Vol. 2, 447–457.

— 1973. Clay minerals from the Lower New Red Sandstone of south Devon. *Proceedings of the Geologists' Association*, Vol. 84, 429–445.

HEYWORTH, A, and KIDSON, C. 1982. Sea-level changes in south-west England and Wales. *Proceedings of the Geologists' Association*, Vol. 93, 91–111.

HIGGINBOTTOM, I E. 1973. A problem of designing and building for a structure at sea. *Proceedings of the Institution of Civil Engineers*, Vol. 54, 673–697.

HILLIS, R R, and DAY, G A. 1987. Deep events in UK South Western Approaches. 243–249 *in* Deep seismic reflection profiling of the continental lithosphere. MATTHEWS, D, and SMITH, C (editors). *Geophysical Journal of the Royal Astronomical Society*, Vol. 89.

HIRN, A, DAMOTTE, B, TORREILLES, G, and ECORS Scientific Party. 1987. Crustal reflection seismics: the contributions of oblique, low frequency and shear wave illuminations. 287–295 *in* Deep seismic reflection profiling of the continental lithosphere. MATTHEWS, D, and SMITH, C (editors). *Geophysical Journal of the Royal Astronomical Society*, Vol. 89.

HODGSON, J M. 1964. The low-level Pleistocene marine sands and gravels of the west Sussex coastal plain. *Proceedings of the Geologists' Association*, Vol. 75, 547–561.

HOLDER, A P, and BOTT, M H P. 1971. Crustal structure in the vicinity of south-west England. *Geophysical Journal of the Royal Astronomical Society*, Vol. 23, 465–489.

HOLDER, M T, and LEVERIDGE, B E. 1986a. A model for the tectonic evolution of south Cornwall. *Journal of the Geological Society of London*, Vol. 143, 125–134.

— — 1986b. Correlation of the Rhenohercynian Variscides. *Journal of the Geological Society of London*, Vol. 143, 141–147.

HOLLOWAY, S, MILODOWSKI, A E, STRONG, G E, and WARRINGTON, G. 1989. The Sherwood Sandstone Group (Triassic) of the Wessex Basin, southern England. *Proceedings of the Geologists' Association*, Vol. 100, 383–394.

HOUSE, M R. 1963. Devonian ammonoid successions and facies in Devon and Cornwall. *Quarterly Journal of the Geological Society of London*, Vol. 119, 1–27.

HUAULT, M F, and five others. 1975. Evolution of the estuary of the Seine since the last glaciation. *Philosophical Transactions of the Royal Society,* Vol. 279A, 229–231.

HUNTLEY, D A. 1980. Tides on the North-West European Continental Shelf. 301–351 in *The North-West European shelf seas: the sea bed and the sea in motion—II. Physical and chemical oceanography, and physical resources.* BANNER, F T, COLLINS, M B, and MASSIE, K S (editors). (Amsterdam: Elsevier.)

HURICH, C A, SMITHSON, S B, FOUNTAIN, D M, and HUMPHREYS, M C. 1985. Seismic evidence of mylonite reflectivity and deep structure in the Kettle Dome metamorphic core complex, Washington. *Geology*, Vol. 13, 577–580.

INSOLE, A, and DALEY, B. 1985. A revision of the lithostratigraphical nomenclature of the Late Eocene and Early Oligocene strata of the Hampshire Basin, Southern England. *Tertiary Research*, Vol. 7, 67–100.

JARVIS, I, and WOODROFF, P. 1981. The phosphatic chalks and hardgrounds of Boxford and Winterbourne, Berkshire—two tectonically controlled facies in the late Coniacian to early Campanian (Cretaceous) of southern England. *Geological Magazine,* Vol. 118, 175–187.

JEANS, C V. 1978. The origin of the Triassic clay assemblages of Europe with special reference to the Keuper Marl and Rhaetic of parts of England. *Philosophical Transactions of the Royal Society of London*, Vol. 289A, 549–636.

— MERRIMAN, R J, and MITCHELL, J G. 1977. Origin of Middle Jurassic and Lower Cretaceous Fuller's Earth in England. *Clay Minerals*, Vol. 12, 11–44.

JELGERSMA, S. 1979. Sea-level changes in the North Sea Basin. 233–248 *in* The Quaternary history of the North Sea. OELE, E, SCHÜTTENHELM, R T E, and WIGGERS, A J (editors). *Acta Universitatis Upsaliensis: Symposium Universitatis Upsaliensis Annum Quingentesimum Celebrantis: 2.*

— Oele, E, and Wiggers, A J. 1979. Depositional history and coastal development in the Netherlands and the adjacent North Sea since the Eemian. 115–142 in The Quaternary history of the North Sea. Oele, E, Schüttenhelm, R T E, and Wiggers, A J (editors). Acta Universitatis Upsaliensis: Symposium Universitatis Upsaliensis Annum Quingentesimum Celebrantis: 2.

Jenkins, D G, Whittaker, J E, and Carlton, R. 1986. On the age and correlation of the St.Erth Beds, south-west England, based on planktonic foraminifera. Journal of Micropalaeontology, Vol. 5, 93–105.

Jennings, S. and Smyth, C. 1987. Coastal sedimentation in East Sussex during the Holocene. Progress in Oceanography, Vol. 18, 205–241.

Johnson, M A, Kenyon, N H, Belderson, R H, and Stride, A H. 1982. Sand transport. 58–94 in Offshore tidal sands — processes and deposits. Stride, A H (editor). (London: Chapman and Hall.)

Jones, H. 1989. Sand to land. New Civil Engineer, 11-5-89, 26–29.

Kauffman, E G. 1977. Evolutionary rates and biostratigraphy. 109–141 in Concepts and methods of biostratigraphy. Kauffman, E G, and Hazel, J E (editors). (Stroudsburg, Penn: Dowden, Hutchinson and Ross.)

Keen, D H. 1978. The Pleistocene deposits of the Channel Islands. Report of the Institute of Geological Sciences, No. 78/26.

Keen, M C. 1977. Ostracod assemblages and the depositional environments of the Headon, Osborne and Bembrige Beds (Upper Eocene) of the Hampshire Basin. Palaeontology, Vol. 20, 405–445.

Kelland, N C, and Hails, J R. 1972. Bedrock morphology and structures within overlying sediments, Start Bay, southwest England, determined by continuous seismic profiling, side-scan sonar and core sampling. Marine Geology, Vol. 13, M19–M26.

Kellaway, G A, and Hancock, P L. 1983. Structure of the Bristol district, the Forest of Dean and the Malvern Fault Zone. 88–107 in The Variscan Fold Belt in the British Isles. Hancock, P L (editor). (Bristol: Adam Hilger.)

— Redding, J H, Shephard-Thorn, E R, and Destombes, J-P. 1975. The Quaternary history of the English Channel. Philosophical Transactions of the Royal Society of London, Vol. 279A, 189–218.

Kelling, G, and Moshrif, M A. 1977. The orientation of fossil bivalves in a pene-littoral sequence (the Rhaetian of South Wales). Journal of Sedimentary Petrology, Vol. 47, 1342–1346.

Kennedy, W J, and Garrison, R E. 1975. Morphology and genesis of nodular chalks and hardgrounds in the Upper Cretaceous of southern England. Sedimentology, Vol. 22, 311–386.

— and Juignet, P. 1974. Carbonate banks and slump beds in the Upper Cretaceous (Upper Turonian–Santonian) of Haute Normandie, France. Sedimentology, Vol. 21, 1–42.

Kenyon, N H. 1970. Sand ribbons of European tidal seas. Marine Geology, Vol. 9, 25–39.

- and Stride, A H. 1970. The tide-swept continental shelf sediments between the Shetland Isles and France. Sedimentology, Vol. 14, 159–173.

Kidson, C, and Bowen, D Q. 1976. Some comments on the history of the English Channel. Quaternary Newsletter, Vol. 18, 8–9.

King, C. 1981. The stratigraphy of the London Clay and associated deposits. Tertiary Research Special Papers, No. 6.

King, W B R. 1949. The geology of the eastern part of the English Channel. Quarterly Journal of the Geological Society of London, Vol. 104, 327–337.

— 1954. The geological history of the English Channel. Quarterly Journal of the Geological Society of London, Vol. 110, 77–101.

Klemperer, S L. 1988. Crustal thinning and nature of extension in the northern North Sea from deep seismic reflection profiling. Tectonics, Vol. 7, 803–821.

Knill, D C. 1969. The Permian igneous rocks of Devon. Bulletin of the Geological Survey of Great Britain, No. 29, 115–138.

Lake, R D, and Shephard-Thorn, E R. 1987. Geology of the country around Hastings and Dungeness. Memoir of the British Geological Survey, Sheets 320 and 321 (England and Wales).

— Young, B, Wood, C J, and Mortimore, R N. 1987. Geology of the country around Lewes. Memoir of the British Geological Survey, Sheet 319 (England and Wales).

Lake, S D, and Karner, G D. 1987. The structure and evolution of the Wessex Basin, southern England: an example of inversion tectonics. Tectonophysics, Vol. 137, 347–378.

Laming, D J C. 1966. Imbrication, palaeocurrents and other sedimentary features in the Lower New Red Sandstone, Devonshire, England. Journal of Sedimentary Petrology, Vol. 36, 940–959.

Lamplugh, G W, and Kitchin, F L. 1911. On the Mesozoic rocks in some of the coal explorations in Kent. Memoir of the Geological Survey of Great Britain.

— — and Pringle, J. 1923. The concealed Mesozoic rocks in Kent. Memoir of the Geological Survey of Great Britain (4th edition).

Lapierre, F. 1975. Contribution a l'étude géologique et sedimentologique de la Manche orientale. Philosophical Transactions of the Royal Society of London, Vol. 279A, 177–187. [In French.]

Larsonneur, C. 1972. Données sur l'évolution paléogéographique posthercynienne de la Manche. Mémoire du Bureau de Recherches Géologiques et Minières, No. 79, 203–214. [In French.]

— 1977. La cartographie des dépôts meubles sur le plateau continental Français; méthode mise au point et utilisée en Manche. Journal de Recherche Océanographique, Vol. 2, 33–39. [In French.]

— Auffret, J-P, and Smith, A J. 1982a. Carte des paléo-vallées et des bancs sableux de la Manche orientale. 1:500 000 map and explanatory leaflet. (Paris: Bureau de Recherches Géologiques et Minières.)

— Bouysse, P, and Auffret, J-P. 1982b. The superficial sediments of the English Channel and its Western Approaches. Sedimentology, Vol. 29, 851–864.

— Horn, R, and Auffret, J-P. 1975. Géologie de la part méridionale de la Manche centrale. Philosophical Transactions of the Royal Society of London, Vol. 279A, 145–153. [In French.]

— Vaslet, D, and Auffret, J-P. 1979. Carte des sédiments superficiels de la Manche. 1:500 000 map and explanatory leaflet. (Paris: Bureau de Recherches Géologique et Minières.) [In French.]

Lautridou, J P, Monnier, J L, Morzadec, M T, Somme, J, and Tuffreau, A. 1986. The Pleistocene of Northern France. Quaternary Science Reviews, Vol. 5, 387–393.

Le Bourgne, E, Le Mouel, J-L, and Le Pichon, X. 1971. Aeromagnetic survey of south-western Europe. Earth and Planetary Science Letters, Vol. 12, 287–299.

Lefort, J-P. 1979. Les prolongements submerges du Massif Armoricain: étude de géologie et de géophysique marine. Memoire de la Société Géologique de France, Nouvelle Serie, No. 56, 1–68. [In French.]

— and Segoufin, J. 1978. Étude comparée des structures profondes et des anomalies magnetiques allongées reconnues en Manche occidentale et en Baie d'Audierne: existence possible d'une suture cryptique au nord-ouest du Massif Armoricain (France). Tectonophysics, Vol. 46, 65–76. [In French.]

Le Fournier, J. 1980. Modern analogue of transgressive sand bodies off eastern English Channel. Bulletin des Centres de Recherches Exploration-Production Elf-Aquitaine, No. 4, 99–118.

Leveridge, B E, Holder, M T, and Day, G A. 1984. Thrust nappe tectonics in the Devonian of south Cornwall and the western English Channel. 103–112 in Variscan tectonics of the North Atlantic region. Hutton, D H W, and Sanderson D J (editors). Special Publication of the Geological Society of London, No. 14.

LISTER, T R, COCKS, L R M, and RUSHTON, A. 1969. The basement beds in the Bobbing borehole, Kent. *Geological Magazine*, Vol. 106, 601–603.

LOTT, G K, KNOX, R W O'B, BIGG, P J, DAVEY, R J, and MORTON, A C. 1980. Aptian–Cenomanian stratigraphy in boreholes from offshore south-west England. *Report of the Institute of Geological Sciences,* No. 80/8.

— SOBEY, R A, WARRINGTON, G, and WHITTAKER A. 1982. The Mercia Mudstone Group (Triassic) in the western Wessex Basin. *Proceedings of the Ussher Society*, Vol. 5, 340–346.

MARTIN, A. J. 1967. Bathonian sediments in southern England. *Proceedings of the Geologists' Association*, Vol. 78, 473–488.

MARTIN, J B. 1841. Description of bones of the Mammoth found in the deep sea of the Bristol Channel and German Ocean. *Transactions of the Geological Society of London*, 2nd Series, Vol. 6, 161–163.

MATTHEWS, D H. 1986. Seismic reflections from the lower crust around Britain. 11–21 *in* The nature of the lower continental crust. DAWSON, J B, CARSWELL, D A, HALL, J, and WEDEPOHL, K H (editors). *Special Publication of the Geological Society of London*, No. 24.

— and CHEADLE, M J. 1986. Deep reflections from the Caledonides and Variscides west of Britain and comparison with the Himalayas. 5–19 *in* Reflection seismology: a global perspective. BARAZANGI, M, and BROWN, L (editors). *Geodynamics Series, American Geophysical Union*, Vol. 13.

MCDONOUGH, D T, and FOUNTAIN, D M. 1988. Reflection characteristics of a mylonite zone based on compressional wave velocities of rock samples. *Geophysical Journal*, Vol. 93, 547–558.

MCGEARY, S, CHEADLE, M J, WARNER, M R, and BLUNDELL, D J. 1987. Crustal structure of the continental shelf around Britain derived from BIRPS deep seismic profiling. 33–41 *in* Petroleum geology of North West Europe. BROOKS, J, and GLENNIE, K W (editors). (London: Graham and Trotman.)

MCKENZIE, D P. 1978. Some remarks on the development of sedimentary basins. *Earth and Planetary Science Letters*, Vol. 40, 25–32.

MCLIMANS, R K, and VIDETICH, P E. 1987. Reservoir diagenesis and oil migration: Middle Jurassic Great Oolite Limestone, Wealden Basin, Southern England. 119–128 in *Petroleum geology of North West Europe*. BROOKS, J, and GLENNIE, K W (editors). (London: Graham and Trotman.)

MÉGNIEN, C. 1980. Synthèse géologique du bassin de Paris. *Mémoires du Bureau de Recherches Géologiques et Minières*, Nos. 101–103. [In French.]

—and DEBRAND-PASSARD, S. 1980. Synthèse géologique du bassin de Paris. Vol. 2. Atlas. *Mémoires du Bureau de Recherches Géologiques et Minières*, No. 102. [In French.]

MEISSNER, R, MATTHEWS, D, and WEVER, Th. 1986. The 'Moho' in and around Great Britain. *Annales Geophysicae*, Vol. 4B, 659–663.

— WEVER, Th, and FLUH, E R. 1987. The Moho in Europe—implications for crustal development. *Annales Geophysicae*, Vol. 5B, 357–364.

MELVILLE, R V, and FRESHNEY, E C. 1982. *British regional geology: the Hampshire Basin and adjoining areas* (4th edition). (London: HMSO for Institute of Geological Sciences.)

MEREU, R F, MUELLER, S, and FOUNTAIN, D M (editors). 1989. Properties and processes of Earth's lower crust. *Geophysical Monograph, American Geophysical Union, International Union of Geodesy and Geophysics,* No. 51. , Vol. 6, 1–339.

MILNER, A R, GARDINER, B G, FRASER, N C, and TAYLOR, M A. 1990. Vertebrates from the Otter Sandstone Formation of Devon. *Palaeontology*, Vol. 33, 873–892.

MILODOWSKI, A E, and five others. 1986. Diagenetic influences on the aquifer properties of the Sherwood Sandstone in the Wessex Basin. *Investigation into the geothermal potential of the UK.* (Keyworth: British Geological Survey.)

MOGI, A. 1979. *An atlas of the sea floor around Japan: aspects of submarine geomorphology.* (Tokyo: University of Tokyo Press.)

MONTFORD, H M. 1970. The terrestrial environment during Upper Cretaceous and Tertiary times. *Proceedings of the Geologists' Association*. Vol. 81, 181–204.

MORTIMER, M G, and CHALONER, W G. 1972. The palynology of the concealed Devonian rocks of southern England. *Bulletin of the Geological Survey of Great Britain*, No. 39, 1–56.

MORTIMORE, R N, and POMEROL, B. 1987. Correlation of the Upper Cretaceous White Chalk (Turonian to Campanian) in the Anglo-Paris Basin. *Proceedings of the Geologists' Association*, Vol. 98, 97–143.

— and WOOD C J. 1983. The distribution of flint in the English Chalk, with particular reference to the 'Brandon Flint Series' and the high Turonian flint maximum. 7–20 in *The scientific study of flint and chert*. SIEVEKING G DE G, and HART M B (editors). (Cambridge: Cambridge University Press.)

MORTON, A C. 1982. Heavy minerals of Hampshire Basin Palaeogene strata. *Geological Magazine*, Vol. 119, 436–476.

— 1989. Heavy minerals in seabed sediments on the southern part of the UK continental shelf. *British Geological Survey Technical Report*, WH/89/190R.

MORZADEC-KERFOURN, M-T, and DELIBRIAS, G. 1972. Analyses polliniques et datations radiocarbone des sédiments Quaternaires prélevés en Manche centrale et orientale. *Mémoires du Bureau de Recherches Géologiques et Minières*, No. 79, 160–165. [In French.]

MURRAY, J W, and WRIGHT, C A. 1974. Palaeogene foraminiferida and palaeoecology, Hampshire and Paris Basins and the English Channel. *Special Papers in Palaeontology*, No. 14.

OELE, E, and SCHÜTTENHELM, R T E. 1979. Development of the North Sea after the Saalian glaciation. 191–215 *in* The Quaternary history of the North Sea. OELE, E, SCHÜTTENHELM, R T E, and WIGGERS, A J (editors). *Acta Universitatis Upsaliensis: Symposium Universitatis Upsaliensis Annum Quingentesimum Celebrantis*: 2.

ORBELL, G. 1973. Palynology of the British Rhaeto-Lias. *Bulletin of the Geological Survey of Great Britain*, No. 44, 1–44.

OSCHMANN, W. 1988. Upper Kimmeridgian and Portlandian marine macrobenthonic associations from southern England and northern France. *Facies*, Vol. 18, 49–82.

OWEN, H G. 1971. Middle Albian stratigraphy in the Anglo-Paris Basin. *Bulletin of the British Museum (Natural History), Geology*, Vol. 8, 1–164.

PAEPE, R, and BAETEMAN, C. 1979. The Belgian coastal plain during the Quaternary. 143–146 *in* The Quaternary history of the North Sea. OELE, E, SCHÜTTENHELM, R T E, and WIGGERS, A J (editors). *Acta Universitatis Upsaliensis: Symposium Universitatis Upsaliensis Annum Quingentesimum Celebrantis*.2.

PATON, R A. 1974. Capitosauroid labyrinthodonts from the Trias of England. *Palaeontology*, Vol. 17, 253–289.

PENN, I E. 1985. Quelques aspects de la géologie profonde du Sud de l'Angleterre et leurs relations avec la géologie profonde en France. *Documents du Bureau de Recherche Géologiques et Minières*, 95–12.

— MERRIMAN, R J, and WYATT, R J. 1979. The Bathonian strata of the Bath–Frome area. *Report of the Institute of Geological Sciences*, No. 78/22.

— and seven others. 1987. Principal features of the hydrocarbon prospectivity of the Wessex–Channel Basin, UK. 109–118 in *Petroleum geology of North West Europe*. BROOKS, J, and GLENNIE, K W (editors). (London: Graham and Trotman.)

— DINGWALL, R G, and KNOX, R W O'B. 1980. The Inferior Oolite (Bajocian) sequence from a borehole in Lyme Bay, Dorset. *Report of the Institute of Geological Sciences*, No. 79/3.

PINET, B, MONTADERT, L, MASCLE, A, CAZES, M, and BOIS, C. 1987. New insights on the structure and the formation of sedimentary basins from deep seismic profiling in Western Europe. 11–31 in *Petroleum geology of North West Europe*, BROOKS, J, and GLENNIE, K W (editors). (London: Graham and Trotman.)

PINGREE, R D. 1980. Physical oceanography of the Celtic Sea and English Channel. 415–465 in *The North-West European shelf seas: the sea bed and the sea in motion—II. Physical and chemical oceanography, and physical resources.* BANNER, F T, COLLINS, M B, and MASSIE, K S (editors). (Amsterdam: Elsevier.)

PLINT, A G. 1982. Eocene sedimentation and tectonics in the Hampshire Basin. *Journal of the Geological Society*, Vol. 139, 249–254.

— 1988. Global eustacy and the Eocene sequence in the Hampshire Basin, England. *Basin Research*, Vol. 1, 11–22.

POMEROL, C. 1972. Colloque sur la géologie de la Manche: introduction. *Mémoires du Bureau de Recherches Géologiques et Minières*, No. 79. [In French.]

— 1980. *Geology of France, with twelve itineries.* (Paris: Masson.)

— 1982. *The Cenozoic era.* (Chichester: Ellis Horwood Ltd.)

— BAILEY, H W, MONCIARDINI, C, and MORTIMORE, R N. 1987. Lithostratigraphy and biostratigraphy of the Lewes and Seaford Chalk. A link across the Anglo-Paris Basin at the Turonian–Senonian boundary. *Cretaceous Research*, Vol. 8, 289–304.

POOLE, E G. 1978. The stratigraphy of the Withycombe Farm Borehole, near Banbury, Oxfordshire. *Bulletin of the Geological Survey of Great Britain*, No. 68.

PREVOST, C. 1839. Reunion extraordinaire de la Société Géologique de France a Boulogne. *Bulletin de la Société Géologique de France*, Series 1, No. 10, 399–402. [In French.]

PRUVOST, P, and PRINGLE, J. 1924. A synopsis of the geology of the Boulonnais, including a correlation of the Mesozoic rocks with those in England. *Proceedings of the Geologists' Association*, Vol. 35, 29–55.

QUINE, M L. 1988. Sedimentology of the Chalk of coastal Haute Normandie, France. Unpublished PhD thesis, University of London.

RAWSON, P F, and seven others. 1978. A correlation of Cretaceous rocks in the British Isles. *Special Report of the Geological Society of London*, No. 9.

— and RILEY, L A. 1982. Latest Jurassic–early Cretaceous events and the 'Late Cimmerian Unconformity' in the North Sea area. *Bulletin of the American Association of Petroleum Geologists*, Vol. 66/12, 2628–2648.

RAYNER, D H. 1981. *The stratigraphy of the British Isles* (2nd edition). (London: Cambridge University Press.)

REID, C. 1892. The Pleistocene deposits of the Sussex coast and their equivalents in other districts. *Quarterly Journal of the Geological Society of London*, Vol. 48, 344–361.

— 1902. The geology of the country around Southampton (explanation of sheet 315). *Memoir of the Geological Survey of Great Britain*.

REID, E M, and CHANDLER, M E J. 1933. *The flora of the London Clay.* (London: British Museum, Natural History.)

RHYS, G H, LOTT, G K, and CALVER, M A (editors). 1982. The Winterborne Kingston borehole, Dorset, England. *Report of the Institute of Geological Sciences*, No. 81/3.

ROBASZYNSKI, F, and AMÉDRO, F. 1986. The Cretaceous of the Boulonnais (France) and a comparison with the Cretaceous of Kent (United Kingdom). *Proceedings of the Geologists' Association*, Vol. 97, 171–208.

ROBERT, J. 1971. Results of a sparker reconnaissance survey of the eastern and central English Channel. *Report of the Institute of Geological Sciences*, No. 70/15, 35–41.

ROBERT, J P, and VILLE, P. 1971a. Boulogne-sur-mer–Rouen. Carte géologique et structurale de la Marge Continentale Française. Sheets 0–49, 0-50. 1:250 000. (Paris: Bureau de Recherches Géologiques et Minières.)

— — 1971b. Caen-Wight. Carte géologique et structurale de la Marge Continentale Française. Sheets 2–49, 2–50. 1:250 000. (Paris: Bureau de Recherches Géologiques et Minières.)

ROBINSON, A H W. 1961. The hydrography of Start Bay and its relationship to beach changes at Hallsands. *Geographical Journal*, Vol. 127, 63–77.

ROEP, T B, HOLST, H, VISSERS, R L M, PAGNIER, H, and POSTMA, D. 1975. Deposits of southward flowing Pleistocene rivers in the Channel region, near Wissant, NW France. *Palaeogeography, Palaeoclimatology, Palaeoecology*, Vol. 17, 289–308.

RUFFEL, A H. 1990. Stratigraphy and structure of the Mercia Mudstone Group (Triassic) in the western part of the Wessex Basin. *Proceedings of the Ussher Society*, Vol. 7, 263–267.

SAGER, G, and SAMMLER, R. 1975. *Atlas der Gezeitenströme für die Nordsee, den Kanal und die Irische See.* (Rostock: Seehydrographischer Dienst der Deutschen Demokratischen Republik.)

SAVIN, S M. 1977. The history of the earth's surface temperature during the past 100 million years. *Annual Review of Earth and Planetary Sciences*, Vol. 5, 315–355.

SELLWOOD, B W. 1970. The relation of trace fossils to small sedimentary cycles in the British Lias. 454–489 in *Trace fossils*. CRIMES, T P, and HARPER, J C (editors). (Liverpool: Seel House Press.)

— 1972. Regional environmental changes across a Lower Jurassic stage-boundary in Britain. *Palaeontology*, Vol. 15, 125–157.

SELWOOD, E B, and seven others. 1984. Geology of the country around Newton Abbot. *Memoir of the British Geological Survey*. 1:50 000 sheet 339, New Series (England and Wales).

SHEPHARD-THORN, E R. 1975. The Quaternary of the Weald—a review. *Proceedings of the Geologists' Association*, Vol. 86, 537–547.

— 1988. Geology of the country around Ramsgate and Dover. *Memoir of the British Geological Survey*, Sheets 274 and 279 (England and Wales).

— BERRY, F G, and WYATT, R J. 1982. *Geological notes and local details for 1:10 000 sheets SU80NW, NE, SW, SE; SU90NW, NE, SW, SE; TQ00NW, SW (West Sussex coastal plain between Chichester and Littlehampton).* (Keyworth: Institute of Geological Sciences.)

— LAKE, R D, and ATITULLAH, E A, 1972. Basement control of structures in the Mesozoic rocks in the Strait of Dover region, and its reflexion in certain features of the present land and submarine topography. *Philosophical Transactions of the Royal Society of London*, Vol. 272A, 99–113.

SHOTTON, F W. 1986. Glaciations in the United Kingdom. *Quaternary Science Reviews*, Vol. 5, 239–297.

SIBRAVA, V. 1986. Correlation of European glaciations and their relation to the deep-sea record. *Quaternary Science Reviews*, Vol. 5, 433–441.

SIMMS, M J, and RUFFEL, A H. 1990. Climate and biotic changes in the late Triassic. *Journal of the Geological Society of London*, Vol. 147, 321–327.

SMART, J G O, BISON, G, and WORSSAM, B C. 1966. Geology of the country around Canterbury and Folkestone. *Memoir of the Geological Survey of Great Britain*, Sheets 289, 305 and 306.

SMITH, A G, HURLEY, A M, and BRIDEN, J C. 1981. *Phanerozoic palaeocontinental world maps.* (Cambridge: Cambridge University Press.)

SMITH, A J. 1984. Structural evolution of the English Channel. *Annales de la Société Géologique du Nord*, Vol. C111, 253–264.

— 1985. Catastrophic origin for the palaeovalley system of the eastern English Channel. *Marine Geology*, Vol. 64, 65–75.

— 1989. The English Channel—by geological design or catastrophic accident? *Proceedings of the Geologists' Association*, Vol. 100, 325–337.

— and CURRY, D. 1975. The structure and geological evolution of the English Channel. *Philosophical Transactions of the Royal Society of London*, Vol. 279A, 3–20.

SMITH, D B, BRUNSTROM, R G W, MANNING, P I, SIMPSON, S, and SHOTTON, F W. 1974. A correlation of the Permian rocks in the British Isles. *Special Publication of the Geological Society of London*, No. 5.

SMITH, N J P. 1985. Structure contour and subcrop maps of the Pre-Permian surface of the United Kingdom (south). *British Geological Survey 150th Anniversary Publication.* (Keyworth: British Geological Survey.)

SMITH, S A. 1990. The sedimentary and accretionary styles of an ancient gravel-bed stream: the Budleigh Salterton Pebble Beds (Lower Triassic), south west England. *Sedimentary Geology,* Vol. 67, 199–219.

— and EDWARDS, R A. In press. Regional sedimentological variations in Lower Triassic fluvial conglomerates (Budleigh Salterton Pebble Beds), south west England: some implications for palaeogeography and basin evolution. *Geological Journal.*

SNELLING, N J (editor). 1985. The chronology of the Geological Record. *Memoir of the Geological Society of London,* No. 10.

SOMMÉ, J. 1979. Quaternary coastlines in northern France. 147–158 *in* The Quaternary history of the North Sea. OELE, E, SCHÜTTENHELM, R T E, and WIGGERS, A J (editors). *Acta Universitatis Upsaliensis: Symposium Universitatis Upsaliensis Annum Quingentesimum Celebrantis.* 2.

SPENCER, P S, and ISAAC, K P. 1983. Triassic vertebrates from the Otter Sandstone Formation of Devon, England. *Proceedings of the Geologists' Association,* Vol. 94, 267–269.

STAMP, L D. 1927. The Thames drainage system and the age of the Strait of Dover. *Geographical Journal,* Vol. 70, 386–390.

STEVENSON, C R, and WARRINGTON, G. 1971. Jurassic and Cretaceous rocks of Wessex: highest Keuper deposits: written discussion to report of field meeting. *Proceedings of the Geologists' Association,* Vol. 82, 297–300.

STEWART, D J. 1981. A meander-belt sandstone of the Lower Cretaceous of southern England. *Sedimentology,* Vol. 28, 1–20.

— 1983. Possible suspended-load channel deposits from the Wealden Group (Lower Cretaceous) of Southern England. *Special Publication of the International Association of Sedimentologists,* Vol. 3, 369–384.

STONELEY, P. 1982. The structural development of the Wessex Basin. *Journal of the Geological Society of London,* Vol. 139, 543–554.

STRIDE, A H. 1960. Recognition of folds and faults on rock surfaces beneath the sea. *Nature, London,* Vol. 185, 837.

— 1963. Current swept sea-floors near the southern half of Great Britain. *Quarterly Journal of the Geological Society of London,* Vol. 119, 175–199.

— (editor). 1982. *Offshore tidal sands—processes and deposits.* (London: Chapman and Hall.)

— 1990. Growth and burial of the English Channel unconformity. *Proceedings of the Geologists' Association,* Vol. 101, 335–340.

— BELDERSON, R H, and KENYON, N H. 1972. Longitudinal furrows and depositional sand bodies of the English Channel. *Mémoires du Bureau de Recherches Géologiques et Minières,* No. 79, 233–240.

STRONG, G E. 1987. Petrographical notes on marine grab and core samples from localities in the Wight and Dungeness–Boulogne areas, English Channel. *Stratigraphy and Sedimentology Research Group Report,* No. SRG/87/7. (Keyworth: British Geological Survey.)

TAITT, A H, and KENT, P E. 1958. *Deep boreholes at Portsdown (Hants) and Henfield (Sussex).* (London: British Petroleum.)

TALBOT, M R. 1973. Major sedimentary cycles in the Corallian Beds (Oxfordian) of southern England. *Palaeogeography, Palaeoclimatology Palaeoecology,* Vol. 14, 293–313.

TERRIS, A P, and BULLERWELL, W. 1965. Investigations into the underground structure of southern England. *Report of the British Association for the Advancement of Science,* Vol. 22, 232–252.

THOMAS, L P, and HOLLIDAY, D W. 1982. Southampton No. 1 (Western Esplanade) geothermal well: geological well completion report. *Report of the Deep Geology Unit, Institute of Geological Sciences,* Vol. 82/3.

THOMÉ DE GAMOND, M A. 1857. *Étude pour l'avant-projet d'un tunnel Sous-Marin entre l'Angleterre et la France.* (Paris: Librarie des Corps Impériaux des Ponts et Chaussées et des Mines.) [In French.]

TOPLEY, W. 1872. Geology of the Straits of Dover. *Quarterly Journal of Science,* Vol. 2, 208–223.

TOWNSON, W G. 1975. Lithostratigraphy and deposition of the type Portlandian. *Journal of the Geological Society of London,* Vol.131, 619–68.

TRAPPE, H. 1990. Thermal basin modelling by means of deep seismic profiling: a tentative approach. 1–14 in *The potential of deep seismic profiling for hydrocarbon exploration.* PINET, B, and BOIS, C (editors). (Paris: Editions Technip.)

VAIL, P R, and seven others. 1977. Seismic stratigraphy and global changes of sea level. *Memoir of the American Association of Petroleum Geologists,* No. 26, 49–212.

VENABLES, E M. 1962. The London Clay of Bognor Regis. *Proceedings of the Geologists' Association,* Vol. 73, 245–271.

WALKER, A D. 1969. The reptile fauna of the 'Lower Keuper' Sandstone. *Geological Magazine,* Vol. 106, 470–476.

WALLACE, P. 1968. The sub-Mesozoic palaeogeology and palaeogeography of northeastern France and the Strait of Dover. *Palaeogeography, Palaeoclimatology, Palaeoecology,* Vol. 4, 241–255.

— 1969. The sedimentology and palaeoecology of the Devonian of the Ferques Inlier, northern France. *Quarterly Journal of the Geological Society of London,* Vol. 125, 83–124.

WARNER, M R. 1987. Seismic reflections from the Moho—the effect of isostasy. *Geophysical Journal of the Royal Astronomical Society,* Vol. 88, 425–435.

WARRINGTON, G. 1971. Palynology of the New Red Sandstone sequence of the South Devon Coast. *Proceedings of the Ussher Society,* Vol. 2, 307–314.

— 1974. Les évaporites du Trias brittanique. *Bulletin de la Société Géologique de France,* Vol. 7, No. 6, 708–723.

— 1981. The indigenous micropalaeontology of British Triassic shelf sea deposits. 61–70 in *Microfossils from Recent and fossil shelf seas.* NEALE, J W, and BRASIER, M D (editors). (Chichester: Ellis Horwood Ltd.)

— and eight others. 1980. A correlation of Triassic rocks in the British Isles. *Special Report of the Geological Society of London,* No. 13.

— and IVIMEY-COOK, H C. 1991. Triassic. In *Atlas of palaeogeography and lithofacies.* COPE, J W C, INGHAM, J K, and RAWSON, P F (editors). (London: Geological Society.)

— and OWENS, B (compilers). 1977. Micropalaeontological biostratigraphy of offshore samples from south-west Britain. *Report of the Institute of Geological Sciences,* No. 77/7.

— and SCRIVENER, R C. 1980. The Lyme Regis (1901) Borehole succession and its relationship to the Triassic sequence of the east Devon coast. *Proceedings of the Ussher Society,* Vol. 5, 24–32.

— — 1988. Late Permian fossils from Devon: regional geological implications. *Proceedings of the Ussher Society,* Vol. 7, 95–96.

— — 1990. The Permian of Devon, England. *Review of Palaeobotany and Palynology,* Vol. 66, 263–272.

— and WHITTAKER, A. 1984. The Blue Anchor Formation (late Triassic) in Somerset. *Proceedings of the Ussher Society,* Vol. 6, 100–107.

WENZEL, F, SANDMEIER, K-J, and WALDE, W. 1987. Properties of the lower crust from modelling refraction and reflection data. *Journal of Geophysical Research,* Vol. 92B, 11, 575-11, 583.

WERNICKE, B. 1985. Uniform sense simple shear of the continental lithosphere. *Canadian Journal of Earth Sciences,* Vol. 22, 108–125.

WEST, R G. 1972. Relative land-sea-level changes in south eastern England during the Pleistocene. *Philosophical Transactions of the Royal Society of London,* Vol. 272A, 87–98.

— DEVOY, R J N, FUNNELL, B M, and ROBINSON, J E. 1984. Pleistocene deposits at Earnley, Bracklesham Bay, Sussex.

Philosophical Transactions of the Royal Society of London, Vol. 306B, 137–157.

— and SPARKS, B W. 1960. Coastal interglacial deposits of the English Channel. *Philosophical Transactions of the Royal Society of London*, Vol. 243B, 95–133.

WHITTAKER, A. 1975. A postulated post-Hercynian rift valley system in southern Britain. *Geological Magazine*, Vol. 112, 137–49.

— (editor) 1985. *Atlas of onshore sedimentary basins in England and Wales: Post-Carboniferous tectonics and stratigraphy.* (Glasgow: Blackie.)

— and CHADWICK, R A. 1984. The large-scale structure of the Earth's crust beneath southern Britain. *Geological Magazine*, Vol. 121, 621–624.

— — and PENN, I E. 1986. Deep crustal traverse across southern Britain from seismic reflection profiles. *Bulletin de la Société Géologique de France*, Series 8, Vol. 2, 55–68.

— HOLLIDAY, D W, and PENN, I E. 1985. Geophysical logs in British stratigraphy. *Special Report of the Geological Society of London*, No. 18.

WIGNALL, P B. 1990. Benthic palaeoecology of the Late Jurassic Kimmeridge Clay of England. *Palaeontology Special Paper*, No. 43.

WILLIAMS, G D, and BROOKS, M. 1985. A reinterpretation of the concealed Variscan structure beneath southern England by section balancing. *Journal of the Geological Society of London*, Vol. 142, 689–695.

WILSON, R C L. 1968a. Upper Oxfordian palaeogeography of southern England. *Palaeogeography, Palaeoclimatology, Palaeoecology*, Vol. 4, 5–28.

— 1968b. Carbonate facies variation within the Osmington Oolite Series in Southern England. *Palaeogeography, Palaeoclimatology, Palaeoecology*, Vol. 4, 89–123.

WILSON, V, WELCH, F B A, ROBBIE, J A, and GREEN, G W. 1958. Geology of the country around Bridport and Yeovil. *Memoir of the Geological Survey of Great Britain.*

WINGFIELD, R T R. 1989. Glacial incisions indicating Middle and Upper Pleistocene ice limits off Britain. *Terra Nova*, Vol. 1, 538–548.

— 1990. The origin of major incisions within the Pleistocene deposits of the North Sea. *Marine Geology*, Vol. 91, 31–52.

WOOD, A. 1974. Submerged platforms of marine abrasion around the coasts of south-western Britain. *Nature, London*, Vol. 252, 563.

WRAY, J L. 1977. Calcareous algae. *Developments in palaeontology and stratigraphy*, Vol. 4. (Amsterdam: Elsevier.)

WRIGHT, C A. 1972. The recognition of a planktonic foraminiferid datum in the London Clay of the Hampshire Basin. *Proceedings of the Geologists' Association*, Vol. 83, 413–419.

WYMER, J. 1988. Palaeolithic archaeology and the British Quaternary sequence. *Quaternary Science Reviews*, Vol. 7, 79–98.

YOUNG, B, and LAKE, R D. 1988. Geology of the country around Brighton and Worthing. *Memoir of the British Geological Survey*, Sheets 318 and 333 (England and Wales).

ZAGWIJN, W H. 1974. The palaeogeographic evolution of the Netherlands during the Quaternary. *Geologie en Mijnbouw*, Vol. 53, 369–385.

— 1979. Early and Middle Pleistocene coastlines in the southern North Sea basin. 31–42 *in* The Quaternary history of the North Sea. OELE, E, SCHÜTTENHELM, R T E, and WIGGERS, A J (editors). *Acta Universitatis Upsaliensis: Symposium Universitatis Upsaliensis Annum Quingentesimum Celebrantis*: 2.

ZIEGLER, P A. 1981. Evolution of sedimentary basins in north-west Europe. 3–39 in *Petroleum geology of the continental shelf of North-West Europe.* ILLING, L V, and HOBSON, G D (editors). (London: Heyden and Son.)

— 1982. *Geological atlas of Western and Central Europe.* (Amsterdam: Shell Internationale Petroleum Maatschappij BV.)

INDEX

106

BRITISH GEOLOGICAL SURVEY

Keyworth, Nottingham NG12 5GG
(0602) 363100

Murchison House, West Mains Road, Edinburgh EH9 3LA
031-667 1000

London Information Office, Natural History Museum
Earth Galleries, Exhibition Road, London SW7 2DE
071 589 4090

The full range of Survey publications is available through the
Sales Desks at Keyworth and at Murchison House,
Edinburgh, and in the BGS London Information Office in
the Natural History Museum Earth Galleries. The adjacent
bookshop stocks the more popular books for sale over the
counter. Most BGS books and reports are listed in HMSO's
Sectional List 45, and can be bought from HMSO and
through HMSO agents and retailers. Maps are listed in the
BGS Map Catalogue, and can be bought BGS approved
stockists and agents as well as direct from BGS.

*The British Geological Survey carries out the geological survey of
Great Britain and Northern Ireland (the latter as an agency
service for the government of Northern Ireland), and of the
surrounding continental shelf, as well as its basic research
projects. It also undertakes programmes of British technical aid
in geology in developing countries as arranged by the Overseas
Development Administration.*

*The British Geological Survey is a component body of the
Natural Environment Research Council.*

HMSO publications are available from:

HMSO Publications Centre
(Mail, fax and telephone orders only)
PO Box 276, London SW8 5DT
Telephone orders 071-873 9090
General enquiries 071-873 0011
Queueing system in operation for both numbers
Fax orders 071-873 8200

HMSO Bookshops
49 High Holborn, London WC1V 6HB
(Counter service only)
071-873 001   Fax 071-873 8200
258 Broad Street, Birmingham B1 2HE
021-643 3740   Fax 021-643 6510
Southey House, 33 Wine Street, Bristol BS1 2BQ
0272-264306   Fax 0272-294515
9 Princess Street, Manchester M60 8AS
061-834 7201   Fax 061-883 0634
16 Arthur Street, Belfast BT1 4GD
0232-238451   Fax 0232-235401
71 Lothian Road, Edinburgh EH3 9AZ
031-228 4181   Fax 031-229 2734

HMSO's Accredited Agents
(see Yellow Pages)

And through good booksellers